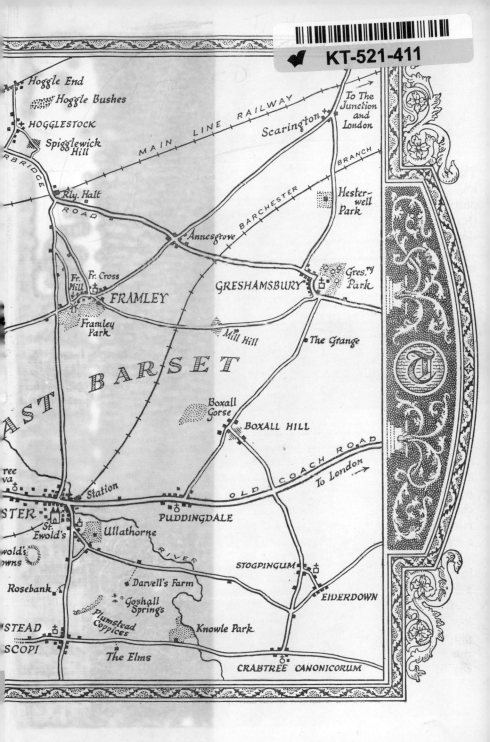

Hoggle End
Hoggle Bushes
HOGGLESTOCK
Spigglewick Hill

MAIN LINE RAILWAY

Scarington

To The Junction and London

RBRIDGE ROAD

Rly. Halt

BARCHESTER

BRANCH

Hester-well Park

Annesgrove

Fr. Mill Fr. Cross

FRAMLEY

GRESHAMSBURY

Gres.ry Park

Framley Park

Mill Hill

The Grange

BARSET

Boxall Gorse

BOXALL HILL

AST

OLD COACH ROAD

To London

ree va

Station

STER-
St. Ewold's

Ullathorne

PUDDINGDALE

RIVER

STOGPINGUM

wold's
owns

Rosebank

Darvell's Farm

Goshall Springs

Plumstead Coppices

Knowle Park

EIDERDOWN

STEAD
SCOPI

The Elms

CRABTREE CANONICORUM

The Bedside Barsetshire

THE BEDSIDE
BARSETSHIRE

compiled by
LANCE O. TINGAY

illustrated by
GWEN RAVERAT

"That she-Beelzebub."

FABER AND FABER LIMITED
24 Russell Square
London

First published in mcmxlix
by Faber and Faber Limited
24 Russell Square London W.C.1
Printed in Great Britain by
R. MacLehose and Company Limited
The University Press Glasgow

To the memory of
a great literary craftsman
ANTHONY TROLLOPE

Preface

The fame of Anthony Trollope is too well known for that great writer to need introduction. He suffered twenty years of neglect after his death in 1882, but since 1900 or thereabouts his work has steadily gained ground.

This book, which has been a labour of love, is for the most part an anthology of his finest work. For non-Trollopians it is hoped that it will serve as an introduction to, and not as a substitute for, his greatest novels, the six Chronicles of Barsetshire. They are:

The Warden (published 1855), indicated by "W."

Barchester Towers (published 1857), indicated by "B.T."

Doctor Thorne (published 1858), indicated by "D.T."

Framley Parsonage (published 1861), indicated by "F.P."

The Small House at Allington (published 1864), indicated by "S.H.A."

The Last Chronicle of Barset (published 1867), indicated by "L.C."

The essay "Map Making in Barsetshire", and the map of Barsetshire, were first published, albeit in less revised form, in "The Trollopian".

L. O. T.

Contents

In Praise of Barsetshire   *page* 15

The Barset Anthology:

Barsetshire   25
A Barsetshire Worthy—Archdeacon Grantly   27
Two Bishops—and another—and Bertie   30
The Obstinacy of Septimus Harding   32
The Proudies Entertain   39
Mrs Proudie Vanquished   54
A Love Scene   60
Mr Slope Vanquished   75
Politics   80
Dr Fillgrave refuses a Fee   83
The Duke Entertains   97
Frank takes a Brother's Privilege   108
Sir Louis Dines Out   115
Mary comes into Money   126
Mothercraft   136
Mrs Proudie Intervenes   137
Two Barsetshire Scandals   143
Mark Robarts Signs a Bill   144
Mark Robarts is Adamant   148
Some Barset Women   154
Mesdames Grantly and Proudie get together   156
Bailiffs at Framley   161
Johnny Eames does well   172
Crosbie starts his Honeymoon   178
On the Press, Art, and Dickens   184

Contents

Josiah Crawley charged with Theft   186

The Bishop sends his Inhibition   198

Caleb Thumble returns to Barchester   208

Josiah Crawley at the Palace   220

Mrs Proudie goes too far   233

Grace Crawley and the Archdeacon   245

R.I.P.   254

MAP MAKING IN BARSETSHIRE   269

A HANDY GUIDE TO BARSETSHIRE   283

WHO'S WHO IN BARSETSHIRE   291

MAP OF BARSETSHIRE   *end-papers*

In
Praise of
Barsetshire

In Praise of Barsetshire

Barsetshire is the most nostalgic of English counties. The lakes and mountains of Cumberland and Westmorland, the peaks of Derbyshire, the rich cornlands of Suffolk, the sweeping broads of Norfolk, the rolling downs of Sussex, the fine orchards of Kent, the lush fields of Devon—what are they compared with the dear, familiar acres of Barset?

It is not especially picturesque (though its woods are fine) and there is little scenic splendour to attract the tourist. Its roads are poor, full of ruts and pot holes, muddy in winter, dusty in summer. Nor is Barchester, architecturally, amongst the most impressive of cathedral cities. Hiram's Hospital is worth a visit but, even so, this old building, so charming and peaceful on a warm, summer evening, strikes damp and cold in the winter; the nearness of the river is by no means an unmixed blessing when the mist begins to rise. The cathedral, its stones mellowed with age, is an imposing edifice, but falls short of the glories of Ely, Canterbury, Lincoln or York, and lacks the magnificence of Salisbury and the dignity of Winchester; it cannot match the awe of Durham, and both Bath and Lichfield have more to show the visitor.

The fact is, Barset has never aspired to be a great English county, nor Barchester a great English city. It figures but seldom in the pages of history. The spiritual upheavals of the Reformation passed it by. Barcastrian clerics contrived to remain undisturbed, and their flock was content that it should be so. King Charles and Parliament pursued their struggle elsewhere, and as for Monmouth and his rebels, what were they to the people of Barset? What cared they, so long as there were Thornes at Ullathorne, and Greshams at Greshamsbury?

Yet when men, in distant corners of the world, think longingly of home and England, they dream of Barsetshire. They recall its homely cottages, its great houses, its leafy woods and narrow lanes; they reflect on mundane Barchester High Street and the chemist's shop over which lived dear old Septimus Harding; on the cloistered cathedral shades; they think of the prosperous parsonages, of Plumstead and Framley, or, maybe, of the less prosperous Puddingdale and the poverty-ridden Hogglestock; they ponder on the splendours of Gatherum Castle, on the shallow tinsel of Courcy Castle; they think of all that is most sweet in old England; they dream of home.

In creating Barsetshire Anthony Trollope did more than he knew. It is, as Nathaniel Hawthorne once wrote, "as real as if some giant had hewn a great lump out of the earth and put it under a glass case, with all its inhabitants going about their daily business, and not suspecting that they were made a show of." It is nothing more or less than a microcosm of England and English life—a phase of English life that has vanished for ever, existing only here and there in forgotten corners of the country, and preserved only in its full savour and freshness and sweetness in the evergreen pages of the six immortal Barset novels.

Few to-day would really wish to see a return of the top-heavy social structure of the mid-Victorians. In that upper middle class world of Trollope there was much that was false and shallow and cruel. There was abuse and mockery of basic human rights. It would be pleasant to have been, let us say, a younger brother of Lord Lufton. But who would willingly have been a brickmaker, living and working amid the dank hovels at the side of the canal? What woman would want to have been Josiah Crawley's wife?

But what many of us sigh for are some of the values of that distant world. Trollope's upper middle class knew what it stood for and was not afraid to defend it. It believed in absolute values of right and wrong. Expediency was a word little used. It did not boast of its social obligations. It strove to fulfil them. It paid lip service to good, moral lives, and believed in them as well; the majority of men and women were not afraid to try to lead Christian lives. The upper middle class cherished the sanctity of the home. It would have perished to defend it.

Archdeacon Grantly thundered and roared in defence of the church he believed in. He took care, no doubt, to provide for himself comfortably, but who will not know that he would have beggared himself if, by so doing, he could have preserved the Church of England? He guarded temporalities as the bulwark of the spiritual values that lay behind.

A man was as good as his word. The rules of social conduct were laid down, and not broken with impunity. A man could not fix his own rules and cry defiance at his neighbour. It was a world of law and order, not of anarchy. People had faith in God, and in themselves.

Trollope believed in the world he portrayed, and who would say his values were wrong? He was not blind to its faults, and he never hesitated to paint them.

The word "gentleman" is rarely used now in the sense that Trollope used it. No one had a clearer perception of who was a gentleman and who was not, who was a lady and who was not. A gulf is fixed between them. And Trollope was never better than when portraying a gentleman who fails to fulfil the obligations of his caste.

Sir Louis Scatcherd, for instance, was not a gentleman. Not even Eton could make him so, and when he drinks himself to death neither Trollope nor his readers spare a tear for him. Yet there is never a doubt about the status of Adolphus Crosbie and, richly though he deserves his thrashing at the hands of Johnny Eames, he always retains a sneaking sympathy on the part of the reader. He is punished but not cast beyond the pale.

Now this conception of what is the conduct of a gentleman and what is not, can be easily derided, but, for all that, it implies a standard of values well worth while, and of which Trollope was well aware. He, at least, would not have been surprised to see the children and grandchildren of his "gentlemen" sacrificing themselves in two world wars for the sake of values rated above their own lives.

Noblesse oblige! Is it not worth something?

Trollope was essentially a realist. His characters are rarely (and never in Barsetshire) wholly good or wholly bad. The best of them have their vices. The worst have their virtues. They are always individuals, never types. One loves them as one loves one's friends, without being blind to their faults.

Mrs Proudie is a detestable woman, narrow minded, priggish, domineering, tyrannical, and, sometimes, hardly a "lady". But what a woman! What strength of character! Who, having once met her, does not want to do so again? I would do much to have the privilege of bowing low over her hand as she stands on the head of the stairs receiving her guests (stipulating but one condition—that I should not have to live with her).

Then there is the beloved Septimus Harding, kind, gentle and well meaning. Oh, so well meaning, that every time he does anything his friends have to rally round to help him out of the mess! Yet so blind is he to his curious little faults that one cannot but sympathize with Archdeacon Grantly (who hated "scruples" because his knowledge of the world made him suspect them) when he loses patience with his father-in-law.

Archdeacon Grantly! There is a man and a half. One begins, in *The Warden*, by respecting him (despite the Rabelais in the locked drawer) but one has grown to love him before one has finished *The Last Chronicle*.

Were I asked that old question "if you could be someone else whom would you choose?" I should select the person of the most minor of minor canons attached to Barchester Cathedral. I should choose thus for the sake of being able to stand, albeit disregarded, snubbed and disdained, in an obscure corner of the chapter house while, warming his coat tails before the fire, the great archdeacon barked his commands, bringing the dean to heel, the chancellor to order, and the rest of the chapter to unquestioning obedience. What a tower of strength to a side! What a calamity to have him against one!

Every Trollopian must regret he never attains the dignity of a bishopric. No man deserved the staff and mitre more. But would he have made a good bishop? Compromise is half the art of ruling, and in no place more than amid the parties and factions, the quarrels temporal and spiritual, doctrinal and political, of a diocese of the Church of England. Archdeacon Grantly was never cast for a role where indecision can be more potent than decision. He was born to lead a faction and, in so doing, he served his church. He would ask no better epitaph.

Barsetshire, of course, must be taken with its faults as well as its virtues. This is no place to digress on Queen Anne's Bounty, the Ecclesiastical Commissioners, or the evils of pluralities; but it does go against natural justice that Mark Robarts, at Framley, should bask in the benefits of nine hundred a year and have little to do, while Josiah Crawley should wear himself out in drab, dreary Hogglestock on little more than a labourer's wage. The perpetual curacy of Hogglestock was a crying scandal in Barsetshire, and never remedied. Septimus Harding might have done well to let the intricacies of his own conscience get on the best they may, and have devoted more energy to such an evil.

On his death bed Mr Harding strove to remedy the effects, if not the causes, of this evil, and one takes leave of Barsetshire as Crawley settles down to the comforts of St Ewold's rectory. But did Crawley become content? Did he take his three hundred and fifty a year (a fair income in those days, after all) and give little dinner parties, and learn to drink his wine, and take pride in the sleekness of his black coat? I doubt it. Crawley was born to find a grievance and to set his face against the world. He all but found martyrdom at Hogglestock. How did he find it at St Ewold's?

Amongst Trollope's many finely drawn characters that of Crawley ranks amongst the best, and the able craftsmanship of Trollope's pen verges towards heights of genius. With acute, subtle strokes he lays bare a man's soul, and paints the tortuous workings of a taut, sensitive mind with an ability transcending anything he did before or since.

The Last Chronicle is, at the same time, both the best and worst of the six Barsetshire novels. It is easily the most enthralling, despite the awkwardness and blatant artificiality of some of its plot. Its structure is often poor, and it is the only Barset tale with that ugly division between the main plot and the sub-plot—a practice indefensible on artistic grounds and, to-day, not to be defended on commercial ones. Yet the interpolation of matters not strictly Barcastrian within the pages of *The Last Chronicle* is easily remedied by the experienced traveller in the county. Unwanted chapters are easily skipped.

Less simple is the problem of *The Small House at Allington*. Its relationship to the five undisputed members of the Barset *genus* is as thorny a problem, in its own way, as that of the Gospel of St John to the three synoptic gospels, or, on equal plane, that of some of the Sherlock Holmes short stories of Sir Arthur Conan Doyle.

Allington is not in Barsetshire. Lily Dale is not a Barsetshire character (they breed girls like Mary Thorne and Lucy Robarts there). Johnny Eames is not at home in Barchester High Street. A noble farmer like the Earl of Guestwick has no place in the social structure of the county. It is like trying to put cockneys in Manchester, or Glaswegians into Suffolk. They do not belong. They have many merits, but their roots are in the wrong soil, and it is useless their trying to masquerade as Barcastrians.

Trollope was well aware of this, and it was with reluctance that *The Small House* was included in the first collected edition of the immortal *Chronicles of Barsetshire*. He did so, as Michael Sadleir records in his masterly *Trollope, A Commentary*, on the advice of his friends and publishers but against his better judgment. But admitted they have been, and who now can bar the door? Yet Johnny Eames and Lily Dale must understand they lack full family rights in Barset realms. They are guests—welcome guests—but guests withal.

Doctor Thorne is a grand book, and I would not wish to dispute against the dicta of many able critics who say it is the best book Trollope ever wrote. (They always point out at the same time—and with some cynicism, I think—that the plot was suggested by Anthony's brother, Thomas Adolphus. All thanks, then, to Thomas Adolphus.) Yet what greater thanks must be accorded Anthony for that genial, forthright figure of the good doctor. As for Mary Thorne, who does not love her?

In Praise of Barsetshire

Indeed, of all Barset towns and villages—the cathedral city itself apart—I should like best to reside in Greshamsbury. It is a snug, comfortable place, and the way in which the main street turns at right angles—it may be recalled that the entrance to Greshamsbury House lies in the angle, with the park gates on the other side—must add infinite charm to a village where it always seems like a warm Sunday afternoon in June. I have no doubt, too, but that Caleb Oriel is at once the most able and most conscientious parson to be found in the whole of the county.

Framley would be my second choice, were nothing vacant in Greshamsbury, though I doubt if the sermons of Mark Robarts—and certainly not those of his Welsh curate—match the honest sense and deep learning of Oriel. Were I poor I might resent the patronage of the Dowager Lady Lufton, but perhaps find compensation in the charm of the vicar's wife.

Yet, as a rabid Trollopian and fervent lover of Barsetshire, and with critics saying what they like, I plump for *Barchester Towers* as the best novel of them all. It is at once the foundation and corner stone of the whole wonderful structure of Barsetshire. It has more good chapters, more fine characters, more rich scenes and more colour than any other. Where else can one find people like the obnoxious Mr Slope, and the dazzling Signora Madeline Vesey Neroni? Where else does Archdeacon Grantly evince such terrible and awful wrath? Take away the other chronicles (which heaven forbid!) and Barsetshire would still remain. Take away *Barchester Towers*, and the county would be like the rim of a wheel without its hub.

We are introduced to Barsetshire for the first time in *The Warden*, but in that short novel the full glory and intimacy of the Barcastrian scene is only hinted at. We see the place, as it were, in the guise of a week-end visitor, and can do little more than go round Hiram's Hospital in the company of Mr Harding. We get a glimpse of the palace, but old Bishop Grantly is ageing fast, and we cannot linger in the palace rooms.

It is in *Barchester Towers* that our brief acquaintance ripens into something so much more, into something so rich and fascinating, that by the time we are invited out to the rural sports at Ullathorne we can claim standing as accepted residents. We are on visiting terms with at least the minor canons, and have been there long enough to take our stand with the Grantly faction in the great dispute with the Proudie party. By no means strangers to the drawing-room at Plumstead, we support our side hot and strong. We have "arrived"; we have left our cards and they have been returned.

Our friendships have begun, and we can explore the rest of Barset at our leisure, wandering through Greshamsbury Park, taking tea at Framley, listening to family secrets at Courcy, learning much of the miseries at Hogglestock, and, even, attaining the glory of a dinner with the great Duke at Gatherum itself. The great houses and the lesser, the rich parsonages and the poor, all open wide their doors and bid us welcome. As we get to know the Barset folk we learn much of their whims and foibles, of their snobberies and weaknesses; but the more we learn their faults the more we respect and like them. We forgive them readily. They are our friends for ever.

What real county can claim so much?

LANCE O. TINGAY

The Barset Anthology

Barsetshire

There is a county in the west of England not so full of life, indeed, nor so widely spoken of as some of its manufacturing leviathan brethren in the north, but which is, nevertheless, very dear to those who know it well. Its green pastures, its waving wheat, its deep and shady and—let us add—dirty lanes, its paths and stiles, its tawny-coloured, well-built rural churches, its avenues of beeches, and frequent Tudor mansions, its constant county hunt, its social graces, and the general air of clanship which pervades it, has made it to its own inhabitants a favoured land of Goshen. It is purely agricultural; agricultural in its produce, agricultural in its poor, and agricultural in its pleasures. There are towns in it, of course, depots from whence are brought seeds and groceries, ribbons and fire-shovels; in which markets are held and county balls are carried on; which return members to Parliament, generally—in spite of Reform Bills, past, present, and coming in—in accordance with the dictates of some neighbouring land magnate: from whence emanate the country postmen, and where is located the supply of post-horses necessary for county visitings. But these towns add nothing to the importance of the county; they consist, with the exception of the assize town, of dull, all but death-like single streets. Each possesses two pumps, three hotels, ten shops, fifteen beer-houses, a beadle, and a market place.

D. T.

A Barsetshire Worthy—
Archdeacon Grantly

His Symbolism

. . . the decorous breeches, and neat black gaiters showing so admirably that well-turned leg, betokened the decency, the outward beauty, and grace of our church establishment.

W.

The Archdeacon becomes Human

He has all the dignity of an ancient saint with the sleekness of a modern bishop; he is always the same; he is always the archdeacon; unlike Homer, he never nods. Even with his father-in-law, even with the bishop and dean, he maintains that sonorous tone and lofty deportment which strikes awe into the young hearts of Barchester, and absolutely cows the whole parish of Plumstead Episcopi. 'Tis only when he has exchanged that ever-new shovel hat for a tasselled nightcap, and those shining black habiliments for his accustomed *robe de nuit*, that Dr Grantly talks, and looks, and thinks like an ordinary man.

W.

THE ARCHDEACON PREPARES A SERMON

He then walked across the room and locked the door; and having so prepared himself, he threw himself into his easy chair, took from a secret drawer beneath his table a volume of Rabelais, and began to amuse himself with the witty mischief of Panurge; and so passed the archdeacon's morning on that day.

W.

THE ARCHDEACON BREAKFASTS

The tea consumed was the very best, the coffee the very blackest, the cream the very thickest; there was dry toast and buttered toast, muffins and crumpets; hot bread and cold bread, white bread and brown bread, home-made bread and bakers' bread, wheaten bread and oaten bread, and if there be other breads than these, they were there; there were eggs in napkins, and crispy bits of bacon under silver covers; and there were little fishes in a little box, and devilled kidneys frizzling on a hot-water dish; which, by-the-by, were placed closely contiguous to the plate of the worthy archdeacon himself. Over and above this, on a snow-white napkin, spread upon the sideboard, was a huge ham and a huge sirloin; the latter having laden the dinner table on the previous evening. Such was the ordinary fare at Plumstead Episcopi.

W.

THE ARCHDEACON COMPROMISES

He certainly was not prepared to cross himself, or to advocate the real presence; but, without going this length, there were various observances, by adopting which he could plainly show his antipathy to such men as Dr Proudie and Mr Slope.

B. T.

THE ARCHDEACON EMULATES ST FRANCIS

. . . as he walked across the hallowed close . . . the ravens . . . cawed with a peculiar reverence as he wended his way . . .

W.

THE ARCHDEACON LETS OFF STEAM

"Good heavens!" exclaimed the archdeacon, as he placed his foot on the gravel walk of the close, and raising his hat with one hand, passed the other somewhat violently over his now grizzled locks; smoke issued forth from the uplifted beaver as it were a cloud of wrath, and the safety valve of his anger opened, and emitted a visible steam, preventing positive explosion and probable apoplexy.

B. T.

Two Bishops—and Another—
and Bertie

BISHOP GRANTLY
The bishop did not whistle; we believe that they lose the power of doing so on being consecrated.

W.

BISHOP PROUDIE
He bore with the idolatry of Rome, tolerated even the infidelity of Socinianism, and was hand in glove with the Presbyterian Synods of Scotland and Ulster.

B. T.

REV MR SLOPE (I)
His face is nearly of the same colour as his hair, though perhaps a little redder: it is not unlike beef—beef, however, one would say, of a bad quality.

B. T.

REV MR SLOPE (II)
His nose . . . is his redeeming feature: it is pronounced, straight and well formed; though I myself should have liked it better did it

not possess a somewhat spongy, porous appearance, as though it had been cleverly formed out of a red coloured cork.

B. T.

ETHELBERT STANHOPE (I)

. . . he had been converted to the Mother Church . . . was already an acolyte of the Jesuits . . . and was about to start with others to Palestine on a mission for converting Jews. He did go to Judea, but being unable to convert the Jews, was converted by them.

B. T.

ETHELBERT STANHOPE (II)

He was habitually addicted to making love to ladies . . .

B. T.

The Obstinacy of
Septimus Harding

"**D**r Grantly is here, sir," greeted his ears before the door was well open, "and Mrs Grantly; they have a sitting-room above, and are waiting up for you."

There was something in the tone of the man's voice which seemed to indicate that even he looked upon the warden as a runaway school-boy, just recaptured by his guardian, and that he pitied the culprit, though he could not but be horrified at the crime.

The warden endeavoured to appear unconcerned, as he said, "Oh, indeed! I'll go upstairs at once;" but he failed signally: there was perhaps a ray of comfort in the presence of his married daughter; that is to say, of comparative comfort, seeing that his son-in-law was there: but how much would he have preferred that they should both have been safe at Plumstead Episcopi! However, upstairs he went, the waiter slowly preceding him; and on the door being opened the archdeacon was discovered standing in the middle of the room, erect, indeed, as usual, but oh! how sorrowful! and on a dingy sofa behind him reclined his patient wife.

"Papa, I thought you were never coming back," said the lady; "it's twelve o'clock."

"Yes, my dear," said the warden. "The attorney-general named ten for my meeting; to be sure ten is late, but what could I do, you know? Great men will have their own way."

And he gave his daughter a kiss, and shook hands with the doctor, and again tried to look unconcerned.

"And you have absolutely been with the attorney-general?" asked the archdeacon.

Mr Harding signified that he had.

"Good heavens, how unfortunate!" And the archdeacon raised his huge hands in the manner in which his friends are so accustomed to see him express disapprobation and astonishment. "What will Sir Abraham think of it? Did you not know that it is not customary for clients to go direct to their counsel?"

"Isn't it?" asked the warden, innocently. "Well, at any rate, I've done it now. Sir Abraham didn't seem to think it so very strange."

The archdeacon gave a sigh that would have moved a man-of-war.

"But, papa, what did you say to Sir Abraham?" asked the lady.

"I asked him, my dear, to explain John Hiram's will to me. He couldn't explain it in the only way which would have satisfied me, and so I resigned the wardenship."

"Resigned it!" said the archdeacon, in a solemn voice, sad and low, but yet sufficiently audible; a sort of whisper that Macready would have envied, and the galleries have applauded with a couple of rounds. "Resigned it! Good heavens!" and the dignitary of the church sank back horrified into a horsehair armchair.

"At least I told Sir Abraham that I would resign; and of course I must now do so."

"Not at all," said the archdeacon, catching a ray of hope. "Nothing that you say in such a way to your own counsel can be in any way binding on you; of course you were there to ask his advice. I'm sure Sir Abraham did not advise any such step."

Mr Harding could not say that he had.

"I am sure he disadvised you from it," continued the reverend cross-examiner.

Mr Harding could not deny this.

"I'm sure Sir Abraham must have advised you to consult your friends."

To this proposition also Mr Harding was obliged to assent.

"Then your threat of resignation amounts to nothing, and we are just where we were before."

Mr Harding was now standing on the rug, moving uneasily from one foot to the other. He made no distinct answer to the archdeacon's last proposition, for his mind was chiefly engaged on thinking how he could escape to bed. That his resignation was a thing finally fixed on, a fact all but completed, was not in his mind a matter of any doubt; he knew his own weakness; he knew how prone he was to be led; but he was not weak enough to give way now, to go back from the position to which his conscience had driven him, after having purposely come to London to declare his determination: he did not in the least doubt his resolution, but he greatly doubted his power of defending it against his son-in-law.

"You must be very tired, Susan," said he: "wouldn't you like to go to bed?"

But Susan didn't want to go till her husband went—she had an idea that her papa might be bullied if she were away: she wasn't tired at all, or at least she said so.

The archdeacon was pacing the room, expressing, by certain noddles of his head, his opinion of the utter fatuity of his father-in-law.

"Why," at last he said—and angels might have blushed at the rebuke expressed in his tone and emphasis—"Why did you go off from Barchester so suddenly? Why did you take such a step without giving us notice, after what had passed at the palace?"

The warden hung his head, and made no reply; he could not condescend to say that he had not intended to give his son-in-law the slip; and as he had not the courage to avow it, he said nothing.

"Papa has been too much for you," said the lady.

The archdeacon took another turn, and again ejaculated, "Good heavens!" this time in a very low whisper, but still audible.

"I think I'll go to bed," said the warden, taking up a side candle.

"At any rate, you'll promise me to take no further step without consultation," said the archdeacon. Mr Harding made no answer, but slowly proceeded to light his candle. "Of course," continued the other, "such a declaration as that you made to Sir Abraham means nothing. Come, warden, promise me this. The whole affair, you see, is already settled, and that with very little trouble or expense. Bold has been compelled to abandon his action, and all you have to do is to remain quiet at the hospital." Mr Harding still made no reply, but looked meekly into his son-in-law's face. The archdeacon thought he knew his father-in-law, but he was mistaken; he thought that he had already talked over a vacillating man to resign his promise. "Come," said he, "promise Susan to give up this idea of resigning the wardenship."

The warden looked at his daughter, thinking probably at the moment that if Eleanor were contented with him, he need not so much regard his other child, and said, "I am sure Susan will not ask me to break my word, or to do what I know to be wrong."

"Papa," said she, "it would be madness in you to throw up your preferment. What are you to live on?"

"God, that feeds the young ravens, will take care of me also," said Mr Harding, with a smile, as though afraid of giving offence by making his reference to scripture too solemn.

"Pish!" said the archdeacon, turning away rapidly; "if the ravens persisted in refusing the food prepared for them, they wouldn't be fed." A clergyman generally dislikes to be met in argument by a scriptural quotation; he feels as affronted as a doctor does, when recommended by an old woman to take some favourite dose, or as a lawyer when an unprofessional man attempts to put him down by a quibble.

"I shall have the living of Crabtree," modestly suggested the warden.

"Eighty pounds a year!" sneered the archdeacon.

"And the precentorship," said the father-in-law.

"It goes with the wardenship," said the son-in-law. Mr Harding was prepared to argue this point, and began to do so, but Dr Grantly stopped him. "My dear warden," said he, "this is all nonsense. Eighty pounds or a hundred and sixty makes very little difference. You can't live on it—you can't ruin Eleanor's prospects for ever. In point of fact, you can't resign; the bishop wouldn't accept it; the whole thing is settled. What I now want to do is to prevent any inconvenient tittle tattle,—any more newspaper articles."

"That's what I want, too," said the warden.

"And to prevent that," continued the other, "we mustn't let any talk of resignation get abroad."

"But I shall resign," said the warden, very, very meekly.

"Good heavens! Susan, my dear, what can I say to him?"

"But, papa," said Mrs Grantly, getting up, and putting her arm through that of her father, "what is Eleanor to do if you throw away your income?"

A hot tear stood in each of the warden's eyes as he looked round upon his married daughter. Why should one sister who was so rich predict poverty for another? Some such idea as this was on his mind, but he gave no utterance to it. Then he thought of the pelican feeding its young with blood from its own breast, but he gave no utterance to that either; and then of Eleanor waiting for him at home, waiting to congratulate him on the end of all his trouble.

The Obstinacy of Septimus Harding

"Think of Eleanor, papa," said Mrs Grantly.

"I do think of her," said her father.

"And you will not do this rash thing?" The lady was really moved beyond her usual calm composure.

"It can never be rash to do right," said he. "I shall certainly resign this wardenship."

"Then, Mr Harding, there is nothing before you but ruin," said the archdeacon, now moved beyond all endurance, "ruin both for you and Eleanor. How do you mean to pay the monstrous expenses of this action?"

Mrs Grantly suggested that, as the action was abandoned, the costs would not be heavy.

"Indeed they will, my dear," continued he. "One cannot have the attorney-general up at twelve o'clock at night for nothing;—but of course your father has not thought of this."

"I will sell my furniture," said the warden.

"Furniture!" ejaculated the other, with a most powerful sneer.

"Come, archdeacon," said the lady, "we needn't mind that at present. You know you never expected papa to pay the costs."

"Such absurdity is enough to provoke Job," said the archdeacon, marching quickly up and down the room. "Your father is like a child. Eight hundred pounds a year!—eight hundred and eighty with the house—with nothing to do. The very place for him. And to throw that up because some scoundrel writes an article in a newspaper! Well—I have done my duty. If he chooses to ruin his child I cannot help it;" and he stood still at the fireplace, and looked at himself in a dingy mirror which stood on the chimney-piece.

There was a pause for about a minute, and then the warden, finding that nothing else was coming, lighted his candle, and quietly said, "Good night."

"Good night, papa," said the lady.

And so the warden retired: but, as he closed the door behind him, he heard the well-known ejaculation—slower, lower, more solemn, more ponderous than ever—"Good heavens!"

W.

37

HUMANITY

    The cross-grainedness of men is so great that things will often be forced to go wrong, even when they have the strongest possible natural tendency of their own to go right.

L. C.

VENERABLE WISDOM

    "I always button up my pocket when I hear of scruples."—*Archdeacon Grantly*.

L. C.

The Proudies Entertain

"**B**ishop of Barchester, I presume?" said Bertie Stanhope, putting out his hand, frankly; "I am delighted to make your acquaintance. We are in rather close quarters here, a'nt we?"

In truth they were. They had been crowded up behind the head of the sofa: the bishop in waiting to receive his guest, and the other in carrying her; and they now had hardly room to move themselves.

The bishop gave his hand quickly, and made his little studied bow, and was delighted to make——. He couldn't go on, for he did not know whether his friend was a signor, or a count, or a prince.

"My sister really puts you all to great trouble," said Bertie.

"Not at all!" The bishop was delighted to have the opportunity of welcoming the Signora Vicinironi—so at least he said—and attempted to force his way round to the front of the sofa. He had, at any rate, learnt that his strange guests were brother and sister. The man, he presumed, must be Signor Vicinironi—or count, or prince, as it might be. It was wonderful what good English he spoke. There was just a twang of foreign accent, and no more.

"Do you like Barchester on the whole?" asked Bertie.

The bishop, looking dignified, said that he did like Barchester.

"You've not been here very long, I believe," said Bertie.

"No—not long," said the bishop, and tried again to make his way between the back of the sofa and a heavy rector, who was staring over it at the grimaces of the signora.

"You weren't a bishop before, were you?"

Dr Proudie explained that this was the first diocese he had held.

"Ah—I thought so," said Bertie; "but you are changed about sometimes, a'nt you?"

"Translations are occasionally made," said Dr Proudie; "but not so frequently as in former days."

"They've cut them all down to pretty nearly the same figure, haven't they?" said Bertie.

To this the bishop could not bring himself to make any answer, but again attempted to move the rector.

"But the work, I suppose, is different?" continued Bertie. "Is there much to do here, at Barchester?" This was said exactly in the tone that a young Admiralty clerk might use in asking the same question of a brother acolyte at the Treasury.

"The work of a bishop of the Church of England", said Dr Proudie, with considerable dignity, "is not easy. The responsibility which he has to bear is very great indeed."

"Is it?" said Bertie, opening wide his wonderful blue eyes. "Well, I never was afraid of responsibility. I once had thoughts of being a bishop myself."

"Had thoughts of being a bishop!" said Dr Proudie, much amazed.

"That is, a parson—a parson first, you know, and a bishop afterwards. If I had once begun, I'd have stuck to it. But, on the whole, I like the Church of Rome the best."

The bishop could not discuss the point, so he remained silent.

"Now, there's my father," continued Bertie; "he hasn't stuck to it. I fancy he didn't like saying the same thing over so often. By the by, Bishop, have you seen my father?"

The bishop was more amazed than ever. Had he seen his father? "No," he replied; "he had not yet had the pleasure: he hoped he might;" and, as he said so, he resolved to bear heavy on that fat, immovable rector, if ever he had the power of doing so.

"He's in the room somewhere," said Bertie, "and he'll turn up soon. By the by, do you know much about the Jews?"

At last the bishop saw a way out. "I beg your pardon," said he, "but I'm forced to go round the room."

"Well—I believe I'll follow in your wake," said Bertie. "Terribly hot—isn't it?" This he addressed to the fat rector with whom he had brought himself into the closest contact. "They've got this sofa

40

into the worst possible part of the room; suppose we move it. Take care, Madeline."

The sofa had certainly been so placed that those who were behind it found great difficulty in getting out;—there was but a narrow gangway, which one person could stop. This was a bad arrangement, and one which Bertie thought it might be well to improve.

"Take care, Madeline," said he; and turning to the fat rector added, "Just help me with a slight push."

The rector's weight was resting on the sofa, and unwittingly lent all its impetus to accelerate and increase the motion which Bertie intentionally originated. The sofa rushed from its moorings, and ran half-way into the middle of the room. Mrs Proudie was standing with Mr Slope in front of the signora, and had been trying to be condescending and sociable; but she was not in the very best of tempers; for she found that, whenever she spoke to the lady, the lady replied by speaking to Mr Slope. Mr Slope was a favourite, no doubt; but Mrs Proudie had no idea of being less thought of than the chaplain. She was beginning to be stately, stiff, and offended when unfortunately the castor of the sofa caught itself in her lace train, and carried away there is no saying how much of her garniture. Gathers were heard to go, stitches to crack, plaits to fly open, flounces were seen to fall, and breadths to expose themselves;—a long ruin of rent lace disfigured the carpet, and still clung to the vile wheel on which the sofa moved.

So, when a granite battery is raised, excellent to the eyes of warfaring men, is its strength and symmetry admired. It is the work of years. Its neat embrasures, its finished parapets, its casemated stories, show all the skill of modern science. But, anon, a small spark is applied to the treacherous fusee—a cloud of dust arises to the heavens—and then nothing is to be seen but dirt and dust and ugly fragments.

We know what was the wrath of Juno when her beauty was despised. We know, too, what storms of passion even celestial minds can yield. As Juno may have looked at Paris on Mount Ida, so did Mrs Proudie look on Ethelbert Stanhope when he pushed the leg of the sofa into her lace train.

"Oh, you idiot, Bertie!" said the signora, seeing what had been done, and what were to be the consequences.

"Idiot!" re-echoed Mrs Proudie, as though the word were not half strong enough to express the required meaning. "I'll let him know——;" and then looking round to learn, at a glance, the worst, she saw that at present it behoved her to collect the scattered *débris* of her dress.

Bertie, when he saw what he had done, rushed over to the sofa, and threw himself on one knee before the offended lady. His object, doubtless, was to liberate the torn lace from the castor; but he looked as though he were imploring pardon from a goddess.

"Unhand it, sir!" said Mrs Proudie. From what scrap of dramatic poetry she had extracted the word cannot be said; but it must have rested on her memory, and now seemed opportunely dignified for the occasion.

"I'll fly to the looms of the fairies to repair the damage, if you'll only forgive me," said Ethelbert, still on his knees.

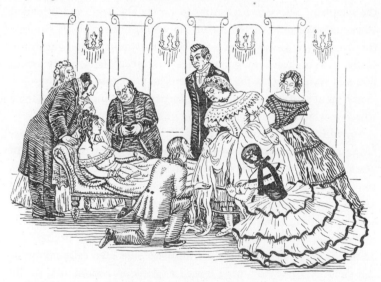

"Unhand it, sir!" said Mrs Proudie, with redoubled emphasis, and all but furious wrath. This allusion to the fairies was a direct mockery, and intended to turn her into ridicule. So at least it seemed to her. "Unhand it, sir!" she almost screamed.

"It's not me; it's the cursed sofa," said Bertie, looking imploringly in her face, and holding up both his hands to show that he was not touching her belongings, but still remaining on his knees.

Hereupon the signora laughed; not loud, indeed, but yet audibly. And as the tigress bereft of her young will turn with equal anger on any within reach, so did Mrs Proudie turn upon her female guest.

"Madam!" she said—and it is beyond the power of prose to tell of the fire which flashed from her eyes.

The signora stared her full in the face for a moment, and then turning to her brother said playfully, "Bertie, you idiot, get up."

By this time the bishop, and Mr Slope, and her three daughters were around her, and had collected together the wide ruins of her magnificence. The girls fell into circular rank behind their mother, and thus following her and carrying out the fragments, they left the reception rooms in a manner not altogether devoid of dignity. Mrs Proudie had to retire and re-array herself.

As soon as the constellation had swept by, Ethelbert rose from his knees, and turning with mock anger to the fat rector, said: "After all it was your doing, sir—not mine. But perhaps you are waiting for preferment, and so I bore it."

Whereupon there was a laugh against the fat rector, in which both the bishop and the chaplain joined; and thus things got themselves again into order.

"Oh! my lord, I am so sorry for this accident," said the signora, putting out her hand so as to force the bishop to take it. "My brother is so thoughtless. Pray sit down, and let me have the pleasure of making your acquaintance. Though I am so poor a creature as to want a sofa, I am not so selfish as to require it all." Madeline could always dispose herself so as to make room for a gentleman, though, as she declared, the crinoline of her lady friends was much too bulky to be so accommodated.

"It was solely for the pleasure of meeting you that I have had myself dragged here," she continued. "Of course, with your occupation, one cannot even hope that you should have time to come to us, that is, in the way of calling. And at your English dinner-parties all is so dull and so stately. Do you know, my lord, that in coming to England my only consolation has been the thought that I should know you;" and she looked at him with the look of a she-devil.

The bishop, however, thought that she looked very like an angel, and accepting the proffered seat, sat down beside her. He uttered some platitude as to his deep obligation for the trouble she had taken, and wondered more and more who she was.

"Of course you know my sad story?" she continued.

The bishop didn't know a word of it. He knew, however, or thought he knew, that she couldn't walk into a room like other people, and so made the most of that. He put on a look of ineffable distress, and said that he was aware how God had afflicted her.

The signora just touched the corner of her eyes with the most lovely of pocket-handkerchiefs. Yes, she said—she had been sorely tried—tried, she thought, beyond the common endurance of humanity; but while her child was left to her, everything was left. "Oh! my lord," she exclaimed, "you must see that infant—the last bud of a wondrous tree: you must let a mother hope that you will lay your holy hands on her innocent head, and consecrate her for female virtues. May I hope it?" said she, looking into the bishop's eye, and touching the bishop's arm with her hand.

The bishop was but a man, and said she might. After all, what was it but a request that he would confirm her daughter?—a request, indeed, very unnecessary to make, as he should do so as a matter of course, if the young lady came forward in the usual way.

"The blood of Tiberius," said the signora, in all but a whisper; "the blood of Tiberius flows in her veins. She is the last of the Neros!"

The bishop had heard of the last of the Visigoths, and had floating in his brain some indistinct idea of the last of the Mohicans, but to have the last of the Neros thus brought before him for a blessing was very staggering. Still, he liked the lady: she had a proper way of thinking, and talked with more propriety than her brother. But who were they? It was not quite clear that that blue madman with the silky beard was not a Prince Vicinironi. The lady was married, and was of course one of the Vicinironis by right of the husband. So the bishop went on learning.

"When will you see her?" said the signora with a start.

"See whom?" said the bishop.

"My child," said the mother.

"What is the young lady's age?" asked the bishop.

"She is just seven," said the signora.

"Oh," said the bishop, shaking his head, "she is much too young—very much too young."

"But in sunny Italy, you know, we do not count by the years," and the signora gave the bishop one of her sweetest smiles.

"But indeed, she is a great deal too young," persisted the bishop, "we never confirm before——"

"But you might speak to her; you might let her hear from your consecrated lips, that she is not a castaway because she is a Roman; that she may be a Nero and yet a Christian; that she may owe her black locks and dark cheeks to the blood of the pagan Caesars, and yet herself be a child of grace; you will tell her this, won't you, my friend?"

The friend said he would, and asked if the child could say her catechism.

"No," said the signora, "I would not allow her to learn lessons such as those in a land ridden over by priests, and polluted by the idolatry of Rome. It was here, in Barchester, that she must first be taught to lisp those holy words. Oh, that you could be her instructor!"

Now, Dr Proudie certainly liked the lady, but, seeing that he was a bishop, it was not probable that he was going to instruct a little girl in the first rudiments of her catechism; so he said he'd send a teacher.

"But you'll see her, yourself, my lord?"

The bishop said he would, but where should he call?

"At papa's house," said the signora, with an air of some little surprise at the question.

The bishop actually wanted the courage to ask her who was her papa; so he was forced at last to leave her without fathoming the mystery. Mrs Proudie, in her second best, had now returned to the rooms, and her husband thought it as well that he should not remain in too close conversation with the lady whom his wife appeared to hold in such slight esteem. Presently he came across his youngest daughter.

"Netta," said he, "do you know who is the father of that Signora Vicinironi?"

"It isn't Vicinironi, papa," said Netta; "but Vesey Neroni, and she's Doctor Stanhope's daughter. But I must go and do the civil to Griselda Grantly; I declare nobody has spoken a word to the poor girl this evening."

Dr Stanhope! Dr Vesey Stanhope! Dr Vesey Stanhope's daughter, of whose marriage with a dissolute Italian scamp he now remembered to have heard something! And that impertinent blue cub who had examined him as to his episcopal bearings was old Stanhope's son, and the lady who had entreated him to come and teach her child the catechism was old Stanhope's daughter! the daughter of one of his own prebendaries! As these things flashed across his mind, he was nearly as angry as his wife had been. Nevertheless, he could not but own that the mother of the last of the Neros was an agreeable woman.

Dr Proudie tripped out into the adjoining room, in which were congregated a crowd of Grantlyite clergymen, among whom the archdeacon was standing pre-eminent, while the old dean was sitting buried in a huge armchair by the fire-place. The bishop was very anxious to be gracious, and, if possible, to diminish the bitterness which his chaplain had occasioned. Let Mr Slope do the *fortiter in re*, he himself would pour in the *suaviter in modo*.

"Pray don't stir, Mr Dean, pray don't stir," he said, as the old man essayed to get up; "I take it as a great kindness your coming to such an *omnium gatherum* as this. Well, Mr Archdeacon, after all, we have not been so hard upon you at Oxford."

"No," said the archdeacon, "you've only drawn our teeth and cut out our tongues; you've allowed us still to breathe and swallow."

"Ha, ha, ha!" laughed the bishop. "It's not quite so easy to cut out the tongue of an Oxford magnate—and as for teeth—ha, ha, ha! Why, in the way we've left the matter, it's very odd if the heads of colleges don't have their own way quite as fully as when the hebdomadal board was in all its glory; what do you say, Mr Dean?"

"An old man, my lord, never likes changes," said the dean.

"You must have been sad bunglers if it is so," said the archdeacon; "and indeed, to tell the truth, I think you have bungled it. At any rate, you must own this; you have not done the half what you boasted you would do."

"Now, as regards your system of professors——" began the chancellor slowly. He was never destined to get beyond such beginning.

"Talking of professors," said a soft clear voice, close behind the chancellor's elbow; "how much you Englishmen might learn from Germany; only you are all too proud."

The bishop looking round, perceived that that abominable young Stanhope had pursued him. The dean stared at him, as though he were some unearthly apparition; so also did two or three prebendaries and minor canons. The archdeacon laughed.

"The German professors are men of learning," said Mr Harding, "but——"

"German professors!" groaned out the chancellor, as though his nervous system had received a shock which nothing but a week of Oxford air could cure.

"Yes," continued Ethelbert; not at all understanding why a German professor should be contemptible in the eyes of an Oxford don. "Not but what the name is best earned at Oxford. In Germany the professors do teach; at Oxford, I believe they only profess to do so, and sometimes not even that. You'll have those universities of yours about your ears soon, if you don't consent to take a lesson from Germany."

There was no answering this. Dignified clergymen of sixty years of age could not condescend to discuss such a matter with a young man with such clothes and such a beard.

47

"Have you got good water out at Plumstead, Mr Archdeacon?" said the bishop, by way of changing the conversation.

"Pretty good," said Dr Grantly.

"But by no means so good as his wine, my lord," said a witty minor canon.

"Nor so generally used," said another; "that is for inward application."

"Ha, ha, ha!" laughed the bishop, "a good cellar of wine is a very comfortable thing in a house."

"Your German professors, sir, prefer beer, I believe," said the sarcastic, little, meagre prebendary.

"They don't think much of either," said Ethelbert; "and that perhaps accounts for their superiority. Now the Jewish professor——"

The insult was becoming too deep for the spirit of Oxford to endure, so the archdeacon walked off one way and the chancellor another, followed by their disciples, and the bishop and the young reformer were left together on the hearth-rug.

"I was a Jew once myself," began Bertie.

The bishop was determined not to stand another examination, or be led on any terms into Palestine; so he again remembered that he had to do something very particular, and left young Stanhope with the dean. The dean did not get the worst of it, for Ethelbert gave him a true account of his remarkable doings in the Holy Land.

"Oh, Mr Harding," said the bishop, overtaking the *ci-devant* warden; "I wanted to say one word about the hospital. You know, of course, that it is to be filled up."

Mr Harding's heart beat a little, and he said that he had heard so.

"Of course," continued the bishop, "there can be only one man whom I could wish to see in that situation. I don't know what your own views may be, Mr Harding——"

"They are very simply told, my lord," said the other; "to take the place if it be offered me, and to put up with the want of it should another man get it."

The bishop professed himself delighted to hear it; Mr Harding might be quite sure that no other man would get it. There were some few circumstances which would in a slight degree change the nature of the duties. Mr Harding was probably aware of this, and would, perhaps, not object to discuss the matter with Mr Slope. It was a subject to which Mr Slope had given a good deal of attention.

Mr Harding felt, he knew not why, oppressed and annoyed. What could Mr Slope do to him? He knew that there were to be changes. The nature of them must be communicated to the warden through somebody, and through whom so naturally as the bishop's chaplain? 'Twas thus he tried to argue himself back to an easy mind, but in vain.

Mr Slope in the meantime had taken the seat which the bishop had vacated on the signora's sofa, and remained with that lady till it was time to marshal the folk to supper. Not with contented eyes had Mrs Proudie seen this. Had not this woman laughed at her distress, and had not Mr Slope heard it? Was she not an intriguing Italian woman, half wife and half not, full of affectation, airs and impudence? Was she not horribly bedizened with velvet and pearls, with velvet and pearls, too, which had not been torn off her back? Above all, did she not pretend to be more beautiful than her neighbours? To say that Mrs Proudie was jealous would give a wrong idea of her feelings. She had not the slightest desire that Mr Slope should be in love with herself. But she desired the incense of Mr Slope's spiritual and temporal services, and did not choose that they should be turned out of their course to such an object as Signora Neroni. She considered also that Mr Slope ought in duty to hate the signora; and it appeared from his manner that he was very far from hating her.

"Come, Mr Slope," she said, sweeping by, and looking all that she felt; "can't you make yourself useful? Do pray take Mrs Grantly down to supper."

Mrs Grantly heard and escaped. The words were hardly out of Mrs Proudie's mouth, before the intended victim had struck her hand through the arm of one of her husband's curates, and saved herself. What would the archdeacon have said had he seen her walking down-stairs with Mr Slope?

Mr Slope heard also, but was by no means so obedient as was

expected. Indeed, the period of Mr Slope's obedience to Mrs Proudie was drawing to a close. He did not wish yet to break with her, nor to break with her at all, if it could be avoided. But he intended to be master in that palace, and as she had made the same resolution it was not improbable that they might come to blows.

Before leaving the signora he arranged a little table before her, and begged to know what he should bring her. She was quite indifferent, she said—nothing—anything. It was now she felt the misery of her position, now that she must be left alone. Well, a little chicken, some ham, and a glass of champagne.

Mr Slope had to explain, not without blushing for his patron, that there was no champagne.

Sherry would do just as well. And then Mr Slope descended with the learned Miss Trefoil on his arm. Could she tell him, he asked, whether the ferns of Barsetshire were equal to those of Cumberland? His strongest worldly passion was for ferns—and before she could answer him he left her wedged between the door and the sideboard. It was fifty minutes before she escaped, and even then unfed.

"You are not leaving us, Mr Slope," said the watchful lady of the house, seeing her slave escaping towards the door, with stores of provisions held high above the heads of the guests.

Mr Slope explained that the Signora Neroni was in want of her supper.

"Pray, Mr Slope, let her brother take it to her," said Mrs Proudie, quite out loud. "It is out of the question that you should be so employed. Pray, Mr Slope, oblige me; I am sure Mr Stanhope will wait upon his sister."

Ethelbert was most agreeably occupied in the further corner of the room, making himself both useful and agreeable to Mrs Proudie's youngest daughter.

"I couldn't get out, madam, if Madeline were starving for her supper," said he; "I'm physically fixed, unless I could fly."

The lady's anger was increased by seeing that her daughter also had gone over to the enemy; and when she saw, that in spite of her remonstrances, in the teeth of her positive orders, Mr Slope went off to the drawing-room, the cup of her indignation ran over, and she could not restrain herself. "Such manners I never saw," she said, muttering. "I cannot, and will not permit it;" and then, after fussing and fuming for a few minutes, she pushed her way through the crowd, and followed Mr Slope.

When she reached the room above, she found it absolutely deserted except by the guilty pair. The signora was sitting very comfortably up to her supper, and Mr Slope was leaning over her and administering to her wants. They had been discussing the merits of Sabbath-day schools, and the lady had suggested that as she could not possibly go to the children, she might be indulged in the wish of her heart by having the children brought to her.

"And when shall it be, Mr Slope?" said she.

Mr Slope was saved the necessity of committing himself to a promise by the entry of Mrs Proudie. She swept close up to the sofa so as to confront the guilty pair, stared full at them for a moment, and then said as she passed on to the next room, "Mr Slope, his lordship is especially desirous of your attendance below; you will greatly oblige me if you will join him." And so she stalked on.

Mr Slope muttered something in reply, and prepared to go down-stairs. As for the bishop's wanting him, he knew his lady patroness well enough to take that assertion at what it was worth; but he did not wish to make himself the hero of a scene, or to become conspicuous for more gallantry than the occasion required.

"Is she always like this?" said the signora.

"Yes—always—madam," said Mrs Proudie, returning; "always the same—always equally adverse to impropriety of conduct of every description;" and she stalked back through the room again, following Mr Slope out of the door.

The signora couldn't follow her, or she certainly would have done so. But she laughed loud, and sent the sound of it ringing through the lobby and down the stairs after Mrs Proudie's feet. Had she been as active as Grimaldi, she could probably have taken no better revenge.

"Mr Slope," said Mrs Proudie, catching the delinquent at the door, "I am surprised that you should leave my company to attend on such a painted Jezebel as that."

"But she's lame, Mrs Proudie, and cannot move. Somebody must have waited upon her."

"Lame," said Mrs Proudie; "I'd lame her if she belonged to me. What business had she here at all?—such impertinence—such affectation."

In the hall and adjacent rooms all manner of cloaking and shawling was going on, and the Barchester folk were getting themselves gone. Mrs Proudie did her best to smirk at each and every one as they made their adieux, but she was hardly successful. Her temper had been tried fearfully. By slow degrees, the guests went.

"Send back the carriage quick," said Ethelbert, as Dr and Mrs Stanhope took their departure.

The younger Stanhopes were left to the very last, and an uncomfortable party they made with the bishop's family. They all went into the dining-room, and then the bishop, observing that "the lady" was alone in the drawing-room, they followed him up. Mrs Proudie kept Mr Slope and her daughters in close conversation, resolving that he should not be indulged, nor they polluted. The bishop, in mortal dread of Bertie and the Jews, tried to converse with Charlotte Stanhope about the climate of Italy. Bertie and the signora had no resource but in each other.

"Did you get your supper at last, Madeline?" said the impudent or else mischievous young man.

"Oh yes," said Madeline; "Mr Slope was so very kind as to bring it me. I fear, however, he put himself to more inconvenience than I wished."

Mrs Proudie looked at her, but said nothing. The meaning of her look might have been thus translated: "If ever you find yourself within these walls again, I'll give you leave to be as impudent and affected, and as mischievous as you please."

At last the carriage returned with the three Italian servants, and La Signora Madeline Vesey Neroni was carried out, as she had been carried in.

The Proudies Entertain

The lady of the palace retired to her chamber by no means contented with the result of her first grand party at Barchester.

B. T.

IMMORTALITY

As for Mrs Proudie, our hopes for her are that she may live for ever.

B. T.

MRS PROUDIE'S SMALL TALK

"Idolatry is, I believe, more rampant than ever in Rome," said she; "and I fear there is no such thing at all as Sabbath observances."

D. T.

Mrs Proudie Vanquished

It was hardly an hour since Mrs Proudie had left her husband's apartment victorious, and yet so indomitable was her courage that she now returned thither panting for another combat. She was greatly angry with what she thought was his duplicity. He had so clearly given her a promise on this matter of the hospital. He had been already so absolutely vanquished on that point. Mrs Proudie began to feel that if every affair was to be thus discussed and battled about twice and even thrice, the work of the diocese would be too much, even for her.

Without knocking at the door she walked quickly into her husband's room, and found him seated at his office table, with Mr Slope opposite to him. Between his fingers was the very note which he had written to the archbishop in her presence—and it was open! Yes, he had absolutely violated the seal which had been made sacred by her approval. They were sitting in deep conclave, and it was too clear that the purport of the archbishop's invitation had been absolutely canvassed again, after it had been already debated and decided on in obedience to her behests! Mr Slope rose from his chair, and bowed slightly. The two opposing spirits looked each other fully in the face, and they knew that they were looking each at an enemy.

"What is this, bishop, about Mr Quiverful?" said she, coming to the end of the table and standing there.

Mr Slope did not allow the bishop to answer, but replied himself. "I have been out to Puddingdale this morning, ma'am, and have seen Mr Quiverful. Mr Quiverful has abandoned his claim to the hospital, because he is now aware that Mr Harding is desirous to fill his old place. Under these circumstances I have strongly advised his lordship to nominate Mr Harding."

"Mr Quiverful has not abandoned anything," said the lady, with a very imperious voice. "His lordship's word has been pledged to him, and it must be respected."

The bishop still remained silent. He was anxiously desirous of making his old enemy bite the dust beneath his feet. His new ally had told him that nothing was more easy for him than to do so. The ally was there now at his elbow to help him, and yet his courage failed him. It is so hard to conquer when the prestige of former victories is all against one. It is so hard for the cock who has once been beaten out of his yard to resume his courage and again take a proud place upon a dunghill.

"Perhaps I ought not to interfere," said Mr Slope, "but yet——"

"Certainly you ought not," said the infuriated dame.

"But yet," continued Mr Slope, not regarding the interruption, "I have thought it my imperative duty to recommend the bishop not to slight Mr Harding's claims."

"Mr Harding should have known his own mind," said the lady.

"If Mr Harding be not replaced at the hospital, his lordship will have to encounter much ill will, not only in the diocese, but in the world at large. Besides, taking a higher ground, his lordship, as I understand, feels it to be his duty to gratify, in this matter, so very worthy a man and so good a clergyman as Mr Harding."

"And what is to become of the Sabbath-day school, and of the Sunday services in the hospital?" said Mrs Proudie, with something very nearly approaching to a sneer on her face.

"I understand that Mr Harding makes no objection to the Sabbath-day school," said Mr Slope. "And as to the hospital services, that matter will be best discussed after his appointment. If he has any permanent objection, then, I fear the matter must rest."

"You have a very easy conscience in such matters, Mr Slope," said she.

"I should not have an easy conscience," he rejoined, "but a conscience very far from being easy, if anything said or done by me should lead the bishop to act unadvisedly in this matter. It is clear that in the interview I had with Mr Harding, I misunderstood him——"

"And it is equally clear that you have misunderstood Mr Quiverful," said she, now at the top of her wrath. "What business have you at all with these interviews? Who desired you to go to Mr Quiverful this morning? Who commissioned you to manage this affair? Will you answer me, sir?—who sent you to Mr Quiverful this morning?"

There was a dead pause in the room. Mr Slope had risen from his chair, and was standing with his hand on the back of it, looking at first very solemn and now very black. Mrs Proudie was standing as she had at first placed herself, at the end of the table, and as she interrogated her foe she struck her hand upon it with almost more than feminine vigour. The bishop was sitting in his easy chair twiddling his thumbs, turning his eyes now to his wife, and now to his chaplain, as each took up the cudgels. How comfortable it would be if they could fight it out between them without the necessity of any interference on his part; fight it out so that one should kill the other utterly, as far as diocesan life was concerned, so that he, the bishop, might know clearly by whom it behoved him to be led. There would be the comfort of quiet in either case; but if the bishop had a wish as to which might prove the victor, that wish was certainly not antagonistic to Mr Slope.

"Better the d—— you know than the d—— you don't know", is an old saying, and perhaps a true one; but the bishop had not yet realized the truth of it.

"Will you answer me, sir?" she repeated. "Who instructed you to call on Mr Quiverful this morning?" There was another pause. "Do you intend to answer me, sir?"

"I think, Mrs Proudie, that under all the circumstances it will be better for me not to answer such a question," said Mr Slope. Mr Slope had many tones in his voice, all duly under his command; among them was a sanctified low tone, and a sanctified loud tone; and he now used the former.

"Did anyone send you, sir?"

"Mrs Proudie," said Mr Slope, "I am quite aware how much I

owe to your kindness. I am aware also what is due by courtesy from a gentleman to a lady. But there are higher considerations than either of those, and I hope I shall be forgiven if I now allow myself to be actuated solely by them. My duty in this matter is to his lordship, and I can admit of no questioning but from him. He has approved of what I have done, and you must excuse me if I say, that having that approval and my own, I want none other."

What horrid words were these which greeted the ear of Mrs Proudie? The matter was indeed too clear. There was premeditated mutiny in the camp. Not only had ill-conditioned minds become insubordinate by the fruition of a little power, but sedition had been overtly taught and preached. The bishop had not yet been twelve months in his chair, and rebellion had already reared her hideous head within the palace. Anarchy and misrule would quickly follow, unless she took immediate and strong measures to put down the conspiracy which she had detected.

"Mr Slope," she said, with slow and dignified voice, differing much from that which she had hitherto used, "Mr Slope, I will trouble you, if you please, to leave the apartment. I wish to speak to my lord alone."

Mr Slope also felt that everything depended on the present interview. Should the bishop now be repetticoated, his thraldom would be complete and for ever. The present moment was peculiarly propitious for rebellion. The bishop had clearly committed himself by breaking the seal of the answer to the archbishop; he had therefore fear to influence him. Mr Slope had told him that no consideration ought to induce him to refuse the archbishop's invitation; he had therefore hope to influence him. He had accepted Mr Quiverful's resignation, and therefore dreaded having to renew that matter with his wife. He had been screwed up to the pitch of asserting a will of his own, and might possibly be carried on till by an absolute success he should have been taught how possible it was to succeed. Now was the moment for victory or rout. It was now that Mr Slope must make himself master of the diocese, or else resign his place and begin his search for fortune again. He saw all this plainly. After what had taken place any compromise between him and the lady was impossible. Let him once leave the room at her bidding, and leave the bishop in her hands, and he might at once pack up his port-manteau and bid adieu to episcopal honours, Mrs Bold, and the Signora Neroni.

And yet it was not so easy to keep his ground when he was bidden by a lady to go; or to continue to make a third in a party between a husband and wife when the wife expressed a wish for a *tête-à-tête* with her husband.

"Mr Slope," she repeated, "I wish to be alone with my lord."

"His lordship has summoned me on most important diocesan business," said Mr Slope, glancing with uneasy eye at Dr Proudie. He felt that he must trust something to the bishop, and yet that trust was so woefully ill-placed. "My leaving him at the present moment is, I fear, impossible."

"Do you bandy words with me, you ungrateful man?" said she.

"My lord, will you do me the favour to beg Mr Slope to leave the room?"

My lord scratched his head, but for the moment said nothing. This was as much as Mr Slope expected from him, and was on the whole, for him, an active exercise of marital rights.

"My lord," said the lady, "is Mr Slope to leave this room, or am I?"

Here Mrs Proudie made a false step. She should not have alluded to the possibility of retreat on her part. She should not have expressed the idea that her order for Mr Slope's expulsion could be treated otherwise than by immediate obedience. In answer to such a question the bishop naturally said in his own mind, perhaps it might be as well that Mrs Proudie did so. He did say so in his own mind, but externally he again scratched his head and again twiddled his thumbs.

Mrs Proudie was boiling over with wrath. Alas, alas! could she but have kept her temper as her enemy did, she would have conquered as she had ever conquered. But divine anger got the better of her, as it has done of other heroines, and she fell.

"My lord," said she, "am I to be vouchsafed an answer or am I not?"

At last he broke his deep silence and proclaimed himself a Slopeite. "Why, my dear," said he, "Mr Slope and I are very busy."

That was all. There was nothing more necessary. He had gone to the battle-field, stood the dust and heat of the day, encountered the fury of the foe, and won the victory. How easy is success to those who will only be true to themselves!

B. T.

A PILLAR OF THE CHURCH

The bishop shook in his shoes. When Mrs Proudie began to talk of the souls of the people he always shook in his shoes.

L. C.

A Love Scene

There is an old song which gives us some very good advice about courting:

> *It's gude to be off with auld luve*
> *Before ye be on wi' the new.*

Of the wisdom of this maxim Mr Slope was ignorant, and accordingly, having written his letter to Mrs Bold he proceeded to call upon the Signora Neroni. Indeed it was hard to say which was the old love and which the new, Mr Slope having been smitten with both so nearly at the same time. Perhaps he thought it not amiss to have two strings to his bow. But two strings to Cupid's bow are always dangerous to him on whose behalf they are to be used. A man should remember that between two stools he may fall to the ground.

But in sooth Mr Slope was pursuing Mrs Bold in obedience to his better instincts, and the signora in obedience to his worser. Had he won the widow and worn her, no one could have blamed him. You, O reader, and I and Eleanor's other friends would have received the story of such a winning with much disgust and disappointment; but we should have been angry with Eleanor, not with Mr Slope. Bishop, male and female, dean and chapter, and diocesan clergy in full congress, could have found nothing to disapprove of in such an alliance. Convocation itself, that mysterious and mighty synod, could in no wise have fallen foul of it. The possession of £1000 a year and a beautiful wife would not at all have hurt the voice of the pulpit charmer, or lessened the grace and piety of the exemplary clergyman.

But not of such a nature were likely to be his dealings with the Signora Neroni. In the first place he knew that her husband was living, and therefore he could not woo her honestly. Then again she had nothing to recommend her to his honest wooing, had such been possible. She was not only portionless, but also from misfortune un-fitted to be chosen as the wife of any man who wanted a useful mate. Mr Slope was aware that she was a helpless, hopeless cripple.

But Mr Slope could not help himself. He knew that he was wrong in devoting his time to the back drawing-room in Dr Stanhope's house. He knew that what took place there would, if divulged, utterly ruin him with Mrs Bold. He knew that scandal would soon come upon his heels and spread abroad among the black coats of Barchester some tidings, exaggerated tidings, of the sighs which he poured into the lady's ears. He knew that he was acting against the recognized principles of his life, against those laws of conduct by which he hoped to achieve much higher success. But, as we have said, he could not help himself. Passion, for the first time in his life, passion was too strong for him.

As for the signora, no such plea can be put forward for her, for in truth she cared no more for Mr Slope than she did for twenty others who had been at her feet before him. She willingly, nay greedily, accepted his homage. He was the finest fly that Barchester had hitherto afforded to her web; and the signora was a powerful spider that made wondrous webs, and could in no way live without catching flies. Her taste in this respect was abominable, for she had no use for the victims when caught. She could not eat them matrimonially, as young lady spiders do whose webs are most frequently of their mother's weaving. Nor could she devour them by any escapade of a less legitimate description. Her unfortunate affliction precluded her from all hope of levanting with a lover. It would be impossible to run away with a lady who required three servants to move her from a sofa.

The signora was subdued by no passion. Her time for love was gone. She had lived out her heart, such heart as she had ever had, in her early years, at an age when Mr Slope was thinking of the second book of Euclid and his unpaid bill at the buttery hatch. In age the lady was younger than the gentleman; but in feelings, in knowledge of the affairs of love, in intrigue, he was immeasurably her junior. It was necessary to her to have some man at her feet. It was the one customary excitement of her life. She delighted in the exercise of power which this gave her; it was now nearly the only food for her ambition; she would boast to her sister that she could make a fool of any man, and the sister, as little imbued with feminine delicacy as herself, good naturedly thought it but fair that such amusement should be afforded to a poor invalid who was debarred from the ordinary pleasures of life.

Mr Slope was madly in love, but hardly knew it. The signora spitted him, as a boy does a cockchafer on a cork, that she might enjoy the energetic agony of his gyrations. And she knew very well what she was doing.

Mr Slope having added to his person all such adornments as are possible to a clergyman making a morning visit, such as a clean neck tie, clean handkerchief, new gloves, and a *soupçon* of not unnecessary scent, called about three o'clock at the doctor's door. At about this hour the signora was almost always alone in the back drawing-room. The mother had not come down. The doctor was out or in his own room. Bertie was out, and Charlotte at any rate left the room if anyone called whose object was specially with her sister. Such was her idea of being charitable and sisterly.

Mr Slope, as was his custom, asked for Mr Stanhope, and was told, as was the servant's custom, that the signora was in the drawing-room. Up-stairs he accordingly went. He found her, as he always did, lying on her sofa with a French volume before her, and a beautiful little inlaid writing case open on her table. At the moment of his entrance she was in the act of writing.

"Ah, my friend," said she, putting out her left hand to him across her desk, "I did not expect you to-day and was this very instant writing to you——"

Mr Slope, taking the soft, fair, delicate hand in his, and very soft and fair and delicate it was, bowed over it his huge red head and kissed it. It was a sight to see, a deed to record if the author could fitly do it, a picture to put on canvas. Mr Slope was big, awkward, cumbrous, and having his heart in his pursuit was ill at ease. The lady was fair, as we have said, and delicate; everything about her was fine and refined; her hand in his looked like a rose lying among carrots, and when he kissed it he looked as a cow might do on finding such a flower among her food. She was graceful as a couchant goddess, and, moreover, as self-possessed as Venus must have been when courting Adonis.

Oh, that such grace and such beauty should have condescended to waste itself on such a pursuit!

"I was in the act of writing to you," said she, "but now my scrawl may go into the basket;" and she raised the sheet of gilded note-paper from off her desk as though to tear it.

"Indeed it shall not," said he, laying the embargo of half a stone weight of human flesh and blood upon the devoted paper. "Nothing that you write for my eyes, signora, shall be so desecrated;" and he took up the letter, put that also among the carrots and fed on it, and then proceeded to read it.

"Gracious me! Mr Slope," said she, "I hope you don't mean to say that you keep all the trash I write to you. Half my time I don't know what I write, and when I do, I know it is only fit for the back of the fire. I hope you have not that ugly trick of keeping letters."

"At any rate, I don't throw them into a waste-paper basket. If destruction is their doomed lot, they perish worthily, and are burnt on a pyre, as Dido was of old."

"With a steel pen stuck through them, of course," said she, to make the simile more complete. "Of all the ladies of my acquaintance I think Lady Dido was the most absurd. Why did she not do as Cleopatra did? Why did she not take out her ships and insist on going with him? She could not bear to lose the land she had got by a swindle; and then she could not bear the loss of her lover. So she fell between two stools. Mr Slope, whatever you do, never mingle love and business."

Mr Slope blushed up to his eyes, and over his mottled forehead to the very roots of his hair. He felt sure that the signora knew all about his intentions with reference to Mrs Bold. His conscience told him that he was detected. His doom was to be spoken; he was to be punished for his duplicity, and rejected by the beautiful creature before him. Poor man. He little dreamt that had all his intentions with reference to Mrs Bold been known to the signora, it would only have added zest to that lady's amusement. It was all very well to have Mr Slope at her feet, to show her power by making an utter fool of a clergyman, to gratify her own infidelity by thus proving the little strength which religion had in controlling the passions even of a religious man; but it would be an increased gratification if she could be made to understand that she was at the same time alluring her victim away from another, whose love, if secured, would be in every way beneficent and salutary.

The signora had indeed discovered with the keen instinct of such a woman, that Mr Slope was bent on matrimony with Mrs Bold, but in alluding to Dido she had not thought of it. She instantly perceived, however, from her lover's blushes, what was on his mind, and was not slow in taking advantage of it.

She looked him full in the face, not angrily, nor yet with a smile, but with an intense and overpowering gaze; and then holding up her forefinger, and slightly shaking her head, she said:

"Whatever you do, my friend, do not mingle love and business. Either stick to your treasure and your city of wealth, or else follow your love like a true man. But never attempt both. If you do, you'll have to die with a broken heart as did poor Dido. Which is it to be with you, Mr Slope, love or money?"

Mr Slope was not so ready with a pathetic answer as he usually was with touching episodes in his extempore sermons. He felt that he ought to say something pretty, something also that should remove the impression on the mind of his lady-love. But he was rather put about how to do it.

"Love," said he, "true overpowering love, must be the strongest passion a man can feel; it must control every other wish, and put aside every other pursuit. But with me love will never act in that way unless it be returned;" and he threw upon the signora a look of tenderness which was intended to make up for all the deficiencies of his speech.

"Take my advice," said she. "Never mind love. After all, what is it? The dream of a few weeks. That is all its joy. The disappointment of a life is its Nemesis. Who was ever successful in true love? Success in love argues that the love is false. True love is always despondent or tragical. Juliet loved, Haidee loved, Dido loved, and what came of it? Troilus loved and ceased to be a man."

"Troilus loved and was fooled," said the more manly chaplain. "A man may love and yet not be a Troilus. All women are not Cressida."

"No; all women are not Cressida. The falsehood is not always on the woman's side. Imogen was true, but how was she rewarded? Her lord believed her to be the paramour of the first he who came near her in his absence. Desdemona was true and was smothered. Ophelia was true and went mad. There is no happiness in love, except at the end of an English novel. But in wealth, money, houses, lands, goods and chattels, in the good things of this world, yes, in them there is something tangible, something that can be retained and enjoyed."

"Oh no," said Mr Slope, feeling himself bound to enter some protest against so very unorthodox a doctrine, "this world's wealth will make no one happy."

"And what will make you happy—you—you?" said she, raising herself up, and speaking to him with energy across the table. "From what source do you look for happiness? Do not say that you look for none? I shall not believe you. It is a search in which every human being spends an existence."

"And the search is always in vain," said Mr Slope. "We look for happiness on earth, while we ought to be content to hope for it in heaven."

"Pshaw! you preach a doctrine which you know you don't believe. It is the way with you all. If you know that there is no earthly happiness, why do you long to be a bishop or a dean? Why do you want lands and income?"

"I have the natural ambition of a man," said he.

"Of course you have, and the natural passions; and therefore I say you don't believe the doctrine you preach. St Paul was an enthusiast. He believed so that his ambition and passions did not war against his creed. So does the Eastern fanatic who passes half his life erect upon a pillar. As for me, I will believe in no belief that does not make itself manifest by outward signs. I will think no preaching sincere that is not recommended by the practice of the preacher."

Mr Slope was startled and horrified, but he felt that he could not answer. How could he stand up and preach the lessons of his Master, being there as he was, on the devil's business? He was a true believer, otherwise this would have been nothing to him. He had audacity for most things, but he had not audacity to make a plaything of the Lord's word. All this the signora understood, and felt much interest as she saw her cockchafer whirl round upon her pin.

"Your wit delights in such arguments," said he, "but your heart and your reason do not go along with them."

"My heart!" said she; "you quite mistake the principles of my composition if you imagine that there is such a thing about me." After all, there was very little that was false in anything that the signora said. If Mr Slope allowed himself to be deceived, it was his own fault. Nothing could have been more open than her declarations about herself.

The little writing table with her desk was still standing before her, a barrier, as it were, against the enemy. She was sitting as nearly upright as she ever did, and he had brought a chair close to the sofa, so that there was only the corner of the table between him and her. It so happened that as she spoke her hand lay upon the table, and as Mr Slope answered her he put his hand upon hers.

"No heart!" said he. "That is a heavy charge which you bring against yourself, and one of which I cannot find you guilty——"

She withdrew her hand, not quickly and angrily, as though insulted by his touch, but gently and slowly.

"You are in no condition to give a verdict on the matter," said she, "as you have not tried me. No; don't say that you intend doing so, for you know you have no intention of the kind; nor indeed have I either. As for you, you will take your vows where they will result in

66

something more substantial than the pursuit of such a ghostlike, ghastly love as mine——"

"Your love should be sufficient to satisfy the dream of a monarch," said Mr Slope, not quite clear as to the meaning of his words.

"Say an archbishop, Mr Slope," said she. Poor fellow! she was very cruel to him. He went round again upon his cork on this allusion to his profession. He tried, however, to smile, and gently accused her of joking on a matter which was, he said, to him of such vital moment.

"Why—what gulls do you men make of us," she replied. "How you fool us to the top of our bent; and of all men you clergymen are the most fluent of your honeyed caressing words. Now look me in the face, Mr Slope, boldly and openly."

Mr Slope did look at her with a languishing loving eye, and as he did so, he again put forth his hand to get hold of hers.

"I told you to look at me boldly, Mr Slope; but confine your boldness to your eyes."

"Oh, Madeline!" he sighed.

"Well, my name is Madeline," said she; "but none except my own family usually call me so. Now look me in the face, Mr Slope. Am I to understand that you say you love me?"

Mr Slope never had said so. If he had come there with any formed plan at all, his intention was to make love to the lady without uttering any such declaration. It was, however, quite impossible that he should now deny his love. He had, therefore, nothing for it but to go down on his knees distractedly against the sofa, and swear that he did love her with a love passing the love of man.

The signora received the assurance with very little palpitation or appearance of surprise. "And now answer me another question," said she. "When are you to be married to my dear friend Eleanor Bold?"

Poor Mr Slope went round and round in mortal agony. In such a condition as his it was really very hard for him to know what answer to give. And yet no answer would be his surest condemnation. He might as well at once plead guilty to the charge brought against him.

"And why do you accuse me of such dissimulation?" said he.

"Dissimulation! I said nothing of dissimulation. I made no charge against you, and make none. Pray, don't defend yourself to me. You

swear that you are devoted to my beauty, and yet you are on the eve of matrimony with another. I feel this to be rather a compliment. It is to Mrs Bold that you must defend yourself. That you may find difficult; unless, indeed, you can keep her in the dark. You clergymen are cleverer than other men."

"Signora, I have told you that I loved you, and now you rail at me?"

"Rail at you. God bless the man; what would he have? Come, answer me this at your leisure—not without thinking now, but leisurely and with consideration—Are you not going to be married to Mrs Bold?"

"I am not," said he. And as he said it, he almost hated, with an exquisite hatred, the woman whom he could not help loving with an exquisite love.

"But surely you are a worshipper of hers?"

"I am not," said Mr Slope, to whom the word worshipper was peculiarly distasteful. The signora had conceived that it would be so.

"I wonder at that," said she. "Do you not admire her? To my eyes she is the perfection of English beauty. And then she is rich too. I should have thought she was just the person to attract you. Come, Mr Slope, let me give you advice on this matter. Marry the charming widow; she will be a good mother to your children, and an excellent mistress of a clergyman's household."

"Oh, Signora, how can you be so cruel?"

"Cruel," said she, changing the voice of banter which she had been using for one which was expressively earnest in its tone; "is that cruelty?"

"How can I love another, while my heart is entirely your own?"

"If that were cruelty, Mr Slope, what might you say of me if I were to declare that I returned your passion? What would you think if I bound you even by a lover's oath to do daily penance at this couch of mine? What can I give in return for a man's love? Ah, dear friend, you have not realized the conditions of my fate."

Mr Slope was not on his knees all this time. After his declaration of love he had risen from them as quickly as he thought consistent with the new position which he now filled, and as he stood was leaning on the back of his chair. This outburst of tenderness on the signora's part quite overcame him, and made him feel for the moment that he could sacrifice everything to be assured of the love of the beautiful creature before him, maimed, lame, and already married as she was.

"And can I not sympathise with your lot?" said he, now seating himself on her sofa, and pushing away the table with his foot.

"Sympathy is so near to pity!" said she. "If you pity me, cripple as I am, I shall spurn you from me."

"Oh, Madeline, I will only love you," and again he caught her hand and devoured it with kisses. Now she did not draw it from him, but sat there as he kissed it, looking at him with her great eyes, just as a great spider would look at a great fly that was quite securely caught.

"Suppose Signor Neroni were to come to Barchester," said she, "would you make his acquaintance?"

"Signor Neroni!" said he.

"Would you introduce him to the bishop, and Mrs Proudie, and the young ladies?" said she, again having recourse to that horrid quizzing voice which Mr Slope so particularly hated.

"Why do you ask such a question?" said he.

"Because it is necessary that you should know that there is a Signor Neroni. I think you had forgotten it."

"If I thought that you retained for that wretch one particle of love of which he was never worthy, I would die before I would distract you by telling you what I feel. No! were your husband the master of your heart, I might perhaps love you; but you should never know it."

"My heart again! how you talk. And you consider, then, that if a husband be not master of his wife's heart, he has no right to her fealty; if a wife ceases to love, she may cease to be true. Is that your doctrine on this matter, as a minister of the Church of England?"

Mr Slope tried hard within himself to cast off the pollution with which he felt that he was defiling his soul. He strove to tear himself away from the noxious siren that had bewitched him. But he could not do it. He could not be again heart free. He had looked for rapturous joy in loving this lovely creature, and he already found that he met with little but disappointment and self-rebuke. He had come across the fruit of the Dead Sea, so sweet and delicious to the eye, so bitter and nauseous to the taste. He had put the apple to his mouth, and it had turned to ashes between his teeth. Yet he could not tear himself away. He knew, he could not but know, that she jeered at him, ridiculed his love, and insulted the weakness of his religion. But she half permitted his adoration, and that half permission added such fuel to his fire that all the fountain of his piety could not quench it. He began to feel savage, irritated, and revengeful. He meditated some severity of speech, some taunt that should cut her, as her taunts cut him. He reflected as he stood there for a moment, silent before her, that if he desired to quell her proud spirit, he should do so by being prouder even than herself; that if he wished to have her at his feet suppliant for his love it behoved him to conquer her by indifference. All this passed through his mind. As far as dead knowledge went, he knew, or thought he knew, how a woman should be tamed. But when he essayed to bring his tactics to bear, he failed like a child. What chance has dead knowledge with experience in any of the transactions between man and man? What possible chance between man and woman? Mr Slope loved furiously, insanely and truly; but he had never played the game of love. The signora did not love at all, but she was up to every move of the board. It was Philidor pitted against a school-boy.

And so she continued to insult him, and he continued to bear it.

"Sacrifice the world for love!" said she, in answer to some renewed vapid declaration of his passion; "how often has the same thing been said, and how invariably with the same falsehood!"

"Falsehood," said he. "Do you say that I am false to you? Do you say that my love is not real?"

"False? Of course it is false, false as the father of falsehood—if indeed falsehoods need a sire and are not self-begotten since the world began. You are ready to sacrifice the world for love? Come, let us see what you will sacrifice. I care nothing for nuptial vows. The wretch, I think you were kind enough to call him so, whom I swore to love and obey, is so base that he can only be thought of with repulsive disgust. In the council chamber of my heart I have divorced him. To me that is as good as though aged lords had gloated for months on the details of his licentious life. I care nothing for what the world can say. Will you be as frank? Will you take me to your home as your wife? Will you call me Mrs Slope before bishop, dean, and prebendaries?" The poor tortured wretch stood silent, not knowing what to say. "What! You won't do that. Tell me, then, what part of the world is it that you will sacrifice for my charms?"

"Were you free to marry, I would take you to my house to-morrow and wish no higher privilege."

"I am free," said she, almost starting up in her energy. For though there was no truth in her pretended regard for her clerical admirer, there was a mixture of real feeling in the scorn and satire with which she spoke of love and marriage generally. "I am free; free as the winds. Come; will you take me as I am? Have your wish; sacrifice the world, and prove yourself a true man."

Mr Slope should have taken her at her word. She would have drawn back, and he would have had the full advantage of the offer. But he did not. Instead of doing so, he stood wrapt in astonishment, passing his fingers through his lank red hair, and thinking as he stared upon her animated countenance that her wondrous beauty grew more and more wonderful as he gazed on it. "Ha! ha! ha!" she laughed out loud. "Come, Mr Slope; don't talk of sacrificing the world again. People beyond one-and-twenty should never dream of such a thing. You and I, if we have the dregs of any love left in us, if we have the remnants of a passion remaining in our hearts, should husband our resources better. We are not in our *première jeunesse*. The world is a very nice place. Your world, at any rate, is so. You have all manner of fat rectories to get, and possible bishoprics to enjoy. Come, confess; on second thoughts you would not sacrifice such things for the smiles of a lame lady?"

It was impossible for him to answer this. In order to be in any way dignified, he felt that he must be silent.

"Come," said she—"don't boody with me: don't be angry because I speak out some home truths. Alas, the world, as I have found it, has taught me bitter truths. Come, tell me that I am forgiven. Are we not to be friends?" and she again put out her hand to him.

He sat himself down in the chair beside her, and took her proffered hand and leant over her.

"There," said she, with her sweetest softest smile—a smile to withstand which a man should be cased in triple steel, "there; seal your forgiveness on it," and she raised it towards his face. He kissed it again and again, and stretched over her as though desirous of extending the charity of his pardon beyond the hand that was offered to him. She managed, however, to check his ardour. For one so easily allured as this poor chaplain, her hand was surely enough.

"Oh, Madeline!" said he, "tell me that you love me—do you—do you love me?"

"Hush," said she. "There is my mother's step. Our *tête-à-tête* has been of monstrous length. Now you had better go. But we shall see you soon again, shall we not?"

Mr Slope promised that he would call again on the following day.

"And, Mr Slope," she continued, "pray answer my note. You have it in your hand, though I declare during these two hours you have not been gracious enough to read it. It is about the Sabbath school and the children. You know how anxious I am to have them here. I have been learning the catechism myself, on purpose. You must manage it for me next week. I will teach them, at any rate, to submit themselves to their spiritual pastors and masters."

Mr Slope said but little on the subject of Sabbath schools, but he made his adieu, and betook himself home with a sad heart, troubled mind, and uneasy conscience.

B. T.

A Brief Courtship

... Mr Slope, having made a declaration of affection, afterwards withdrew it on finding that the doctor had no immediate worldly funds with which to endow his child. ...

B. T.

Mr Slope looks to Heaven

"Beautiful woman," at last he burst forth; "beautiful woman, you cannot pretend to be ignorant that I adore you. Yes, Eleanor, yes, I love you. I love you with the truest affection which a man can bear to a woman. Next to my hopes of heaven are my hopes of possessing you." (Mr Slope's memory here played him false, or he would not have omitted the deanery.) "How sweet to walk to heaven with you by my side, with you for my guide, mutual guides. Say, Eleanor, dearest Eleanor, shall we walk that sweet path together?"

B. T.

HOW TO GET RICH

There is no road to wealth so easy and respectable as that of matrimony; that is, of course, provided that the aspirant declines the slow course of honest work.

D. T.

SEX APPEAL

Ladies are sometimes less nice in their appreciation of physical disqualifications; and, provided that a man speak to them well, they will listen, though he speak from a mouth never so deformed and hideous.

B. T.

Mr Slope Vanquished

————◦◦◦◦◦◦————

Mr Slope waited about ten minutes more to prove his independence, and then he went into the bishop's room. There, as he had expected, he found Mrs Proudie, together with her husband.

"Hum, ha!—Mr Slope, pray take a chair," said the gentleman bishop.

"Pray be seated, Mr Slope," said the lady bishop.

"Thank ye, thank ye," said Mr Slope, and walking round to the fire, he threw himself into one of the arm-chairs that graced the hearth-rug.

"Mr Slope," said the bishop, "it has become necessary that I should speak to you definitely on a matter that has for some time been pressing itself on my attention."

"May I ask whether the subject is in any way connected with myself?" said Mr Slope.

"It is so,—certainly,—yes, it certainly is connected with yourself, Mr Slope."

"Then, my lord, if I may be allowed to express a wish, I would prefer that no discussion on the subject should take place between us in the presence of a third person."

"Don't alarm yourself, Mr Slope," said Mrs Proudie, "no discussion is at all necessary. The bishop merely intends to express his own wishes."

"I merely intend, Mr Slope, to express my own wishes,—no discussion will be at all necessary," said the bishop, reiterating his wife's words.

"That is more, my lord, than we any of us can be sure of," said Mr Slope; "I cannot, however, force Mrs Proudie to leave the room;

nor can I refuse to remain here if it be your lordship's wish that I should do so."

"It is his lordship's wish, certainly," said Mrs Proudie.

"Mr Slope," began the bishop, in a solemn, serious voice, "it grieves me to have to find fault. It grieves me much to have to find fault with a clergyman; but especially so with a clergyman in your position."

"Why, what have I done amiss, my lord?" demanded Mr Slope, boldly.

"What have you done amiss, Mr Slope?" said Mrs Proudie, standing erect before the culprit, and raising that terrible forefinger. "Do you dare to ask the bishop what you have done amiss? Does not your conscience——"

"Mrs Proudie, pray let it be understood, once for all, that I will have no words with you."

"Ah, sir, but you will have words," said she; "you must have words. Why have you had so many words with that Signora Neroni? Why have you disgraced yourself, you a clergyman too, by constantly consorting with such a woman as that—with a married woman,—with one altogether unfit for a clergyman's society?"

"At any rate, I was introduced to her in your drawing-room," retorted Mr Slope.

"And shamefully you behaved there," said Mrs Proudie, "most shamefully. I was wrong to allow you to remain in the house a day after what I then saw. I should have insisted on your instant dismissal."

"I have yet to learn, Mrs Proudie, that you have the power to insist either on my going from hence or on my staying here."

"What!" said the lady; "I am not to have the privilege of saying who shall and who shall not frequent my own drawing-room! I am not to save my servants and dependents from having their morals corrupted by improper conduct! I am not to save my own daughters from impurity! I will let you see, Mr Slope, whether I have the power or whether I have not. You will have the goodness to understand that you no longer fill any situation about the bishop; and as your room will be immediately wanted in the palace for another chaplain, I must ask you to provide yourself with apartments as soon as may be convenient to you."

"My lord," said Mr Slope, appealing to the bishop, and so turning his back completely on the lady, "will you permit me to ask that I may have from your own lips any decision that you may have come to on this matter?"

"Certainly, Mr Slope, certainly," said the bishop; "that is but reasonable. Well, my decision is that you had better look out for some other preferment. For the situation which you have lately held I do not think that you are well suited."

"And what, my lord, has been my fault?"

"That Signora Neroni is one fault," said Mrs Proudie; "and a very abominable fault she is; very abominable and very disgraceful. Fie, Mr Slope, fie! You an evangelical clergyman indeed!"

"My lord, I desire to know for what fault I am turned out of your lordship's house."

"You hear what Mrs Proudie says," said the bishop.

"When I publish the history of this transaction, my lord, as I decidedly shall do in my own vindication, I presume you will not wish me to state that you have discarded me at your wife's bidding— because she has objected to my being acquainted with another lady, the daughter of one of the prebendaries of the chapter?"

"You may publish what you please, sir," said Mrs Proudie. "But you will not be insane enough to publish any of your doings in Barchester. Do you think I have not heard of your kneelings at that creature's feet—that is, if she has any feet—and of your constant slobbering over her hand? I advise you to beware, Mr Slope, of what you do and say. Clergymen have been unfrocked for less than what you have been guilty of."

"My lord, if this goes on I shall be obliged to indict this woman— Mrs Proudie I mean—for defamation of character."

"I think, Mr Slope, you had better now retire," said the bishop. "I will enclose to you a cheque for any balance that may be due to you; and, under the present circumstances, it will of course be better for all parties that you should leave the palace at the earliest possible moment. I will allow you for your journey back to London, and for your maintenance in Barchester for a week from this date."

"If, however, you wish to remain in this neighbourhood," said Mrs Proudie, "and will solemnly pledge yourself never again to see that woman, and will promise also to be circumspect in your conduct, the bishop will mention your name to Mr Quiverful, who now wants a curate at Puddingdale. The house is, I imagine, quite sufficient for your requirements: and there will, moreover, be a stipend of fifty pounds a year."

"May God forgive you, madam, for the manner in which you have treated me," said Mr Slope, looking at her with a very heavenly look; "and remember this, madam, that you yourself may still have a fall;" and he looked at her with a very worldly look. "As to the bishop, I pity him!" And so saying, Mr Slope left the room. Thus ended the intimacy of the Bishop of Barchester with his first confidential chaplain.

B. T.

HOLY ORDERS (I)

Clergymen are subject to the same passions as other men; and, as far as I can see, give way to them, in one line or in another, almost as frequently.

F. P.

HOLY ORDERS (II)

If we look to our clergymen to be more than men, we shall probably teach ourselves to think that they are less, and can hardly hope to raise the character of the pastor by denying to him the right to entertain the aspirations of a man.

B. T.

PHILOSOPHY (ABSTRACT)

. . . in this world no good is unalloyed, and there is but little evil that has not in it some seed of what is goodly.

W.

PHILOSOPHY (HUMAN)

. . . a man may be very imperfect and yet worth a great deal.

F. P.

Politics

GAMBLING

. . . when a man lays himself out to be a member of Parliament, he plays the highest game and for the highest stakes which the country affords.

D. T.

PARLIAMENTARY TACTICS

Sir Abraham Haphazard was deeply engaged in preparing a bill for the mortification of papists, to be called "Convent Custody Bill", the purport of which was to enable any Protestant clergyman over fifty years of age to search any nun whom he suspected of being in possession of treasonable papers, or jesuitical symbols: and as there were to be a hundred and thirty-seven clauses in the bill, each clause containing a separate thorn for the side of the papist, and as it was known the bill would be fought inch by inch, by fifty maddened Irishmen, the due constructions and adequate dovetailing of it did consume much of Sir Abraham's time. The bill had all its desired effect. Of course it never passed into law; but it so completely divided the ranks of the Irish members, who had bound themselves together to force on the ministry a bill for compelling all men to drink Irish whiskey, and all women to wear Irish poplins, that for the remainder of the session the Great Poplin and Whiskey League was utterly harmless.

W.

HANSARD

"And is this a Christian country?" said he. (Loud cheers; counter cheers from the ministerial benches. "Some doubt as to that," from a voice below the gangway.) "No, it can be no Christian country, in which the head of the bar, the lagal adviser (loud laughter and cheers)—yes, I say the lagal adviser of the crown (great cheers and laughter)—can stand up in his seat in this house (prolonged cheers and laughter), and attempt to lagalise indacant assaults on the bodies of religious ladies."

W.

ANOTHER INJUSTICE

The innocent Irish fell into the trap as they always do. . . .

W.

A PREMIER RESIGNS

What elaborate letters, what eloquent appeals, what indignant remonstrances, he might there have to frame, at such a moment, may be conceived, but not described! How he was preparing his thunder for successful rivals, standing like a British peer with his back to the sea-coal fire, and his hands in his breeches pockets,—how his fine eye was lit up with anger, and his forehead gleamed with patriotism,—how he stamped his foot as he thought of his heavy associates,—how he all but swore as he remembered how much too clever one of them had been,—my creative readers may imagine. But was he so engaged? No: history and truth compel me to deny it. He was sitting easily in a lounging chair, conning over a Newmarket list, and by his elbow on the table was lying open an uncut French novel on which he was engaged.

B. T.

FOREIGN AFFAIRS

He had lived too long abroad to fall into the Englishman's habit of offering each an arm to two ladies at the same time; a habit, by the by, which foreigners regard as an approach to bigamy, or a sort of incipient Mormonism.

B. T.

Dr Fillgrave refuses a Fee

The doctor, that is our doctor, had thought nothing more of the message which had been sent to that other doctor, Dr Fillgrave; nor, in truth did the baronet. Lady Scatcherd had thought of it, but her husband during the rest of the day was not in a humour which allowed her to remind him that he would soon have a new physician on his hands; so she left the difficulty to arrange itself, waiting in some little trepidation till Dr Fillgrave should show himself.

It was well that Sir Roger was not dying for want of his assistance, for when the message reached Barchester, Dr Fillgrave was some five or six miles out of town, at Plumpstead; and as he did not get back till late in the evening, he felt himself necessitated to put off his visit to Boxall Hill till the next morning. Had he chanced to have been made acquainted with that little conversation about the pump, he would probably have postponed it even yet a while longer.

He was, however, by no means sorry to be summoned to the bedside of Sir Roger Scatcherd. It was well known at Barchester, and very well known to Dr Fillgrave, that Sir Roger and Dr Thorne were old friends. It was very well known to him also, that Sir Roger, in all his bodily ailments, had hitherto been contented to entrust his safety to the skill of his old friend. Sir Roger was in his way a great man, and much talked of in Barchester, and rumour had already reached the ears of the Barchester Galen, that the great railway contractor was ill. When, therefore, he received a peremptory summons to go over to Boxall Hill, he could not but think that some pure light had broken in upon Sir Roger's darkness, and taught him at last where to look for true medical accomplishment.

And then, also, Sir Roger was the richest man in the county, and to county practitioners a new patient with large means is a godsend; how much greater a godsend when he be not only acquired, but taken also from some rival practitioner, need hardly be explained.

Dr Fillgrave, therefore, was somewhat elated when, after a very early breakfast, he stepped into the post-chaise which was to carry him to Boxall Hill. Dr Fillgrave's professional advancement had been sufficient to justify the establishment of a brougham, in which he paid his ordinary visits round Barchester; but this was a special occasion, requiring special speed, and about to produce no doubt a special guerdon, and therefore a pair of post-horses were put into request.

It was hardly yet nine when the post-boy somewhat loudly rang the bell at Sir Roger's door; and then Dr Fillgrave, for the first time, found himself in the new grand hall of Boxall Hill House.

"I'll tell my lady," said the servant, showing him into the grand dining-room; and there for some fifteen or twenty minutes Dr Fillgrave walked up and down the length of the Turkey carpet all alone.

Dr Fillgrave was not a tall man, and was perhaps rather more inclined to corpulence than became his height. In his stocking-feet, according to the usually received style of measurement, he was five feet five; and he had a little round abdominal protuberance, which an inch and a half added to the heels of his boots hardly enabled him to carry off as well as he himself would have wished. Of this he was apparently conscious, and it gave to him an air of not being entirely at his ease. There was, however, a personal dignity in his demeanour, a propriety in his gait, and an air of authority in his gestures which should prohibit one of stigmatizing those efforts at altitude as a failure. No doubt he did achieve much; but, nevertheless, the effort would occasionally betray itself, and the story of the frog and the ox would irresistibly force itself into one's mind at those moments when it most behoved Dr Fillgrave to be magnificent.

But if the bulgy roundness of his person and the shortness of his legs in any way detracted from his personal importance, these trifling defects were, he was well aware, more than atoned for by the peculiar dignity of his countenance. If his legs were short, his face was not;

if there was any undue preponderance below the waistcoat, all was in due symmetry above the necktie. His hair was grey, not grizzled nor white, but properly grey; and stood up straight from off his temples on each side with an unbending determination of purpose. His whiskers, which were of an admirable shape, coming down and turning gracefully at the angle of his jaw, were grey also, but somewhat darker than his hair. His enemies in Barchester declared that their perfect shade was produced by a leaden comb. His eyes were not brilliant, but were very effective, and well under command. He was rather short-sighted, and a pair of eye-glasses was always on his nose, or in his hand. His nose was long, and well pronounced, and his chin, also, was sufficiently prominent; but the great feature of his face was his mouth. The amount of secret medical knowledge of which he could give assurance by the pressure of those lips was truly wonderful. By his lips, also, he could be most exquisitely courteous, or most sternly forbidding. And not only could he be either the one or the other; but he could at his will assume any shade of difference between the two, and produce any mixture of sentiment.

When Dr Fillgrave was first shown into Sir Roger's dining-room, he walked up and down the room for a while with easy, jaunty step, with his hands joined together behind his back, calculating the price of the furniture, and counting the heads which might be adequately entertained in a room of such noble proportions; but in seven or eight minutes an air of impatience might have been seen to suffuse his face. Why could he not be shown up into the sick man's room? What necessity could there be for keeping him there, as though he were some apothecary with a box of leeches in his pocket? He then rang the bell, perhaps a little violently. "Does Sir Roger know that I am here?" he said to the servant. "I'll tell my lady," said the man, again vanishing.

For five minutes more he walked up and down, calculating no longer the value of the furniture, but rather that of his own importance. He was not wont to be kept waiting in this way; and though Sir Roger Scatcherd was at present a great and a rich man, Dr Fillgrave had remembered him a very small and a very poor man. He now began to think of Sir Roger as the stone-mason, and to chafe somewhat more violently at being so kept by such a man.

When one is impatient, five minutes is as the duration of all time, and a quarter of an hour is eternity. At the end of twenty minutes the step of Dr Fillgrave up and down the room had become very quick, and he had just made up his mind that he would not stay there all day to the serious detriment, perhaps fatal injury, of his other expectant patients. His hand was again on the bell, and was about to be used with vigour, when the door opened and Lady Scatcherd entered.

The door opened and Lady Scatcherd entered; but she did so very slowly, as though she were afraid to come into her own dining-room. We must go back a little and see how she had been employed during those twenty minutes.

"Oh laws!" Such had been her first exclamation on hearing that the doctor was in the dining-room. She was standing at the time with her housekeeper in a small room in which she kept her linen and jam, and in which, in company with the same housekeeper, she spent the happiest moments of her life.

"Oh laws! now, Hannah, what shall we do?"

"Send 'un up at once to the master, my lady! let John take 'un up."

"There'll be such a row in the house, Hannah; I know there will."

"But sure-ly didn't he send for 'un? Let the master have the row himself, then; that's what I'd do, my lady," added Hannah, seeing that her ladyship still stood trembling in doubt, biting her thumbnail.

"You couldn't go up to the master yourself, could you now, Hannah?" said Lady Scatcherd in her most persuasive tone.

"Why no," said Hannah, after a little deliberation; "no, I'm afeard I couldn't."

"Then I must just face it myself." And up went the wife to tell her lord that the physician for whom he had sent had come to attend his bidding.

In the interview which then took place the baronet had not indeed been violent, but he had been very determined. Nothing on earth, he

86

said, should induce him to see Dr Fillgrave and offend his dear old friend Thorne.

"But, Roger," said her ladyship, half crying, or rather pretending to cry in her vexation, "what shall I do with the man? How shall I get him out of the house?"

"Put him under the pump," said the baronet; and he laughed his peculiar low guttural laugh, which told so plainly of the havoc which brandy had made in his throat.

"That's nonsense, Roger; you know I can't put him under the pump. Now you are ill, and you'd better see him just for five minutes. I'll make it all right with Dr Thorne."

"I'll be d—— if I do, my lady." All the people about Boxall Hill called poor Lady Scatcherd "my lady", as if there was some excellent joke in it; and so, indeed, there was.

"You know you needn't mind nothing he says, nor yet take nothing he sends: and I'll tell him not to come no more. Now do 'ee see him, Roger?"

But there was no coaxing Roger over now, or indeed ever: he was a wilful, headstrong, masterful man; a tyrant always, though never a cruel one; and accustomed to rule his wife and household as despotically as he did his gangs of workmen. Such men it is not easy to coax over.

"You go down and tell him I don't want him, and won't see him, and that's an end of it. If he chose to earn his money, why didn't he come yesterday when he was sent for? I'm well now, and don't want him; and what's more, I won't have him. Winterbones, lock the door."

So Winterbones, who during this interview had been at work at his little table, got up to lock the door, and Lady Scatcherd had no alternative but to pass through it before the last edict was obeyed.

Lady Scatcherd, with slow step, went downstairs and again sought counsel with Hannah, and the two, putting their heads together, agreed that the only cure for the present evil was to be found in a good fee. So Lady Scatcherd, with a five-pound note in her hand,

and trembling in every limb, went forth to encounter the august presence of Dr Fillgrave.

As the door opened, Dr Fillgrave dropped the bell-rope which was in his hand, and bowed low to the lady. Those who knew the doctor well, would have known from his bow that he was not well pleased; it was as much as though he said, "Lady Scatcherd, I am your most obedient humble servant; at any rate it appears that it is your pleasure to treat me as such."

Lady Scatcherd did not understand all this; but she perceived at once that the man was angry.

"I hope Sir Roger does not find himself worse," said the doctor. "The morning is getting on; shall I step up and see him?"

"Hem! ha! oh! Why, you see, Dr Fillgrave, Sir Roger finds hisself vastly better this morning, vastly so."

"I'm very glad to hear it, very; but as the morning is getting on, shall I step up to see Sir Roger?"

"Why, Dr Fillgrave, sir, you see, he finds hisself so much hisself this morning, that he a'most thinks it would be a shame to trouble you."

"A shame to trouble me!" This was a sort of shame which Dr Fillgrave did not at all comprehend. "A shame to trouble me! Why, Lady Scatcherd——"

Lady Scatcherd saw that she had nothing for it but to make the whole matter intelligible. Moreover, seeing that she appreciated more thoroughly the smallness of Dr Fillgrave's person than she did the peculiar greatness of his demeanour, she began to be a shade less afraid of him than she had thought she should have been.

"Yes, Dr Fillgrave; you see, when a man like he gets well, he can't abide the idea of doctors: now yesterday, he was all for sending for you; but to-day he comes to hisself, and don't seem to want no doctor at all."

Then did Dr Fillgrave seem to grow out of his boots, so suddenly did he take upon himself sundry modes of expansive altitude;—to grow out of his boots and to swell upwards, till his angry eyes almost looked down on Lady Scatcherd, and each erect hair bristled up towards the heavens.

"This is very singular, very singular, Lady Scatcherd; very singular indeed; very singular; quite unusual. I have come here from Barchester, at some considerable inconvenience, at some very considerable inconvenience, I may say, to my regular patients; and—and—and—I don't know that anything so very singular ever occurred to me before." And then Dr Fillgrave, with a compression of his lips which almost made the poor woman sink into the ground, moved towards the door.

Then Lady Scatcherd bethought her of her great panacea. "It isn't about the money, you know, doctor," said she; "of course Sir Roger don't expect you to come here with post-horses for nothing." In this, by the by, Lady Scatcherd did not stick quite close to veracity, for Sir Roger, had he known it, would by no means have assented to any payment; and the note which her ladyship held in her hand was taken from her own private purse. "It ain't at all about the money, doctor;" and then she tendered the bank-note, which she thought would immediately make all things smooth.

Now Dr Fillgrave dearly loved a five-pound fee. What physician is so unnatural as not to love it? He dearly loved a five-pound fee; but he loved his dignity better. He was angry also; and like all angry men, he loved his grievance. He felt that he had been badly treated; but if he took the money he would throw away his right to indulge any such feeling. At that moment his outraged dignity and his cherished anger were worth more to him than a five-pound note. He looked at it with wishful but still averted eyes, and then sternly refused the tender.

"No, madam," said he; "no, no;" and with his right hand raised with his eye-glasses in it, he motioned away the tempting paper. "No; I should have been happy to have given Sir Roger the benefit of any medical skill I may have, seeing that I was specially called in——"

"But, doctor; if the man's well, you know——"

"Oh, of course; if he's well, and does not choose to see me, there's an end of it. Should he have any relapse, as my time is valuable, he will perhaps oblige me by sending elsewhere. Madam, good morning.

I will, if you will allow me, ring for my carriage—that is, post-chaise."

"But, doctor, you'll take the money; you must take the money; indeed you'll take the money," said Lady Scatcherd, who had now become really unhappy at the idea that her husband's unpardonable whim had brought this man with post-horses all the way from Barchester, and that he was to be paid nothing for his time nor costs.

"No, madam, no. I could not think of it. Sir Roger, I have no doubt, will know better another time. It is not a question of money; not at all."

"But it is a question of money, doctor; and you really shall, you must." And poor Lady Scatcherd, in her anxiety to acquit herself at any rate of any pecuniary debt to the doctor, came to personal close quarters with him, with the view of forcing the note into his hands.

"Quite impossible, quite impossible," said the doctor, still cherishing his grievance, and valiantly rejecting the root of all evil. "I shall not do anything of the kind, Lady Scatcherd."

"Now, doctor, do 'ee; to oblige me."

"Quite out of the question." And so, with his hands and hat behind his back, in token of his utter refusal to accept any pecuniary accommodation of his injury, he made his way backwards to the door, her ladyship perseveringly pressing him in front. So eager had been the attack on him, that he had not waited to give his order about the post-chaise, but made his way at once towards the hall.

"Now, do 'ee take it, do 'ee," pressed Lady Scatcherd.

"Utterly out of the question," said Dr Fillgrave, with great deliberation, as he backed his way into the hall. As he did so, of course, he turned round,—and he found himself almost in the arms of Dr Thorne.

As Burley must have glared at Bothwell when they rushed together in that dread encounter on the mountain side; as Achilles may have glared at Hector when at last they met, each resolved to test in fatal conflict the prowess of the other, so did Dr Fillgrave glare at his foe from Greshamsbury, when, on turning round on his exalted heel, he found his nose on a level with the top button of Dr Thorne's waistcoat.

And here, if it be not too tedious, let us pause a while to recapitu-
late and add up the undoubted grievances of the Barchester practi-

tioner. He had made no effort to ingratiate himself into the sheepfold
of that other shepherd-dog; it was not by his seeking that he was now
at Boxall Hill; much as he hated Dr Thorne, full sure as he felt of
that man's utter ignorance, of his incapacity to adminster properly
even a black dose, of his murdering propensities, and his low, mean,
unprofessional style of practice; nevertheless, he had done nothing to
undermine him with these Scatcherds. Dr Thorne might have sent
every mother's son at Boxall Hill to his long account, and Dr Fillgrave would not have interfered—would not have interfered unless
specially and duly called upon to do so.

But he had been specially and duly called on. Before such a step was taken some words must undoubtedly have passed on the subject between Thorne and the Scatcherds. Thorne must have known what was to be done. Having been so called, Dr Fillgrave had come—had come all the way in a post-chaise—had been refused admittance to the sick man's room, on the plea that the sick man was no longer sick; and just as he was about to retire fee-less—for the want of the fee was not the less a grievance from the fact of its having been tendered and refused—fee-less, dishonoured, and in dudgeon, he encountered this other doctor—this very rival whom he had been sent to supplant; he encountered him in the very act of going to the sick man's room.

What mad fanatic Burley, what god-succoured insolent Achilles, ever had such cause to swell with wrath as at that moment had Dr Fillgrave? Had I the pen of Molière, I could fitly tell of such medical anger, but with no other pen can it be fitly told. He did swell, and when the huge bulk of his wrath was added to his natural proportions, he loomed gigantic before the eyes of the surrounding followers of Sir Roger.

Dr Thorne stepped back three steps and took his hat from his head, having, in the passage from the hall-door to the dining-room, hitherto omitted to do so. It must be borne in mind that he had no conception whatever that Sir Roger had declined to see the physician for whom he had sent; none whatever that that physician was now about to return, fee-less, to Barchester.

Dr Thorne and Dr Fillgrave were doubtless well-known enemies. All the world of Barchester, and all that portion of the world of London which is concerned with the lancet and the scalping-knife, were well aware of this: they were continually writing against each other; continually speaking against each other; but yet they had never hitherto come to that positive personal collision which is held to justify a cut direct. They very rarely saw each other; and when they did meet, it was in some casual way in the streets of Barchester or elsewhere, and on such occasions their habit had been to bow with very cold propriety.

On the present occasion, Dr Thorne of course felt that Dr Fillgrave had the whip-hand of him; and, with a sort of manly feeling on such a point, he conceived it to be most compatible with his own dignity to show, under such circumstances, more than his usual courtesy—something, perhaps, amounting almost to cordiality. He had been supplanted, *quoad* doctor, in the house of this rich, eccentric, railway baronet, and he would show that he bore no malice on that account.

So he smiled blandly as he took off his hat, and in a civil speech he expressed a hope that Dr Fillgrave had not found his patient to be in any very unfavourable state.

Here was an aggravation to the already lacerated feelings of the injured man. He had been brought thither to be scoffed and scorned at, that he might be a laughing-stock to his enemies, and food for mirth to the vile-minded. He swelled with noble anger till he would have burst, had it not been for the opportune padding of his frock-coat.

"Sir," said he; "sir:" and he could hardly get his lips open to give vent to the tumult of his heart. Perhaps he was not wrong; for it may be that his lips were more eloquent than would have been his words.

"What's the matter?" said Dr Thorne, opening his eyes wide, and addressing Lady Scatcherd over the head and across the hairs of the irritated man below him. "What on earth is the matter? Is anything wrong with Sir Roger?"

"Oh laws, doctor!" said her ladyship. "Oh laws; I'm sure it ain't my fault. Here's Dr Fillgrave in a taking, and I'm quite ready to pay him—quite. If a man gets paid, what more can he want?" And she again held out the five-pound note over Dr Fillgrave's head.

What more, indeed, Lady Scatcherd, can any of us want, if only we could keep our tempers and feelings a little in abeyance? Dr Fillgrave, however, could not so keep his; and, therefore, he did want something more, though at the present moment he could have hardly said what.

Lady Scatcherd's courage was somewhat resuscitated by the presence of her ancient trusty ally; and, moreover, she began to conceive that the little man before her was unreasonable beyond all conscience in his anger, seeing that that for which he was ready to work had been offered to him without any work at all.

"Madam," said he, again turning round at Lady Scatcherd, "I was never before treated in such a way in any house in Barsetshire—never—never."

"Good heavens, Dr Fillgrave!" said he of Greshamsbury, "what's the matter?"

"I'll let you know what is the matter, sir," said he, turning round again as quickly as before. "I'll let you know what is the matter. I'll publish this, sir, to the medical world;" and as he shrieked out the words of the threat, he stood on tiptoes and brandished his eye-glasses up almost into his enemy's face.

"Don't be angry with Dr Thorne," said Lady Scatcherd. "Any ways, you needn't be angry with him. If you must be angry with anybody——"

"I shall be angry with him, madam," ejaculated Dr Fillgrave, making another sudden demi-pirouette. "I am angry with him—or, rather, I despise him;" and completing the circle, Dr Fillgrave again brought himself round in full front of his foe.

Dr Thorne raised his eyebrows and looked inquiringly at Lady Scatcherd; but there was a quiet sarcastic motion round his mouth which by no means had the effect of throwing oil on the troubled waters.

"I'll publish the whole of this transaction to the medical world, Dr Thorne—the whole of it; and if that has not the effect of rescuing the people of Greshamsbury out of your hands, then—then—then, I don't know what will. Is my carriage—that is, post-chaise there?" and Dr Fillgrave, speaking very loudly, turned majestically to one of the servants.

"What have I done to you, Dr Fillgrave," said Dr Thorne, now absolutely laughing, "that you should determine to take my bread out of my mouth? I am not interfering with your patient. I have come here simply with reference to money matters appertaining to Sir Roger."

"Money matters! Very well—very well; money matters. That is your idea of medical practice! Very well—very well. Is my post-chaise at the door? I'll publish it all to the medical world—every word—every word of it, every word of it."

"Publish what, you unreasonable man?"

"Man! sir; whom do you call a man? I'll let you know whether I'm a man—post-chaise there!"

"Don't 'ee call him names now, doctor; don't 'ee, pray don't 'ee," said Lady Scatcherd.

By this time they had all got somewhat nearer the hall-door; but the Scatcherd retainers were too fond of the row to absent themselves willingly at Dr Fillgrave's bidding, and it did not appear that any one went in search of the post-chaise.

"Man! sir; I'll let you know what it is to speak to me in that style. I think, sir, you hardly know who I am."

"All that I know of you at present is, that you are my friend Sir Roger's physician, and I cannot conceive what has occurred to make you so angry." And as he spoke, Dr Thorne looked carefully at him to see whether that pump-discipline had in truth been applied. There were no signs whatever that cold water had been thrown upon Dr Fillgrave.

"My post-chaise—is my post-chaise there? The medical world shall know all; you may be sure, sir, the medical world shall know it all;" and thus, ordering his post-chaise, and threatening Dr Thorne with the medical world, Dr Fillgrave made his way to the door.

But the moment he put on his hat he returned. "No, madam," said he. "No; it is quite out of the question; such an affair is not to be arranged by such means. I'll publish it all to the medical world—post-chaise there!" and then, using all his force, he flung as far as he could into the hall a light bit of paper. It fell at Dr Thorne's feet, who raising it, found that it was a five-pound note.

"I put it into his hat just while he was in his tantrum," said Lady Scatcherd. "And I thought that perhaps he would not find it till he got to Barchester. Well, I wish he'd been paid, certainly, although Sir Roger wouldn't see him;" and in this manner Dr Thorne got some glimpse of understanding into the cause of the great offence.

D. T.

Dr Fillgrave refuses a Fee

HIPPOCRATES—AND DOCTOR THORNE

A physician should take his fee without letting his left hand know what his right hand was doing; it should be taken without a thought, without a look, without a move of the facial muscles; the true physician should hardly be aware that the last friendly grasp of the hand had been made more precious by the touch of gold. Whereas, that fellow Thorne would lug out half a crown from his breeches pocket and give it in change for a ten-shilling piece.

D. T.

The Duke Entertains

The Duke of Omnium was, as we have said, a bachelor. Not the less on that account did he on certain rare gala days entertain the beauty of the county at his magnificent rural seat, or the female fashion of London in Belgrave Square; but on this occasion the dinner at Gatherum Castle—for such was the name of his mansion—was to be confined to the lords of the creation. It was to be one of those days on which he collected round his board all the notables of the county, in order that his popularity might not wane, or the established glory of his hospitable house become dim.

On such an occasion it was not probable that Lord de Courcy would be one of the guests. The party, indeed, who went from Courcy Castle was not large, and consisted of the Honourable George, Mr Moffat, and Frank Gresham. They went in a tax-cart, with a tandem horse, driven very knowingly by George de Courcy; and the fourth seat on the back of the vehicle was occupied by a servant, who was to look after the horses at Gatherum.

The Honourable George drove either well or luckily, for he reached the duke's house in safety; but he drove very fast. Poor Miss Dunstable! what would have been her lot had anything but good happened to that vehicle, so richly freighted with her three lovers! They did not quarrel as to the prize, and all reached Gatherum Castle in good-humour with each other.

The castle was a new building of white stone, lately erected at an enormous cost by one of the first architects of the day. It was an immense pile, and seemed to cover ground enough for a moderate-sized town. But, nevertheless, report said that when it was completed, the noble owner found that he had no rooms to live in; and that, on this account, when disposed to study his own comfort, he resided in a house of perhaps one-tenth the size, built by his grandfather in another county.

Gatherum Castle would probably be called Italian in its style of architecture; though it may, I think, be doubted whether any such edifice, or anything like it, was ever seen in any part of Italy. It was a vast edifice; irregular in height—or it appeared to be so—having long wings on each side too high to be passed over by the eye as mere adjuncts to the mansion, and a portico so large as to make the house behind it look like another building of a greater altitude. This portico was supported by Ionic columns, and was in itself doubtless a beautiful structure. It was approached by a flight of steps, very broad and very grand; but, as an approach by a flight of steps hardly suits an Englishman's house, to the immediate entrance of which it is necessary that his carriage should drive, there was another front door in one of the wings which was commonly used. A carriage, however, could on very stupendously grand occasions—the visits, for instance, of queens and kings, and royal dukes—be brought up under the portico; as the steps had been so constructed as to admit of a road, with a rather stiff ascent, being made close in front of the wing up into the very porch.

Opening from the porch was the grand hall, which extended up to the top of the house. It was magnificent, indeed; being decorated with many-coloured marbles, and hung round with various trophies of the house of Omnium; banners were there, and armour; the sculptured busts of many noble progenitors; full-length figures in marble of those who had been especially prominent; and every monument of glory that wealth, long years, and great achievements could bring together. If only a man could but live in his hall and be for ever happy there! But the Duke of Omnium could not live happily in his hall; and the fact was, that the architect, in contriving this magnificent entrance for his own honour and fame, had destroyed the duke's house as regards most of the ordinary purposes of residence.

Nevertheless, Gatherum Castle is a very noble pile; and, standing as it does on an eminence, has a very fine effect when seen from many a distant knoll and verdant-wooded hill.

The Duke Entertains

At seven o'clock Mr de Courcy and his friends got down from their drag at the smaller door—for this was no day on which to mount up under the portico; nor was that any suitable vehicle to have been entitled to such honour. Frank felt some excitement a little stronger than that usual to him at such moments, for he had never yet been in company with the Duke of Omnium; and he rather puzzled himself to think on what points he could talk to the man who was the largest landowner in that county in which he himself had so great an interest. He, however, made up his mind that he would allow the duke to choose his own subjects; merely reserving to himself the right of pointing out how deficient in gorse covers was West Barsetshire—that being the duke's division.

They were soon divested of their coats and hats, and, without entering on the magnificence of the great hall, were conducted through rather a narrow passage into rather a small drawing-room—small, that is, in proportion to the number of gentlemen there assembled. There might be about thirty, and Frank was inclined to think that they were almost crowded. A man came forward to greet them when their names were announced; but our hero at once knew that he was not the duke; for this man was fat and short, whereas the duke was thin and tall.

There was a great hubbub going on; for everybody seemed to be talking to his neighbour; or, in default of a neighbour, to himself. It was clear that the exalted rank of their host had put very little constraint on his guests' tongues, for they chatted away with as much freedom as farmers at an ordinary.

"Which is the duke?" at last Frank contrived to whisper to his cousin.

"Oh,—he's not here," said George; "I suppose he'll be in presently. I believe he never shows till just before dinner."

Frank, of course, had nothing further to say; but he already began to feel himself a little snubbed: he thought that the duke, duke though he was, when he asked people to dinner should be there to tell them that he was glad to see them.

More people flashed into the room, and Frank found himself

rather closely wedged in with a stout clergyman of his acquaintance. He was not badly off, for Mr Athill was a friend of his own, who had held a living near Greshamsbury. Lately, however, at the lamented decease of Dr Stanhope—who had died of apoplexy at his villa in Italy—Mr Athill had been presented with the better preferment of Eiderdown, and had, therefore, removed to another part of the county. He was somewhat of a bon-vivant, and a man who thoroughly understood dinner-parties; and with much good nature he took Frank under his special protection.

"You stick to me, Mr Gresham," he said, "when we go into the dining-room. I'm an old hand at the duke's dinners, and know how to make a friend comfortable as well as myself."

"But why doesn't the duke come in?" demanded Frank.

"He'll be here as soon as dinner is ready," said Mr Athill. "Or, rather, the dinner will be ready as soon as he is here. I don't care, therefore, how soon he comes."

Frank did not understand this, but he had nothing to do but to wait and see how things went.

He was beginning to be impatient, for the room was now nearly full, and it seemed evident that no other guests were coming; when suddenly a bell rang, and a gong was sounded, and at the same instant a door that had not yet been used flew open, and a very plainly dressed, plain, tall man entered the room. Frank at once knew that he was at last in the presence of the Duke of Omnium.

But his grace, late as he was in commencing the duties as host, seemed in no hurry to make up for lost time. He quietly stood on the rug, with his back to the empty grate, and spoke one or two words in a very low voice to one or two gentlemen who stood nearest to him. The crowd, in the meanwhile, became suddenly silent. Frank, when he found that the duke did not come and speak to him, felt that he ought to go and speak to the duke; but no one else did so, and when he whispered his surprise to Mr Athill, that gentleman told him that this was the duke's practice on all such occasions.

"Fothergill," said the duke—and it was the only word he had yet spoken out loud—"I believe we are ready for dinner." Now Mr

Fothergill was the duke's land-agent, and he it was who had greeted Frank and his friends at their entrance.

Immediately the gong was again sounded, and another door leading out of the drawing-room into the dining-room was opened. The duke led the way, and then the guests followed. "Stick close to me, Mr Gresham," said Athill, "we'll get about the middle of the table, where we shall be cosy—and on the other side of the room, out of this dreadful draught—I know the place well, Mr Gresham; stick to me."

Mr Athill, who was a pleasant, chatty companion, had hardly seated himself, and was talking to Frank as quickly as he could, when Mr Fothergill, who sat at the bottom of the table, asked him to say grace. It seemed to be quite out of the question that the duke should take any trouble with his guests whatever. Mr Athill consequently dropped the word that he was speaking, and uttered a prayer—if it was a prayer—that they might all have grateful hearts for that which God was about to give them.

If it was a prayer! As far as my own experience goes, such utterances are seldom prayers, seldom can be prayers. And if not prayers, what then? To me it is unintelligible that the full tide of glibbest chatter can be stopped at a moment in the midst of profuse good living, and the Giver thanked becomingly in words of heartfelt praise. Setting aside for the moment what one daily hears and sees, may not one declare that a change so sudden is not within the compass of the human mind? But then, to such reasoning one cannot but add what one does hear and see; one cannot but judge of the ceremony by the manner in which one sees it performed—uttered, that is—and listened to. Clergymen there are—one meets them now and then—who endeavour to give to the dinner-table grace some of the solemnity of a church ritual, and what is the effect? Much the same as though one were to be interrupted for a minute in the midst of one of our church liturgies to hear a drinking-song.

And will it be argued, that a man need be less thankful because, at the moment of receiving, he utters no thanksgiving? or will it be thought that a man is made thankful because what is called a grace is uttered after dinner? It can hardly be imagined that any one will so argue, or so think.

Dinner-graces are, probably, the last remaining relic of certain daily services which the Church in olden days enjoined; nones, complines, and vespers were others. Of the nones and complines we have happily got quit; and it might be well if we could get rid of the dinner-graces also. Let any man ask himself whether, on his own part, they are acts of prayer and thanksgiving—and if not that, what then?

When the large party entered the dining-room one or two gentlemen might be seen to come in from some other door and set themselves at the table near to the duke's chair. These were guests of his own, who were staying in the house, his particular friends, the men with whom he lived: the others were strangers whom he fed, perhaps once a year, in order that his name might be known in the land as that of one who distributed food and wine hospitably through the county. The food and wine, the attendance also, and the view of the vast repository of plate he vouchsafed willingly to his county neighbours;—but it was beyond his good nature to talk to them. To judge by the present appearance of most of them, they were quite as well satisfied to be left alone.

Frank was altogether a stranger there, but Mr Athill knew every one at the table.

"That's Apjohn," said he: "don't you know Mr Apjohn, the attorney from Barchester? he's always here; he does some of Fothergill's law business and makes himself useful. If any fellow knows the value of a good dinner, he does. You'll see that the duke's hospitality will not be thrown away upon him."

"It's very much thrown away upon me, I know," said Frank, who could not at all put up with the idea of sitting down to dinner without having been spoken to by his host.

"Oh, nonsense!" said his clerical friend; "you'll enjoy yourself amazingly by and by. There is not such champagne in any other house in Barsetshire; and then the claret——" And Mr Athill pressed his lips together and gently shook his head, meaning to

signify by the motion that the claret of Gatherum Castle was sufficient atonement for any penance which a man might have to go
through in his mode of obtaining it.

"Who's that funny little man sitting there, next but one to Mr de
Courcy? I never saw such a queer fellow in my life."

"Don't you know old Bolus? Well, I thought every one in Barsetshire knew Bolus; you especially should do so, as he is such a dear
friend of Dr Thorne."

"A dear friend of Dr Thorne?"

"Yes; he was apothecary at Scarington in the old days, before Dr
Fillgrave came into vogue. I remember when Bolus was thought to
be a very good sort of a doctor."

"Is he—is he——" whispered Frank, "is he by way of a gentleman?"

"Ha! ha! ha! Well, I suppose we must be charitable, and say that
he is quite as good, at any rate, as many others there are here——"
and Mr Athill, as he spoke, whispered into Frank's ear. "You see,
there's Finnie here, another Barchester attorney. Now, I really think
where Finnie goes Bolus may go too."

"The more the merrier, I suppose," said Frank.

"Well, something a little like that. I wonder why Thorne is not
here. I'm sure he was asked."

"Perhaps he did not particularly wish to meet Finnie and Bolus.
Do you know, Mr Athill, I think he was quite right not to come. As
for myself, I wish I was anywhere else."

"Ha! ha! ha! You don't know the duke's ways yet; and what's
more, you're young, you happy fellow! But Thorne should have
more sense; he ought to show himself here."

The gormandizing was now going on at a tremendous rate. Though
the volubility of their tongues had been for a while stopped by the
first shock of the duke's presence, the guests seemed to feel no such
constraint upon their teeth. They fed, one may almost say, rabidly,
and gave their orders to the servants in an eager manner; much
more impressive than that usual at smaller parties. Mr Apjohn, who
sat immediately opposite to Frank, had, by some well-planned

manoeuvre, contrived to get before him the jowl of a salmon; but, unfortunately, he was not for a while equally successful in the article of sauce. A very limited portion—so at least thought Mr Apjohn—had been put on his plate; and a servant, with a huge sauce tureen, absolutely passed behind his back inattentive to his audible requests. Poor Mr Apjohn in his despair turned round to arrest the man by his coat-tails; but he was a moment too late, and all but fell backwards on the floor. As he righted himself he muttered an anathema, and looked with a face of mute anguish at his plate.

"Anything the matter, Apjohn?" said Mr Fothergill kindly, seeing the utter despair written on the poor man's countenance; "can I get anything for you?"

"The sauce!" said Mr Apjohn, in a voice that would have melted a hermit; and as he looked at Mr Fothergill, he pointed at the now distant sinner, who was dispensing his melted ambrosia at least ten heads upwards, away from the unfortunate supplicant.

Mr Fothergill, however, knew where to look for balm for such wounds, and in a minute or two Mr Apjohn was employed quite to his heart's content.

"Well," said Frank to his neighbour, "it may be very well once in a way; but I think that on the whole Dr Thorne is right."

"My dear Mr Gresham, see the world on all sides," said Mr Athill, who had also been somewhat intent on the gratification of his own appetite, though with an energy less evident than that of the gentleman opposite. "See the world on all sides if you have an opportunity; and, believe me, a good dinner now and then is a very good thing."

"Yes, but I don't like eating it with hogs."

"Whish—h! softly, softly, Mr Gresham, or you'll disturb Mr Apjohn's digestion. Upon my word, he'll want it all before he has done. Now, I like this kind of thing once in a way."

"Do you?" said Frank, in a tone that was almost savage.

"Yes; indeed I do. One sees so much character. And, after all, what harm does it do?"

"My idea is that people should live with those whose society is pleasant to them."

"Live—yes, Mr Gresham—I agree with you there. It wouldn't do for me to live with the Duke of Omnium; I shouldn't understand, or probably approve, his ways. Nor should I, perhaps, much like the constant presence of Mr Apjohn. But now and then—once in a year or so—I do own I like to see them both. Here's the cup; now whatever you do, Mr Gresham, don't pass the cup without tasting it."

And so the dinner passed on, slowly enough as Frank thought, but all too quickly for Mr Apjohn. It passed away, and the wine came circulating freely. The tongues again were loosed, the teeth being released from their labours, and under the influence of the claret the duke's presence was forgotten.

But very speedily the coffee was brought. "This will soon be over now," said Frank, to himself, thankfully; for, though he by no means despised good claret, he had lost his temper too completely to enjoy it at the present moment. But he was much mistaken; the farce as yet was only at its commencement. The duke took his cup of coffee, and so did the few friends who sat close to him; but the beverage did not seem to be in great request with the majority of the guests. When the duke had taken his modicum, he rose up and silently retired, saying no word and making no sign. And then the farce commenced.

"Now, gentlemen," said Mr Fothergill, cheerily, "we are all right. Apjohn, is there claret there? Mr Bolus, I know you stick to the Madeira; you are quite right, for there isn't much of it left, and my belief is there'll never be more like it."

And so the duke's hospitality went on, and the duke's guests drank merrily for the next two hours.

"Shan't we see any more of him?" asked Frank.

"Any more of whom?" said Mr Athill.

"Of the duke?"

"Oh, no; you'll see no more of him. He always goes when the coffee comes. It's brought in as an excuse. We've had enough of the light of his countenance to last till next year. The duke and I are excellent friends; have been so these fifteen years; but I never see more of him than that."

"I shall go away," said Frank.

"Nonsense. Mr de Courcy and your other friend won't stir for this hour yet."

"I don't care. I shall walk on, and they may catch me. I may be wrong; but it seems to me that a man insults me when he asks me to dine with him and never speaks to me. I don't care if he be ten times Duke of Omnium; he can't be more than a gentleman, and as such I am his equal." And then, having thus given vent to his feelings in somewhat high-flown language, he walked forth and trudged away along the road towards Courcy.

Frank Gresham had been born and bred a Conservative, whereas the Duke of Omnium was well known as a consistent Whig. There is no one so devoutly resolved to admit of no superior as your Conservative, born and bred, no one so inclined to high domestic despotism as your thoroughgoing consistent old Whig.

When he had proceeded about six miles, Frank was picked up by his friends; but even then his anger had hardly cooled.

"Was the duke as civil as ever when you took your leave of him?" said he to his cousin George, as he took his seat on the drag.

"The juke has jeuced jude wine—lem me tell you that, old fella," hiccupped out the Honourable George, as he touched up the leader under the flank.

D. T.

Dignity

A man rarely carries himself meanly, whom the world holds high in esteem.

L. C.

Snobbery

. . . no one is so hostile to lowly born pretenders to high station as the pure Whig.

B. T.

SINCERITY

When one Esquimaux meets another, do the two, as an invariable rule, ask after each other's health? Is it inherent in all human nature to make this obliging inquiry? Did any reader of this tale ever meet any friend or acquaintance without asking some such question, and did any one ever listen to the reply?

W.

Frank takes a
Brother's Privilege

————••◦━━◦━━◦••————

At ten minutes before four these two heroes might be seen walking up Pall Mall, towards the —— Club. Young Baker walked with an eager disengaged air. Mr Moffat did not know his appearance; he had, therefore, no anxiety to pass along unnoticed. But Frank had in some mysterious way drawn his hat very far over his forehead, and had buttoned his shooting-coat up round his chin. Harry had recommended to him a great-coat, in order that he might the better conceal his face; but Frank had found that the great-coat was an encumbrance to his arm. He put it on, and when thus clothed he had tried the whip, he found that he cut the air with much less potency than in the lighter garment. He contented himself, therefore, with looking down on the pavement as he walked along, letting the long point of the whip stick up from his pocket, and flattering himself that even Mr Moffat would not recognize him at the first glance. Poor Mr Moffat! If he had but had the chance!

And now, having arrived at the front of the club, the two friends for a moment separate: Frank remains standing on the pavement, under the shade of the high stone area-railing, while Harry jauntily skips up three steps at a time, and with a very civil word of inquiry of the hall porter, sends in his card to Mr Moffat—

"MR HENRY BAKER"

Mr Moffat, never having heard of such a gentleman in his life, unwittingly comes out into the hall, and Harry, with his sweetest smile, addresses him.

Now the plan of the campaign had been settled in this wise: Baker was to send into the club for Mr Moffat, and invite that gentleman down into the street. It was probable that the invitation might be declined; and it had been calculated in such case that the two gentlemen would retire for parley into the strangers' room, which was known to be immediately opposite the hall door. Frank was to keep his eye on the portals, and if he found that Mr Moffat did not appear as readily as might be desired, he also was to ascend the steps and hurry into the strangers' room. Then, whether he met Mr Moffat there or elsewhere, or wherever he might meet him, he was to greet him with all the friendly vigour in his power, while Harry disposed of the club porters.

But fortune, who ever favours the brave, specially favoured Frank Gresham on this occasion. Just as Harry Baker had put his card into the servant's hand, Mr Moffat, with his hat on, prepared for the street, appeared in the hall; Mr Baker addressed him with his sweetest smile, and begged the pleasure of saying a word or two as they descended into the street. Had not Mr Moffat been going thither it would have been very improbable that he should have done so at Harry's instance. But, as it was, he merely looked rather solemn at his visitor—it was his wont to look solemn—and continued the descent of the steps.

Frank, his heart leaping the while, saw his prey, and retreated two steps behind the area-railing, the dread weapon already well poised in his hand. Oh! Mr Moffat! Mr Moffat! if there be any goddess to intervene in thy favour, let her come forward now without delay; let her now bear thee off on a cloud if there be one to whom thou art sufficiently dear! But there is no such goddess.

Harry smiled blandly till they were well on the pavement, saying some nothing, and keeping the victim's face averted from the avenging angel; and then, when the raised hand was sufficiently nigh, he withdrew two steps towards the nearest lamp-post. Not for him was the honour of the interview—unless, indeed, succouring policemen might give occasion for some gleam of glory.

But succouring policemen were no more to be come by than goddesses. Where were ye, men, when that savage whip fell about the ears of the poor ex-legislator? In Scotland Yard, sitting dozing on your benches, or talking soft nothings to the housemaids round the corner; for ye were not walking on your beats, nor standing at coign of vantage, to watch the tumults of the day. But had ye been there

what could ye have done? Had Sir Richard himself been on the spot Frank Gresham would still, we may say, have had his five shies at that unfortunate one.

When Harry Baker quickly seceded from the way, Mr Moffat at once saw his fate before him. His hair doubtless stood on end, and his voice refused to give the loud screech with which he sought to invoke the club. An ashy paleness suffused his cheeks, and his tottering steps were unable to bear him away in flight. Once, and twice, the cutting whip came well down across his back. Had he been wise

enough to stand still and take his thrashing in that attitude, it would have been well for him. But men so circumstanced have never such prudence. After two blows he made a dash at the steps, thinking to get back into the club; but Harry, who had by no means reclined in idleness against the lamp-post, here stopped him: "You had better go back into the street;" said Harry, "indeed you had," giving him a shove from off the second step.

Then of course Frank could not do other than hit him anywhere. When a gentleman is dancing about with much energy it is hardly possible to strike him fairly on his back. The blows, therefore, came now on his legs and now on his head; and Frank unfortunately got more than his five or six shies before he was interrupted.

The interruption, however, came all too soon for Frank's idea of justice. Though there be no policemen to take part in a London row, there are always others ready enough to do so; amateur policemen, who generally sympathize with the wrong side, and, in nine cases out of ten, expend their generous energy in protecting thieves and pickpockets. When it was seen with what tremendous ardour that dread weapon fell about the ears of the poor undefended gentleman, interference there was at last, in spite of Harry Baker's best endeavours, and loudest protestations.

"Do not interrupt them, sir," said he; "pray do not. It is a family affair, and they will neither of them like it."

In the teeth, however, of these assurances, rude people did interfere, and after some nine or ten shies Frank found himself encompassed by the arms, and encumbered by the weight, of a very stout gentleman, who hung affectionately about his neck and shoulders; whereas Mr Moffat was already receiving consolation from two motherly females, sitting in a state of syncope on the good-natured knees of a fishmonger's apprentice.

Frank was thoroughly out of breath: nothing came from his lips but half-muttered expletives, and unintelligible denunciations of the iniquity of his foe. But still he struggled to be at him again. We all know how dangerous is the taste of blood; how cruelty will become a custom even with the most tender-hearted. Frank felt that he had hardly fleshed his virgin lash: he thought, almost with despair, that he had not yet at all succeeded as became a man and a brother; his memory told him of but one or two slight touches that had gone well home to the offender. He made a desperate effort to throw off that incubus round his neck and rush again to the combat.

"Harry—Harry; don't let him go—don't let him go," he barely articulated.

"Do you want to murder the man, sir; to murder him?" said the stout gentleman over his shoulder, speaking solemnly into his very ear.

"I don't care," said Frank, struggling manfully but uselessly. "Let me out, I say; I don't care—don't let him go, Harry, whatever you do."

"He has got it pretty tidily," said Harry; "I think that will perhaps do for the present."

By this time there was a considerable concourse. The club steps were crowded with the members; among whom there were many of Mr Moffat's acquaintance. Policemen also now flocked up, and the question arose as to what should be done with the originators of the affray. Frank and Harry found that they were to consider themselves under a gentle arrest, and Mr Moffat, in a fainting state, was carried into the interior of the club.

Frank, in his innocence, had intended to have celebrated this little affair when it was over by a slight repast and a bottle of claret with his friend, and then to have gone back to Cambridge by the mail train. He found, however, that his schemes in this respect were frustrated. He had to get bail to attend at Marlborough Street police-office should he be wanted within the next two or three days; and was given to understand that he would be under the eye of the police, at any rate until Mr Moffat should be out of danger.

"Out of danger!" said Frank to his friend with a startled look. "Why, I hardly got at him." Nevertheless, they did have their slight repast, and also their bottle of claret.

On the second morning after this occurrence, Frank was again sitting in that public room at the Tavistock, and Harry was again sitting opposite to him. The whip was not now so conspicuously produced between them, having been carefully packed up and put away among Frank's other travelling properties. They were so sitting, rather glum, when the door swung open, and a heavy, quick step was heard advancing towards them. It was the squire; whose arrival there had been momentarily expected.

"Frank," said he—"Frank, what on earth is all this?" and as he spoke he stretched out both his hands, the right to his son and the left to his friend.

"He has given a blackguard a licking, that is all," said Harry.

Frank felt that his hand was held with a peculiarly warm grasp; and he could not but think that his father's face, raised though his eyebrows were—though there was on it an intended expression of amazement and, perhaps, regret—nevertheless he could not but think that his father's face looked kindly at him.

"God bless my soul, my dear boy! what have you done to the man?"

"He's not a ha'porth the worse, sir," said Frank, still holding his father's hand.

"Oh, isn't he!" said Harry, shrugging his shoulders. "He must be made of some very tough article then."

"But, my dear boys, I hope there's no danger. I hope there's no danger."

"Danger!" said Frank, who could not yet induce himself to believe that he had been allowed a fair chance with Mr Moffat.

"Oh, Frank! Frank! how could you be so rash? In the middle of Pall Mall, too. Well! well! well! All the women down at Greshamsbury will have it that you have killed him."

"I almost wish I had," said Frank.

"Oh, Frank! Frank! But now tell me——"

And then the father sat well pleased while he heard, chiefly from Harry Baker, the full story of his son's prowess. And then they did not separate without another slight repast and another bottle of claret.

Mr Moffat retired into the country for a while, and then went abroad; having doubtless learnt that the petition was not likely to give him a seat for the city of Barchester. And this was the end of the wooing with Miss Gresham.

D. T.

Turning the Cheek

It is easy to love one's enemy when one is making fine speeches; but so difficult to do so in the actual everyday work of life.

F. P.

Sir Louis Dines Out

The next day Joe did not make his appearance, and Sir Louis, with many execrations, was driven to the terrible necessity of dressing himself. Then came an unexpected difficulty: how were they to get up to the house? Walking out to dinner, though it was merely through the village and up the avenue, seemed to Sir Louis to be a thing impossible. Indeed, he was not well able to walk at all, and positively declared that he should never be able to make his way over the gravel in pumps. His mother would not have thought half as much of walking from Boxall Hill to Greshamsbury and back again. At last, the one village fly was sent for, and the matter was arranged.

When they reached the house, it was easy to see that there was some unwonted bustle. In the drawing-room there was no one but Mr Mortimer Gazebee, who introduced himself to them both. Sir Louis, who knew that he was only an attorney, did not take much notice of him, but the doctor entered into conversation.

"Have you heard that Mr Gresham has come home?" said Mr Gazebee.

"Mr Gresham! I did not know that he had been away."

"Mr Gresham, junior, I mean." No, indeed; the doctor had not heard. Frank had returned unexpectedly just before dinner, and he was now undergoing his father's smiles, his mother's embraces, and his sisters' questions.

"Quite unexpectedly," said Mr Gazebee. "I don't know what has brought him back before his time. I suppose he found London too hot."

"Deuced hot," said the baronet. "I found it so, at least. I don't know what keeps men in London when it's so hot; except those fellows who have business to do: they're paid for it."

Mr Mortimer Gazebee looked at him. He was managing an estate which owed Sir Louis an enormous sum of money, and, therefore, he could not afford to despise the baronet; but he thought to himself, what a very abject fellow the man would be if he were not a baronet, and had not a large fortune!

And then the squire came in. His broad, honest face was covered with a smile when he saw the doctor.

"Thorne," he said, almost in a whisper, "you're the best fellow breathing; I have hardly deserved this." The doctor, as he took his old friend's hand, could not but be glad that he had followed Mary's counsel.

"So Frank has come home?"

"Oh, yes; quite unexpectedly. He was to have stayed a week longer in London. You would hardly know him if you met him. Sir Louis, I beg your pardon." And the squire went up to his other guest, who had remained somewhat sullenly standing in one corner of the room. He was the man of highest rank present, or to be present, and he expected to be treated as such.

"I am happy to have the pleasure of making your acquaintance, Mr Gresham," said the baronet, intending to be very courteous. "Though we have not met before, I very often see your name in my accounts—ha! ha! ha!" and Sir Louis laughed as though he had said something very good.

The meeting between Lady Arabella and the doctor was rather distressing to the former; but she managed to get over it. She shook hands with him graciously, and said that it was a fine day. The doctor said that it was fine, only perhaps a little rainy. And then they went into different parts of the room.

When Frank came in, the doctor hardly did know him. His hair was darker than it had been, and so was his beard, which hung down over his cravat. The doctor had hitherto not been much in favour of long beards, but he could not deny that Frank looked very well with the appendage.

"Oh, doctor, I am so delighted to find you here," said he, coming up to him; "so very, very glad:" and, taking the doctor's arm, he led him away into a window, where they were alone. "And how is Mary?" said he, almost in a whisper. "Oh, I wish she were here! But, doctor, it shall all come in time. But tell me, doctor, there is no news about her, is there?"

"News—what news?"

"Oh, well; no news is good news: you will give her my love, won't you?"

The doctor said that he would. What else could he say? It appeared quite clear to him that some of Mary's fears were groundless.

Frank was again very much altered. It has been said, that though he was a boy at twenty-one, he was a man at twenty-two. But now, at twenty-three, he appeared to be almost a man of the world. His manners were easy, his voice under his control, and words were at his command: he was no longer either shy or noisy; but, perhaps, was open to the charge of seeming, at least, to be too conscious of his own merits. He was, indeed, very handsome; tall, manly and power-fully built, his form was such as women's eyes have ever loved to look upon. "Ah, if he would but marry money!" said Lady Arabella to herself, taken up by a mother's natural admiration for her son. His sisters clung round him before dinner, all talking to him at once. How proud a family of girls are of one big, tall, burly brother!

"You don't mean to tell me, Frank, that you are going to eat soup with that beard?" said the squire, when they were seated round the table. He had not ceased to rally his son as to this patriarchal adorn-ment; but, nevertheless, any one could have seen, with half an eye, that he was as proud of it as were the others.

"Don't I, sir? All I require is a relay of napkins for every course:" and he went to work, covering it with every spoonful, as men with beards always do.

"Well, if you like it!" said the squire, shrugging his shoulders.

"But I do like it," said Frank.

"Oh, papa, you wouldn't have him cut it off," said one of the twins. "It is so handsome."

"I should like to work it into a chair-back instead of floss-silk," said the other twin.

"Thank'ee, Sophy; I'll remember you for that."

"Doesn't it look nice, and grand, and patriarchal?" said Beatrice, turning to her neighbour.

"Patriarchal, certainly," said Mr Oriel. "I should grow one myself if I had not the fear of the archbishop before my eyes."

What was next said to him was in a whisper, audible only to himself.

"Doctor, did you know Wildman, of the 9th? He was left as surgeon at Scutari for two years. Why, my beard to his is only a little down."

"A little way down, you mean," said Mr Gazebee.

"Yes," said Frank, resolutely set against laughing at Mr Gazebee's pun. "Why, his beard descends to his ankles, and he is obliged to tie it in a bag at night, because his feet get entangled in it when he is asleep!"

"Oh, Frank!" said one of the girls.

This was all very well for the squire, and Lady Arabella, and the girls. They were all delighted to praise Frank, and talk about him. Neither did it come amiss to Mr Oriel and the doctor, who had both a personal interest in the young hero. But Sir Louis did not like it at all. He was the only baronet in the room, and yet nobody took any notice of him. He was seated in the post of honour, next to Lady Arabella; but even Lady Arabella seemed to think more of her own son than of him. Seeing how he was ill-used, he meditated revenge; but not the less did it behove him to make some effort to attract attention.

"Was your ladyship long in London, this season?" said he.

Lady Arabella had not been in London at all this year, and it was a sore subject with her. "No," said she, very graciously; "circumstances have kept us at home."

Sir Louis only understood one description of "circumstances". Circumstances, in his idea, meant the want of money, and he immediately took Lady Arabella's speech as a confession of poverty.

"Ah, indeed! I am very sorry for that; that must be very distressing to a person like your ladyship. But things are mending, perhaps?"

Lady Arabella did not in the least understand him. "Mending!" she said, in her peculiar tone of aristocratic indifference; and then turned to Mr Gazebee, who was on the other side of her.

Sir Louis was not going to stand this. He was the first man in the room, and he knew his own importance. It was not to be borne that Lady Arabella should turn to talk to a dirty attorney, and leave him, a baronet, to eat his dinner without notice. If nothing else would move her, he would let her know who was the real owner of the Greshamsbury title-deeds.

"I think I saw your ladyship out to-day, taking a ride." Lady Arabella had driven through the village in her pony-chair.

"I never ride," said she, turning her head for one moment from Mr Gazebee.

"In the one-horse carriage, I mean, my lady. I was delighted with the way you whipped him up round the corner."

Whipped him up round the corner! Lady Arabella could make no answer to this; so she went on talking to Mr Gazebee. Sir Louis, repulsed, but not vanquished—resolved not to be vanquished by any Lady Arabella—turned his attention to his plate for a minute or two, and then recommenced.

"The honour of a glass of wine with you, Lady Arabella," said he.

"I never take wine at dinner," said Lady Arabella. The man was becoming intolerable to her, and she was beginning to fear that it would be necessary for her to fly the room, to get rid of him.

The baronet was again silent for a moment; but he was determined not to be put down.

"This is a nice-looking country about here," said he.

"Yes; very nice," said Mr Gazebee, endeavouring to relieve the lady of the mansion.

"I hardly know which I like best; this, or my own place at Boxall Hill. You have the advantage here in trees, and those sort of things. But, as to the house, why, my box there is very comfortable, very. You'd hardly know the place now, Lady Arabella, if you haven't seen it since my governor bought it. How much do you think he spent about the house and grounds, pineries included, you know, and those sort of things?"

Lady Arabella shook her head.

"Now guess, my lady," said he. But it was not to be supposed that Lady Arabella should guess on such a subject.

"I never guess," said she, with a look of ineffable disgust.

"What do you say, Mr Gazebee?"

"Perhaps a hundred thousand pounds."

"What! for a house? You can't know much about money, nor yet about building, I think, Mr Gazebee."

"Not much", said Mr Gazebee, "as to such magnificent places as Boxall Hill."

"Well, my lady, if you won't guess, I'll tell you. It cost twenty-two thousand four hundred and nineteen pounds four shillings and eightpence. I've all the accounts exact. Now, that's a tidy lot of money for a house for a man to live in."

Sir Louis spoke this in a loud tone, which at least commanded the attention of the table. Lady Arabella, vanquished, bowed her head, and said that it was a large sum; Mr Gazebee went on sedulously eating his dinner; the squire was struck momentarily dumb in the middle of a long chat with the doctor; even Mr Oriel ceased to whisper; and the girls opened their eyes with astonishment. Before the end of his speech, Sir Louis's voice had become very loud.

"Yes, indeed," said Frank; "a very tidy lot of money. I'd have generously dropped the four and eightpence if I'd been the architect."

"It wasn't all one bill; but that's the tot. I can show the bills:" and Sir Louis, well pleased with his triumph, swallowed a glass of wine.

Almost immediately after the cloth was removed, Lady Arabella escaped, and the gentlemen clustered together. Sir Louis found himself next to Mr Oriel, and began to make himself agreeable.

"A very nice girl, Miss Beatrice; very nice."

Now Mr Oriel was a modest man, and, when thus addressed as to his future wife, found it difficult to make any reply.

"You parsons always have your own luck," said Sir Louis. "You get all the beauty, and generally all the money, too. Not much of the latter in this case, though—eh?"

Mr Oriel was dumbfounded. He had never said a word to any creature as to Beatrice's dowry; and when Mr Gresham had told him, with sorrow, that his daughter's portion must be small, he had at once passed away from the subject as one that was hardly fit for conversation, even between him and his future father-in-law; and now he was abruptly questioned on the subject by a man he had never before seen in his life. Of course, he could make no answer.

"The squire has muddled his matters most uncommonly," continued Sir Louis, filling his glass for the second time before he passed the bottle. "What do you suppose now he owes me, alone; just at one lump, you know?"

Mr Oriel had nothing for it but to run. He could make no answer, nor would he sit there to hear tidings as to Mr Gresham's embarrassments. So he fairly retreated, without having said one word to his neighbour, finding such discretion to be the only kind of valour left to him.

"What, Oriel! off already?" said the squire. "Anything the matter?"

"Oh, no; nothing particular. I'm not just quite—I think I'll go out for a few minutes."

"See what it is to be in love," said the squire, half whispering to Dr Thorne. "You're not in the same way, I hope?"

Sir Louis then shifted his seat again, and found himself next to Frank. Mr Gazebee was opposite to him, and the doctor opposite to Frank.

"Parson seems peekish, I think," said the baronet.

"Peekish?" said the squire, inquisitively.

"Rather down on his luck. He's decently well off himself, isn't he?"

There was another pause, and nobody seemed inclined to answer the question.

"I mean, he's got something more than his bare living."

"Oh, yes," said Frank, laughing. "He's got what will buy him bread and cheese when the Rads shut up the Church:—unless, indeed, they shut up the Funds too."

"Ah, there's nothing like land," said Sir Louis: "nothing like the dirty acres; is there, squire?"

"Land is a very good investment, certainly," said Mr Gresham.

"The best going," said the other, who was now, as people say when they mean to be good-natured, slightly under the influence of liquor. "The best going—eh, Gazebee?"

Mr Gazebee gathered himself up, and turned away his head, looking out of the window.

"You lawyers never like to give an opinion without money, ha! ha! ha! Do they, Mr Gresham? You and I have had to pay for plenty of them, and will have to pay for plenty more before they let us alone."

Here Mr Gazebee got up, and followed Mr Oriel out of the room. He was not, of course, on such intimate terms in the house as was Mr Oriel; but he hoped to be forgiven by the ladies in consequence of the severity of the miseries to which he was subjected. He and Mr Oriel were soon to be seen through the dining-room window walking about the grounds with the two eldest Miss Greshams. And Patience Oriel, who had also been of the party, was also to be seen with the twins. Frank looked at his father with almost a malicious smile, and began to think that he too might be better employed out among the walks. Did he think then of a former summer evening, when he had half broken Mary's heart by walking there too lovingly with Patience Oriel?

Sir Louis, if he continued his brilliant career of success, would soon be left the cock of the walk. The squire, to be sure, could not bolt, nor could the doctor very well; but they might be equally vanquished, remaining there in their chairs. Dr Thorne, during all this time, was sitting with tingling ears. Indeed, it may be said that his whole body tingled. He was in a manner responsible for this horrid scene; but what could he do to stop it? He could not take Sir Louis up bodily and carry him away. One idea did occur to him. The fly had been ordered for ten o'clock. He could rush out and send for it instantly.

"You're not going to leave me?" said the squire, in a voice of horror, as he saw the doctor rising from his chair.

"Oh, no, no, no," said the doctor; and then he whispered the purpose of his mission. "I will be back in two minutes." The doctor would have given twenty pounds to have closed the scene at once; but he was not the man to desert his friend in such a strait as that.

"He's a well-meaning fellow, is the doctor," said Sir Louis, when his guardian was out of the room, "very; but he's not up to trap—not at all."

"Up to trap—well, I should say he was; that is, if I know what trap means," said Frank.

"Ah, but that's just the ticket. Do you know? Now I say Dr Thorne's not a man of the world."

"He's about the best man I know, or ever heard of," said the squire. "And if any man ever had a good friend, you have got one in him; and so have I:" and the squire silently drank the doctor's health.

"All very true, I dare say; but yet he's not up to trap. Now look here, squire——"

"If you don't mind, sir," said Frank, "I've got something very particular—perhaps, however——"

"Stay till Thorne returns, Frank."

Frank did stay till Thorne returned, and then escaped.

"Excuse me, doctor," said he, "but I've something very particular to say; I'll explain to-morrow." And then the three were left alone.

Sir Louis was now becoming almost drunk and was knocking his words together. The squire had already attempted to stop the bottle; but the baronet had contrived to get hold of a modicum of Madeira, and there was no preventing him from helping himself; at least, none at that moment.

"As we were saying about lawyers," continued Sir Louis. "Let's see, what were we saying? Why, squire, it's just here. Those fellows will fleece us both if we don't mind what we are after."

"Never mind about lawyers now," said Dr Thorne, angrily.

"Ah, but I do mind; most particularly. That's all very well for you, doctor; you've nothing to lose. You've no great stake in the matter. Why, now, what sum of money of mine do you think those d—— doctors are handling?"

"D—— doctors!" said the squire in a tone of dismay.

"Lawyers, I mean, of course. Why, now, Gresham; we're all totted now, you see; you're down in my books, I take it, for pretty near a hundred thousand pounds."

"Hold your tongue, sir!" said the doctor, getting up.

"Hold my tongue?" said Sir Louis.

"Sir Louis Scatcherd," said the squire, slowly rising from his chair, "we will not, if you please, talk about business at the present moment. Perhaps we had better go to the ladies."

This latter proposition had certainly not come from the squire's heart: going to the ladies was the very last thing for which Sir Louis was now fit. But the squire had said it as being the only recognised formal way he could think of for breaking up the symposium.

"Oh, very well," hiccupped the baronet, "I'm always ready for the ladies," and he stretched out his hand to the decanter to get a last glass of Madeira.

"No," said the doctor, rising stoutly, and speaking with a determined voice. "No; you will have no more wine:" and he took the decanter from him.

"What's all this about?" said Sir Louis, with a drunken laugh.

"Of course he cannot go into the drawing-room, Mr Gresham. If you will leave him here with me, I will stay with him till the fly comes. Pray tell Lady Arabella from me, how sorry I am that this has occurred."

"Lady Arabella! why, what's the matter with her?" said Sir Louis.

The squire would not leave his friend, and they sat together till the fly came. It was not long, for the doctor had dispatched his messenger with much haste.

"I am so heartily ashamed of myself," said the doctor, almost with tears.

The squire took him by the hand affectionately. "I've seen a tipsy man before to-night," said he.

"Yes," said the doctor, "and so have I, but——" He did not express the rest of his thoughts.

D. T.

FILTHY LUCRE

Moneys in possession or in expectation do give a set to the head, and a confidence to the voice, and an assurance to the man, which will help him much in his walk in life—if the owner of them will simply use them, and not abuse them.

S. H. A.

Mary comes into Money

The doctor was up very early the next morning, long before Mary was ready with her teacups. He was up, and in his own study behind the shop, arranging dingy papers, pulling about tin boxes which he had brought down with him from London, and piling on his writing-table one set of documents in one place, and one in another. "I think I understand it all," said he; "but yet I know I shall be bothered. Well, I never will be anybody's trustee again. Let me see!" and then he sat down, and with bewildered look recapitulated to himself sundry heavy items. "What those shares are really worth I cannot understand, and nobody seems able to tell one. They must make it out among them as best they can. Let me see; that's Boxall Hill, and this is Greshamsbury. I'll put a newspaper over Greshamsbury, or the squire will know it!" and then, having made his arrangements, he went to his breakfast.

I know I am wrong, my much and truly honoured critic, about these title-deeds and documents. But when we've got that barrister in hand, then if I go wrong after that, let the blame be on my own shoulders—or on his.

The doctor ate his breakfast quickly, and did not talk much to his niece. But what he did say was of a nature to make her feel strangely happy. She could not analyse her own feelings, or give a reason for her own confidence; but she certainly did feel, and even trust, that something was going to happen after breakfast which would make her more happy than she had been for many months.

"Janet," said he, looking at his watch, "if Mr Gresham and Mr Frank call, show them into my study. What are you going to do with yourself, my dear?"

"I don't know, uncle; you are so mysterious, and I am in such a twitter, that I don't know what to do. Why is Mr Gresham coming here—that is, the squire?"

"Because I have business with him about the Scatcherd property. You know that he owed Sir Louis money. But don't go out, Mary. I want you to be in the way if I should have to call for you. You can stay in the drawing-room, can't you?"

"Oh yes, uncle; or here."

"No, dearest; go into the drawing-room." Mary obediently did as she was bid; and there she sat, for the next three hours, wondering, wondering, wondering. During the greater part of that time, however, she well knew that Mr Gresham, senior, and Mr Gresham, junior, were both with her uncle, below.

At eleven o'clock the doctor's visitors came. He had expected them somewhat earlier, and was beginning to become fidgety. He had so much on his hands that he could not sit still for a moment till he had, at any rate, commenced it. The expected footsteps were at last heard on the gravel-path, and a moment or two afterwards Janet ushered the father and son into the room.

The squire did not look very well. He was worn and sorrowful, and rather pale. The death of his young creditor might be supposed to have given him some relief from his more pressing cares, but the necessity of yielding to Frank's wishes had almost more than balanced this. When a man has daily to reflect that he is poorer than he was the day before, he soon becomes worn and sorrowful.

But Frank was well; both in health and spirits. He also felt, as Mary did, that the day was to bring forth something which should end his present troubles; and he could not but be happy to think that he could now tell Dr Thorne that his father's consent to his marriage had been given.

The doctor shook hands with them both, and then they sat down. They were all rather constrained in their manner; and at first it seemed that nothing but little speeches of compliments were to be made. At last, the squire remarked that Frank had been talking to him about Miss Thorne.

"About Mary?" said the doctor.

"Yes; about Mary," said the squire, correcting himself. It was quite unnecessary that he should use so cold a name as the other, now that he had agreed to the match.

"Well!" said Dr Thorne.

"I suppose it must be so, doctor. He has set his heart upon it, and, God knows, I have nothing to say against her—against her personally. No one could say a word against her. She is a sweet, good girl, excellently brought up; and, as for myself, I have always loved her." Frank drew near to his father, and pressed his hand against the squire's arm, by way of giving him, in some sort, a filial embrace for his kindness.

"Thank you, squire, thank you," said the doctor. "It is very good of you to say that. She is a good girl, and if Frank chooses to take her, he will, in my estimation, have made a good choice."

"Chooses!" said Frank, with all the enthusiasm of a lover.

The squire felt himself perhaps a little ruffled at the way in which the doctor received his gracious intimation; but he did not show it as he went on. "They cannot, you know, doctor, look to be rich people——"

"Ah! well, well," interrupted the doctor.

"I have told Frank so, and I think that you should tell Mary. Frank means to take some land into his hand, and he must farm it as a farmer. I will endeavour to give him three, or perhaps four hundred a year. But you know better——"

"Stop, squire; stop a minute. We will talk about that presently. This death of poor Sir Louis will make a difference."

"Not permanently," said the squire, mournfully.

"And now, Frank," said the doctor, not attending to the squire's last words, "what do you say?"

"What do I say? I say what I said to you in London the other day. I believe Mary loves me; indeed, I won't be affected—I know she does. I have loved her—I was going to say always; and, indeed, I almost might say so. My father knows that this is no light fancy of mine. As to what he says about our being poor, why——"

The doctor was very arbitrary, and would hear neither of them on this subject.

"Mr Gresham," said he, interrupting Frank, "of course I am well aware how very little suited Mary is by birth to marry your only son."

"It is too late to think about it now," said the squire.

"It is not too late for me to justify myself," replied the doctor. "We have long known each other, Mr Gresham, and you said here the other day, that this is a subject as to which we have been both of one mind. Birth and blood are very valuable gifts."

"I certainly think so," said the squire; "but one can't have everything."

"No; one can't have everything."

"If I am satisfied in that matter——" began Frank.

"Stop a moment, my dear boy," said the doctor. "As your father says, one can't have everything. My dear friend"—and he gave his hand to the squire—"do not be angry if I allude for a moment to the estate. It has grieved me to see it melting away—the old family acres that have so long been the heritage of the Greshams."

"We need not talk about that now, Dr Thorne," said Frank, in an almost angry tone.

"But I must, Frank, for one moment, to justify myself. I could not have excused myself in letting Mary think that she could become your wife if I had not hoped that good might come of it."

"Well, good will come of it," said Frank, who did not quite understand at what the doctor was driving.

"I hope so. I have had much doubt about this, and have been sorely perplexed; but now I do hope so. Frank—Mr Gresham—" and then Dr Thorne rose from his chair; but was, for a moment, unable to go on with his tale.

"We will hope that it is all for the best," said the squire.

"I am sure it is," said Frank.

"Yes, I hope it is. I do think it is; I am sure it is, Frank. Mary will not come to you empty-handed. I wish for your sake—yes, and for hers too—that her birth were equal to her fortune, as her worth is superior to both. Mr Gresham, this marriage will, at any rate, put an end to your pecuniary embarrassments—unless, indeed, Frank should prove a hard creditor. My niece is Sir Roger Scatcherd's heir."

The doctor, as soon as he had made the announcement, began to employ himself sedulously about the papers on the table; which, in the confusion caused by his own emotion, he transferred hither and thither in such a manner as to upset all his previous arrangements. "And now," he said, "I might as well explain, as well as I can, of what that fortune consists. Here, this is—no——"

"But, Dr Thorne," said the squire, now perfectly pale, and almost gasping for breath, "what is it you mean?"

"There's not a shadow of doubt," said the doctor. "I've had Sir Abraham Haphazard, and Sir Rickety Giggs, and old Neversaye Die, and Mr Snilam; and they are all of the same opinion. There is not the smallest doubt about it. Of course, she must adminster, and all that; and I'm afraid there'll be a very heavy sum to pay for the tax; for she cannot inherit as a niece, you know. Mr Snilam pointed that out particularly. But, after all that, there'll be—I've got it down on a piece of paper, somewhere—three grains of blue pill. I'm really so bothered, squire, with all these papers, and all those lawyers, that I don't know whether I'm sitting or standing. There's ready money enough to pay all the tax and all the debts. I know that, at any rate."

"You don't mean to say that Mary Thorne is now possessed of all Sir Roger Scatcherd's wealth?" at last ejaculated the squire.

"But that's exactly what I do mean to say," said the doctor, looking up from his papers with a tear in his eye, and a smile on his mouth; "and what is more, squire, you owe her at the present moment exactly—I've got that down too, somewhere, only I am so bothered with these papers. Come, squire, when do you mean to pay her? She's in a great hurry, as young ladies are when they want to get married."

The doctor was inclined to joke if possible, so as to carry off, as it were, some of the great weight of obligation which it might seem that he was throwing on the father and son; but the squire was by no means in a state to understand a joke: hardly as yet in a state to comprehend what was so very serious in this matter.

"Do you mean that Mary is the owner of Boxall Hill?" said he.

"Indeed, I do," said the doctor; and he was just going to add, "and of Greshamsbury also," but he stopped himself.

"What, the whole property there?"

"That's only a small portion," said the doctor. "I almost wish it were all, for then I should not be so bothered. Look here; these are the Boxall Hill title-deeds; that's the simplest part of the whole affair; and Frank may go and settle himself there to-morrow if he pleases."

"Stop a moment, Dr Thorne," said Frank. These were the only words which he had yet uttered since the tidings had been conveyed to him.

"And these, squire, are the Greshamsbury papers:" and the doctor, with considerable ceremony, withdrew the covering news-papers. "Look at them; there they all are once again. When I suggested to Mr Snilam that I supposed they might now all go back to the Greshamsbury muniment room, I thought he would have fainted. As I cannot return them to you, you will have to wait till Frank shall give them up."

"But, Dr Thorne," said Frank.

"Well, my boy."

"Does Mary know all about this?"

"Not a word of it. I mean that you shall tell her."

"Perhaps, under such very altered circumstances——"

"Eh?"

"The change is so great and so sudden, so immense in its effects, that Mary may perhaps wish——"

"Wish! wish what? Wish not to be told of it at all?"

"I shall not think of holding her to her engagement—that is, if—I mean to say, she should have time at any rate for consideration."

"Oh, I understand," said the doctor. "She shall have time for consideration. How much shall we give her, squire? three minutes? Go up to her, Frank: she is in the drawing-room."

Frank went to the door, and then hesitated, and returned. "I could not do it," said he. "I don't think that I understand it all yet.

I am so bewildered that I could not tell her:" and he sat down at the table, and began to sob with emotion.

"And she knows nothing of it?" asked the squire.

"Not a word. I thought that I would keep the pleasure of telling her for Frank."

"She should not be left in suspense," said the squire.

"Come, Frank, go up to her," again urged the doctor. "You've been ready enough with your visits when you knew that you ought to stay away."

"I cannot do it," said Frank, after a pause of some moments; "nor is it right that I should. It would be taking advantage of her."

"Go to her yourself, doctor; it is you that should do it," said the squire.

After some further slight delay, the doctor got up, and did go up-stairs. He, even, was half afraid of the task. "It must be done," he said to himself, as his heavy steps mounted the stairs. "But how to tell it!"

When he entered, Mary was standing half-way up the room, as though she had risen to meet him. Her face was troubled, and her eyes were almost wild. The emotion, the hopes, the fears of that morning had almost been too much for her. She had heard the murmuring of voices in the room below, and had known that one was that of her lover. Whether that discussion was to be for her good or ill she did not know; but she felt that further suspense would almost kill her. "I could wait for years", she thought to herself, "if I did but know. If I lost him, I suppose I should bear it, if I did but know."—Well; she was going to know.

Her uncle met her in the middle of the room. His face was serious, though not sad; too serious to confirm her hopes at that moment of doubt. "What is it, uncle?" she said, taking one of his hands between both of her own. "What is it? Tell me." And as she looked up into his face with her wild eyes, she almost frightened him.

"Mary," he said, gravely, "you have heard much, I know, of Sir Roger Scatcherd's great fortune."

"Yes, yes, yes!"

"Now that poor Sir Louis is dead——"

"Well, uncle, well?"

"It has been left——"

"To Frank! to Mr Gresham! to the squire!" exclaimed Mary, who felt, with an agony of doubt, that this sudden accession of immense wealth might separate her still further from her lover.

"No, Mary, not to the Greshams; but to yourself."

"To me!" she cried, and putting both her hands to her forehead she seemed to be holding her temples together. "To me!"

"Yes, Mary; it is all your own now. To do as you like best with it all—all. May God, in His mercy, enable you to bear the burden, and lighten for you the temptation!"

She had so far moved as to find the nearest chair, and there she was now seated, staring at her uncle with fixed eyes. "Uncle," she said, "what does it mean?" Then he came, and sitting beside her, explained, as best he could, the story of her birth, and her kinship with the Scatcherds. "And where is he, uncle?" she said. "Why does he not come to me?"

"I wanted him to come, but he refused. They are both there now, the father and son; shall I fetch them?"

"Fetch them! whom? the squire? No, uncle; but may we go to them?"

"Surely, Mary."

"But, uncle——"

"Yes, dearest?"

"Is it true? are you sure? For his sake, you know; not for my own. The squire, you know—Oh, uncle! I cannot go."

"They shall come to you."

"No—no. I have gone to him such hundreds of times; I will never allow that he shall be sent to me. But, uncle, is it true?"

The doctor, as he went downstairs, muttered something about Sir Abraham Haphazard, and Sir Rickety Giggs; but these great names were much thrown away upon poor Mary. The doctor entered the room first, and the heiress followed him with downcast eyes, and timid steps. She was at first afraid to advance, but when she did look up, and saw Frank standing alone by the window, her lover restored her courage, and rushing up to him, she threw herself into his arms. "Oh, Frank; my own Frank! my own Frank! we shall never be separated now."

D. T.

FRANK GRESHAM IN WONDERLAND

"Oh! Oh, Mary, do you love me? Don't you love me? Won't you love me? Say you will. Oh, Mary, dearest Mary, will you? Won't you? do you? don't you? Come now, you have a right to give a fellow an answer."

D. T.

PASSION

Gentleman: "Well, Miss——, the long and the short of it is this: here I am; and you can take me or leave me."

Lady—scratching a gutter on the sand with her parasol, so as to allow a little salt water to run out of one hole into another: "Of course, I know that's all nonsense."

134

Mary comes into Money

Gentleman: "Nonsense! By Jove, it isn't nonsense at all: come, Jane; here I am: come, at any rate you can say something."

Lady: "Yes, I suppose I can say something."

Gentleman: "Well, which is it to be; take me or leave me?"

Lady—very slowly, and with a voice perhaps hardly articulate, carrying on, at the same time, her engineering works on a wider scale: "Well, I don't exactly want to leave you."

D. T.

Mothercraft

INFANT WELFARE

The baby was really delightful; he took his food with a will, struck out his toes merrily whenever his legs were uncovered, and did not have fits. These are supposed to be the strongest points of baby perfection. . . .

B. T.

DIET

How it is that poor men's wives, who have no cold fowl and port wine on which to be coshered up, nurse their children without difficulty, whereas the wives of rich men, who eat and drink everything that is good, cannot do so, we will for the present leave to the doctors and the mothers to settle between them.

B. T.

LADIES

They are gifted with the powers of being mothers, but not nursing mothers. Nature gives them bosoms for show, but not for use.

D. T.

Mrs Proudie Intervenes

It was rather late when they all found themselves in the big room of the Mechanics' Institute; but I do not know whether this on the whole did them any harm. Most of Mr Smith's hearers, excepting the party from the palace, were Barchester tradesmen with their wives and families; and they waited, not impatiently, for the big people. And then the lecture was gratis, a fact which is always borne in mind by an Englishman when he comes to reckon up and calculate the way in which he is treated. When he pays his money, then he takes his choice; he may be impatient or not as he likes. His sense of justice teaches him so much, and in accordance with that sense he usually acts. So the people on the benches rose graciously when the palace party entered the room. Seats for them had been kept in the front. There were three armchairs, which were filled, after some little hesitation, by the bishop, Mrs Proudie and Miss Dunstable—Mrs Smith positively declining to take one of them; though, as she admitted, her rank as Lady Papua of the islands did give her some claim. And this remark, as it was made quite out loud, reached Mr Smith's ears as he stood behind a little table on a small raised dais, holding his white kid gloves; and it annoyed him and rather put him out. He did not like that joke about Lady Papua. And then the others of the party sat upon a front bench covered with red cloth.

"We shall find this very hard and very narrow about the second hour," said Mr Sowerby, and Mr Smith on his dais again overheard the words, and dashed his gloves down to the table. He felt that all the room would hear it.

And there were one or two gentlemen on the second seat who shook hands with some of our party. There was Mr Thorne, of Ullathorne, a good-natured old bachelor, whose residence was near enough to Barchester to allow of his coming in without much personal inconvenience; and next to him was Mr Harding, an old clergyman of the chapter, with whom Mrs Proudie shook hands very graciously, making way for him to seat himself close behind her if he would so please. But Mr Harding did not so please. Having paid his respects to the bishop he returned quietly to the side of his old friend Mr Thorne, thereby angering Mrs Proudie, as might easily be seen by her face. And Mr Chadwick also was there, the episcopal man of business for the diocese; but he also adhered to the two gentlemen above named. And now that the bishop and the ladies had taken their places, Mr Harold Smith relifted his gloves and again laid them down, hummed three times distinctly, and then began.

"It was", he said, "the most peculiar characteristic of the present era in the British islands that those who were high placed before the world in rank, wealth, and education were willing to come forward and give their time and knowledge without fee or reward, for the advantage and amelioration of those who did not stand so high in the social scale." And then he paused for a moment, during which Mrs Smith remarked to Miss Dunstable that that was pretty well for a beginning; and Miss Dunstable replied, "that as for herself she felt very grateful to rank, wealth, and education." Mr Sowerby winked to Mr Supplehouse, who opened his eyes very wide and shrugged his shoulders. But the Barchesterians took it all in good part and gave the lecturer the applause of their hands and feet. And then, well pleased, he recommenced—"I do not make these remarks with reference to myself——"

"I hope he's not going to be modest," said Miss Dunstable.

"It will be quite new if he is," replied Mrs Smith.

". . . so much as to many noble and talented lords and members of the lower House who have lately from time to time devoted themselves to this good work." And then he went through a long list of peers and members of Parliament, beginning, of course, with Lord Boanerges, and ending with Mr Green Walker, a young gentleman who had lately been returned by his uncle's interest for the borough of Crewe Junction, and had immediately made his entrance into public life by giving a lecture on the grammarians of the Latin language as exemplified at Eton school. "On the present occasion," Mr Smith continued, "our object is to learn something as to those grand and magnificent islands which lie far away, beyond the Indies, in the Southern Ocean; the lands of which produce rich spices and glorious fruits, and whose seas are embedded with pearls and corals—Papua and the Philippines, Borneo and the Moluccas. My friends, you are familiar with your maps, and you know the track which the equator makes for itself through those distant oceans." And then many heads were turned down, and there was a rustle of leaves; for not a few of those "who stood not so high in the social scale" had brought their maps with them, and refreshed their memories as to the whereabouts of these wondrous islands.

And then Mr Smith also, with a map in his hand, and pointing occasionally to another large map which hung against the wall, went into the geography of the matter. "We might have found that out from our atlases, I think, without coming all the way to Barchester," said that unsympathizing helpmate, Mrs Harold, very cruelly—most illogically too, for there be so many things which we could find out ourselves by search, but which we never do find out unless they be specially told us; and why should not the latitude and longitude of Labuan be one—or rather two of these things? And then, when he had duly marked the path of the line through Borneo, Celebes and Gilolo, through the Macassar strait and the Molucca passage, Mr Harold Smith rose to a higher flight. "But what", said he, "avails all that God can give to man, unless man will open his hand to receive the gift? And what is this opening of the hand but the process of civilization—yes, my friends, the process of civilization? These

South Sea islanders have all that a kind Providence can bestow on them; but that all is as nothing without education. That education and that civilization it is for you to bestow upon them—yes, my friends, for you; for you, citizens of Barchester as you are." And then he paused again, in order that the feet and hands might go to work. The feet and hands did go to work, during which Mr Smith took a slight drink of water. He was now quite in his element and had got into the proper way of punching the table with his fists. A few words dropping from Mr Sowerby did now and again find their way to his ears, but the sound of his own voice had brought with it the accustomed charm, and he ran on from platitude to truism, and from truism back to platitude, with an eloquence that was charming to himself.

"Civilization," he exclaimed, lifting up his eyes and hands to the ceiling. "O Civilization——"

"There will not be a chance for us now for the next hour and a half," said Mr Supplehouse, groaning. Harold Smith cast one eye down at him, but it immediately flew back to the ceiling.

"O Civilization! thou that ennoblest mankind and makest him equal to the gods, what is like unto thee?" Here Mrs Proudie showed evident signs of disapprobation, which no doubt would have been shared by the bishop, had not that worthy prelate been asleep. But Mr Smith continued unobservant; or at any rate regardless. "What is like unto thee? Thou art the irrigating stream which makest fertile the barren plain. Till thou comest all is dark and dreary; but at thy advent the noontide sun shines out, the earth gives forth her increase; the deep bowels of the rocks render up their tribute. Forms which were dull and hideous become endowed with grace and beauty, and vegetable existence rises to the scale of celestial life. Then, too, Genius appears clad in a panoply of translucent armour, grasping in his hand the whole terrestrial surface, and making every rood of earth subservient to his purposes—Genius, the child of Civilization, the mother of the Arts!" The last little bit, taken from the Pedigree of Progress, had a great success, and all Barchester went to work with its hands and feet—all Barchester, except that ill-natured aristocratic front-row together with the three arm-chairs at the corner of it. The aristocratic front-row felt itself to be too intimate with civilization to care much about it; and the three arm-chairs, or rather that special one which contained Mrs Proudie, considered that there was a certain heathenness, a pagan sentimentality almost amounting to infidelity, contained in the lecturer's remarks, with which she, a pillar of the Church, could not put up, seated as she was now in public conclave.

"It is to civilization that we must look", continued Mr Harold Smith, descending from poetry to prose as a lecturer well knows how and thereby showing the value of both—"for any material progress in these islands; and——"

"And to Christianity," shouted Mrs Proudie, to the great amazement of the assembled people, and to the thorough wakening of the bishop, who, jumping up from his chair at the sound of the well-known voice, exclaimed, "Certainly, certainly."

"Hear, hear, hear," said those on the benches who particularly belonged to Mrs Proudie's school of divinity in the city, and among the voices was distinctly heard that of a new verger in whose behalf she had greatly interested herself.

"Oh, yes, Christianity of course," said Harold Smith, upon whom the interruption did not seem to operate favourably.

"Christianity and Sabbath-day observance," exclaimed Mrs Proudie, who, now that she had obtained the ear of the public, seemed well inclined to keep it. "Let us never forget that these islanders can never prosper unless they keep the Sabbath holy." Poor Mr Smith, having been so rudely dragged from his high horse, was never able to mount it again, and completed the lecture in a manner not at all comfortable to himself. He had there, on the table before him, a huge bundle of statistics, with which he had meant to convince the reason of his hearers, after he had taken full possession of their feelings. But they fell very dull and flat. And at the moment when he was interrupted, he was about to explain that that material progress to which he had alluded could not be attained without money; and that it behoved them, the people of Barchester before him, to come forward with their purses like men and brothers. He did also attempt this; but from the moment of that fatal onslaught from the arm-chair, it was clear to him, and to everyone else, that Mrs Proudie was now the hero of the hour. His time had gone by, and the people of Barchester did not care a straw for his appeal. From these causes the lecture was over full twenty minutes earlier than anyone had expected, to the great delight of Messrs Sowerby and Supplehouse, who, on that evening, moved and carried a vote of thanks to Mrs Proudie. For they had gay doings yet before they went to their beds.

"Robarts, here one moment," Mr Sowerby said, as they were standing at the door of the Mechanics' Institute. "Don't you go off with Mr and Mrs Bishop. We are going to have a little supper at the Dragon of Wantly, and, after what we have gone through, upon my word we want it. You can tell one of the palace servants to let you in." Mark considered the proposal wistfully. He would fain have joined the supper party had he dared; but he, like many others of his cloth, had the fear of Mrs Proudie before his eyes. And a very merry supper they had; but poor Mr Harold Smith was not the merriest of the party.

F. P.

AFTER-DINNER SPEECHES

"Fix your eye on one of the bottles, put your thumbs in your waistcoat-pockets; stick out your elbows, bend your knees a little, and then go ahead."—*Hon. George de Courcy*.

D. T.

Two Barsetshire Scandals

Rev. Septimus Harding

. . . he always wears a black frock coat, black knee-breeches, and black gaiters, and somewhat scandalises some of his more hyper-clerical brethren by a black neck-handkerchief.

W.

John Bold

The bishop, in his simple mind, felt no doubt that John Bold, had he so much power, would shut up all cathedrals, and probably all parish churches; distribute all tithes among Methodists, Baptists, and other savage tribes; utterly annihilate the sacred bench, and make shovel hats and lawn sleeves as illegal as cowls, sandals, and sackcloth! Here was a nice man to be initiated into the comfortable arcana of ecclesiastical snuggeries; one who doubted the integrity of parsons, and probably disbelieved the Trinity!

W.

Mark Robarts Signs a Bill

O n that evening before Robarts went away Sowerby asked
him to come up into his bedroom when the whole party
was breaking up, and there got him into an easy chair,
while he, Sowerby, walked up and down the room.

"You can hardly tell, my dear fellow," said he, "the state of
nervous anxiety in which this puts me."

"Why don't you ask her and have done with it? She seems to me
to be fond of your society."

"Ah, it is not that only; there are wheels within wheels:" and then he walked once or twice up and down the room, during which Mark thought that he might as well go to bed.

"Not that I mind telling you everything," said Sowerby. "I am infernally hard up for a little ready money just at the present moment. It may be, and indeed I think it will be, the case that I shall be ruined in this matter for the want of it."

"Could not Harold Smith give it you?"

"Ha, ha, ha! you don't know Harold Smith. Did you ever hear of his lending a man a shilling in his life?"

"Or Supplehouse?"

"Lord love you! You see me and Supplehouse together here, and he comes and stays at my house, and all that; but Supplehouse and I are no friends. Look you here, Mark—I would do more for your little finger than for his whole hand, including the pen which he holds in it. Fothergill indeed might—but then I know Fothergill is pressed himself at the present moment. It is deuced hard, isn't it? I must give up the whole game if I can't put my hand upon £400 within the next two days."

"Ask her for it, herself."

"What, the woman I wish to marry! No, Mark, I'm not quite come to that. I would sooner lose her than that." Mark sat silent, gazing at the fire and wishing that he was in his own bedroom. He had an idea that Mr Sowerby wished him to produce this £400, and he knew also that he had not £400 in the world, and that if he had he would be acting very foolishly to give it to Mr Sowerby. But nevertheless he felt half fascinated by the man, and half afraid of him.

"Lufton owes it to me to do more than this," continued Mr Sowerby, "but then Lufton is not here."

"Why, he has just paid five thousand pounds for you."

"Paid five thousand pounds for me! Indeed he has done no such thing: not a sixpence of it came into my hands. Believe me, Mark, you don't know the whole of that yet. Not that I mean to say a word against Lufton. He is the soul of honour; though so deucedly dilatory in money matters. He thought he was right all through that affair, but no man was ever so confoundedly wrong. Why, don't you remember that that was the very view you took of it yourself?"

"I remember saying that I thought he was mistaken."

"Of course he was mistaken. And dearly the mistake cost me; I had to make good the money for two or three years. And my property is not like his—I wish it were."

"Marry Miss Dunstable, and that will set it all right for you."

"Ah! so I would if I had this money. At any rate I would bring it to the point. Now, I tell you what, Mark, if you'll assist me at this strait I'll never forget it. And the time will come round when I may be able to do something for you."

"I have not got a hundred, no, not fifty pounds by me in the world."

"Of course you've not. Men don't walk about the streets with £400 in their pockets. I don't suppose there's a single man here in the house with such a sum at his bankers', unless it be the duke."

"What is it you want then?"

"Why, your name, to be sure. Believe me, my dear fellow, I would not ask you really to put your hand into your pocket to such a tune as that. Allow me to draw on you for that amount at three months. Long before that time I shall be flush enough." And then, before Mark could answer, he had a bill stamp and pen and ink out on the table before him, and was filling in the bill as though his friend had already given his consent.

"Upon my word, Sowerby, I had rather not do that."

"Why? what are you afraid of?"—Mr Sowerby asked this very sharply. "Did you ever hear of my having neglected to take up a bill when it fell due?" Robarts thought that he had heard of such a thing; but in his confusion he was not exactly sure, and so he said nothing.

"No, my boy; I have not come to that. Look here: just you write, 'Accepted, Mark Robarts,' across that, and then you shall never hear of the transaction again—and you will have obliged me for ever."

"As a clergyman it would be wrong of me," said Robarts.

"As a clergyman! Come, Mark! If you don't like to do as much as

146

that for a friend, say so; but don't let us have that sort of humbug. If there be one class of men whose names would be found more frequent on the backs of bills in the provincial banks than another, clergymen are that class. Come, old fellow, you won't throw me over when I am so hard pushed." Mark Robarts took the pen and signed the bill. It was the first time in his life that he had ever done such an act. Sowerby then shook him cordially by the hand, and he walked off to his own bedroom a wretched man.

F. P.

BUYING A PUP

When a man says to you, "Let us be candid with each other," you feel instinctively that he desires to squeeze you without giving a drop of water himself.

D. T.

Mark Robarts is Adamant

On the next day, at two o'clock punctually, Mark Robarts was at the "Dragon of Wantly", walking up and down the very room in which the party had breakfasted after Harold Smith's lecture, and waiting for the arrival of Mr Sowerby. He had been very well able to divine what was the business on which his friend wished to see him, and he had been rather glad than otherwise to receive the summons. Judging of his friend's character by what he had hitherto seen, he thought that Mr Sowerby would have kept out of the way, unless he had it in his power to make some provision for these terrible bills. So he walked up and down the dingy room, impatient for the expected arrival, and thought himself wickedly ill-used in that Mr Sowerby was not there when the clock struck a quarter to three. But when the clock struck three, Mr Sowerby was there, and Mark Robarts' hopes were nearly at an end.

"Do you mean that they will demand nine hundred pounds?" said Robarts, standing up and glaring angrily at the member of Parliament.

"I fear that they will," said Sowerby. "I think it is best to tell you the worst, in order that we may see what can be done."

"I can do nothing, and will do nothing," said Robarts. "They may do what they choose—what the law allows them." And then he thought of Fanny and his nursery, and Lucy refusing in her pride Lord Lufton's offer, and he turned away his face that the hard man of the world before him might not see the tear gathering in his eye.

"But, Mark, my dear fellow——" said Sowerby, trying to have recourse to the power of his cajoling voice. Robarts, however, would not listen.

"Mr Sowerby," said he, with an attempt at calmness which

betrayed itself at every syllable, "it seems to me that you have robbed me. That I have been a fool, and worse than a fool, I know well; but —but—but I thought that your position in the world would guarantee me from such treatment as this." Mr Sowerby was by no means without feeling, and the words which he now heard cut him very deeply—the more so because it was impossible that he should answer them with an attempt at indignation. He had robbed his friend, and, with all his wit, knew no words at the present moment sufficiently witty to make it seem that he had not done so. "Robarts," said he, "you may say what you like to me now; I shall not resent it."

"Who would care for your resentment?" said the clergyman, turning on him with ferocity. "The resentment of a gentleman is terrible to a gentleman; and the resentment of one just man is terrible to another. Your resentment!"—and then he walked twice the length of the room, leaving Sowerby dumb in his seat. "I wonder whether you ever thought of my wife and children when you were plotting this ruin for me!" And then again he walked the room.

"I suppose you will be calm enough presently to speak of this with some attempt to make a settlement?"

"No; I will make no such attempt. These friends of yours, you tell me, have a claim on me for nine hundred pounds, of which they demand immediate payment. You shall be asked in a court of law how much of that money I have handled. You know that I have never touched—have never wanted to touch—one shilling. I will make no attempt at any settlement. My person is here, and there is my house. Let them do their worst."

"But, Mark——"

"Call me by my name, sir, and drop that affectation of regard. What an ass I have been to be so cozened by a sharper!" Sowerby had by no means expected this. He had always known that Robarts possessed what he, Sowerby, would have called the spirit of a gentleman. He had regarded him as a bold, open, generous fellow, able to take his own part when called on to do so, and by no means disinclined to speak his own mind; but he had not expected from him such a torrent of indignation, or thought that he was capable of such a depth of anger. "If you use such language as that, Robarts, I can only leave you."

"You are welcome. Go. You tell me that you are the messenger of these men who intend to work nine hundred pounds out of me. You have done your part in the plot, and have now brought their message. It seems to me that you had better go back to them. As for me, I want my time to prepare my wife for the destiny before her."

"Robarts, you will be sorry some day for the cruelty of your words."

"I wonder whether you will ever be sorry for the cruelty of your doings, or whether these things are really a joke to you?"

"I am at this moment a ruined man," said Sowerby. "Everything is going from me—my place in the world, the estate of my family, my father's house, my seat in Parliament, the power of living among my countrymen, or, indeed, of living anywhere—but all this does not oppress me now so much as the misery which I have brought upon you."

And then Sowerby also turned away his face, and wiped from his eyes tears which were not artificial. Robarts was still walking up and down the room, but it was not possible for him to continue his reproaches after this. This is always the case. Let a man endure to heap contumely on his own head, and he will silence the contumely of others—for the moment. Sowerby, without meditating on the matter, had had some inkling of this, and immediately saw that there was at last an opening for conversation. "You are unjust to me", said he, "in supposing that I have now no wish to save you. It is solely in the hope of doing so that I have come here."

"And what is your hope? That I should accept another brace of bills, I suppose."

"Not a brace; but one renewed bill for——"

"Look here, Mr Sowerby. On no earthly consideration that can be put before me will I again sign my name to any bill in the guise of an acceptance. I have been very weak, and am ashamed of my weakness; but so much strength as that, I hope, is left to me. I have been very wicked, and am ashamed of my wickedness; but so much right principle as that, I hope, remains. I will put my name to no other bill; not for you, not even for myself."

"But, Robarts, under your present circumstances that will be madness."

"Then I will be mad."

"Have you seen Forrest? If you will speak to him I think you will find that everything can be accommodated."

"I already owe Mr Forrest a hundred and fifty pounds, which I obtained from him when you pressed me for the price of that horse, and I will not increase the debt. What a fool I was again there! Perhaps you do not remember that, when I agreed to buy the horse, the price was to be a contribution to the liquidation of these bills."

"I do remember it; but I will tell you how that was."

"It does not signify. It has been all of a piece."

"But listen to me. I think you would feel for me if you knew all that I have gone through. I pledge you my solemn word that I had no intention of asking you for the money when you took the horse—indeed I had not. But you remember that affair of Lufton's, when he came to you at your hotel in London and was so angry about an outstanding bill."

"I know that he was very unreasonable as far as I was concerned."

"He was so; but that makes no difference. He was resolved, in his rage, to expose the whole affair; and I saw that, if he did so, it would be most injurious to you, seeing that you had just accepted your stall at Barchester." Here the poor prebendary winced terribly. "I moved heaven and earth to get up that bill. Those vultures stuck to their prey when they found the value which I attached to it, and I was forced to raise above a hundred pounds at the moment to obtain possession of it, although every shilling absolutely due on it had long since been paid. Never in my life did I wish to get money as I did to raise that hundred and twenty pounds: and as I hope for mercy in my last moments, I did that for your sake. Lufton could not have injured me in that matter."

"But you told him that you got it for twenty-five pounds."

"Yes, I told him so. I was obliged to tell him that, or I should have apparently condemned myself by showing how anxious I was to get it. And you know I could not have explained all this before him and you. You would have thrown up the stall in disgust." Would that he had! That was Mark's wish now—his futile wish. In what a slough of despond had he come to wallow in consequence of his folly on that night at Gatherum Castle! He had then done a silly thing, and was he now to rue it by almost total ruin? He was sickened also with all these lies. His very soul was dismayed by the dirt through which he was forced to wade. He had become unconsciously connected with the lowest dregs of mankind, and would have to see his name mingled with theirs in the daily newspapers. And for what had he done this? Why had he thus filed his mind and made himself a disgrace to his cloth? In order that he might befriend such a one as Mr Sowerby!

"Well," continued Sowerby, "I did get the money, but you would hardly believe the rigour of the pledge which was exacted from me for repayment. I got it from Harold Smith, and never, in my worst straits, will I again look to him for assistance. I borrowed it only for a fortnight; and in order that I might repay it, I was obliged to ask you for the price of the horse. Mark, it was on your behalf that I did all this—indeed it was."

"And now I am to repay you for your kindness by the loss of all that I have in the world."

"If you will put the affair into the hands of Mr Forrest, nothing need be touched—not a hair of a horse's back; no, not though you should be obliged to pay the whole amount yourself gradually out of your income. You must execute a series of bills, falling due quarterly, and then——"

"I will execute no bill, I will put my name to no paper in the matter; as to that my mind is fully made up. They may come and do their worst." Mr Sowerby persevered for a long time, but he was quite unable to move the parson from this position. He would do nothing towards making what Mr Sowerby called an arrangement, but persisted that he would remain at home at Framley, and that any-one who had a claim upon him might take legal steps. "I shall do nothing myself," he said; "but if proceedings against me be taken, I shall prove that I have never had a shilling of the money." And in this resolution he quitted the Dragon of Wantly. Mr Sowerby at one time said a word as to the expediency of borrowing that sum of money from John Robarts; but as to this Mark would say nothing. Mr Sowerby was not the friend with whom he now intended to hold consultation in such matters. "I am not at present prepared", he said, "to declare what I may do; I must first see what steps others take." And then he took his hat and went off; and mounting his horse in the yard of the Dragon of Wantly—that horse which he had now so many reasons to dislike—he slowly rode back home.

F. P.

THIS WICKED WORLD

. . . it is in this world the man that is in the wrong almost invariably conquers the man that is in the right, and invariably despises him.

B. T.

WISDOM

Wise people, when they are in the wrong, always put themselves right by finding fault with the people against whom they have sinned.

B. T.

Some Barset Women

MISS MONICA THORNE (OF ULLATHORNE)

She would as soon have thought of appearing before her brother without her stockings as without her stays; and Miss Thorne's stays were no trifle.

B. T.

MRS SUSAN GRANTLY

". . . archdeacon". (Mrs Grantly had never assumed a more familiar term than this in addressing her husband) . . .

W.

Some Barset Women

ELEANOR HARDING

You might pass Eleanor Harding in the street without notice, but you could hardly pass an evening with her and not lose your heart.

W.

MADELINE STANHOPE

A sudden half-hour with the Neroni was like falling into a pit.

B. T.

Mesdames Grantly and Proudie get together

———◈———

Olivia Proudie had just accepted a widowed preacher at a district church in Bethnal Green—a man with three children, who was dependent on pew-rents; and Griselda Grantly was engaged to the eldest son of the Marquis of Hartletop! When women are enjoined to forgive their enemies it cannot be intended that such wrongs as these should be included. But Mrs Proudie's courage was nothing daunted. It may be boasted of her that nothing could daunt her courage. Soon after her return to Barchester, she and Olivia—Olivia being very unwilling—had driven over to Plumstead, and, not finding the Grantlys at home, had left their cards; and now, at a proper interval, Mrs Grantly and Griselda returned the visit. It was the first time that Miss Grantly had been seen by the Proudie ladies since the fact of her engagement had become known.

The first bevy of compliments that passed might be likened to a crowd of flowers on a hedge rosebush. They were beautiful to the eye, but were so closely environed by thorns that they could not be plucked without great danger. As long as the compliments were allowed to remain on the hedge—while no attempt was made to garner them and realize their fruits for enjoyment—they did no mischief; but the first finger that was put forth for such a purpose was soon drawn back, marked with spots of blood. "Of course it is a great match for Griselda," said Mrs Grantly, in a whisper the meekness of which would have disarmed an enemy whose weapons were less firmly clutched than those of Mrs Proudie; "but, independently of that, the connection is one which is gratifying in many ways."

"Oh, no doubt," said Mrs Proudie.

"Lord Dumbello is so completely his own master," continued Mrs Grantly, and a slight, unintended semi-tone of triumph mingled itself with the meekness of that whisper.

"And is likely to remain so, from all I hear," said Mrs Proudie, and the scratched hand was at once drawn back.

"Of course the estab——," and then Mrs Proudie, who was blandly continuing her list of congratulations, whispered her sentence close into the ear of Mrs Grantly, so that not a word of what she said might be audible by the young people.

"I never heard a word of it," said Mrs Grantly, gathering herself up, "and I don't believe it."

"Oh, I may be wrong; and I'm sure I hope so. But young men will be young men, you know—and children will take after their parents. I suppose you will see a great deal of the Duke of Omnium now."

But Mrs Grantly was not a woman to be knocked down and trampled on without resistance; and though she had been lacerated by the rosebush she was not as yet placed altogether *hors de combat*. She said some word about the Duke of Omnium very tranquilly, speaking of him merely as a Barsetshire proprietor, and then, smiling with her sweetest smile, expressed a hope that she might soon have the pleasure of becoming acquainted with Mr Tickler; and as she spoke she made a pretty little bow towards Olivia Proudie. Now Mr Tickler was the worthy clergyman attached to the district church at Bethnal Green.

"He'll be down here in August," said Olivia, boldly, determined not to be shamefaced about her love affairs.

"You'll be starring it about the Continent by that time, my dear," said Mrs Proudie to Griselda. "Lord Dumbello is well known at Homburg and Ems, and places of that sort; so you will find yourself quite at home."

"We are going to Rome," said Griselda, majestically.

"I suppose Mr Tickler will come into the diocese soon," said Mrs Grantly. "I remember hearing him very favourably spoken of by Mr Slope, who was a friend of his." Nothing short of a fixed resolve on the part of Mrs Grantly that the time had now come in which she must throw away her shield and stand behind her sword, declare war to the knife, and neither give nor take quarter, could have justified such a speech as this. Any allusion to Mr Slope acted on Mrs Proudie as a red cloth is supposed to act on a bull; but when that allusion connected the name of Mr Slope in a friendly bracket with that of Mrs Proudie's future son-in-law it might be certain that the effect would be terrific. And there was more than this: for that very Mr Slope had once entertained audacious hopes—hopes not thought to be audacious by the young lady herself—with reference to Miss Olivia Proudie. All this Mrs Grantly knew, and, knowing it, still dared to mention his name.

The countenance of Mrs Proudie became darkened with black anger, and the polished smile of her company manners gave place before the outraged feelings of her nature. "The man you speak of,

Mrs Grantly," said she, "was never known as a friend by Mr Tickler."

"Oh, indeed," said Mrs Grantly. "Perhaps I have made a mistake. I am sure I have heard Mr Slope mention him."

"When Mr Slope was running after your sister, Mrs Grantly, and was encouraged by her as he was, you perhaps saw more of him than I did."

"Mrs Proudie, that was never the case."

"I have reason to know that the archdeacon conceived it to be so, and that he was very unhappy about it." Now this, unfortunately, was a fact which Mrs Grantly could not deny.

"The archdeacon may have been mistaken about Mr Slope," she said, "as were some other people at Barchester. But it was you, I think, Mrs Proudie, who were responsible for bringing him here." Mrs Grantly, at this period of the engagement, might have inflicted a fatal wound by referring to poor Olivia's former love affairs, but she was not destitute of generosity. Even in the extremest heat of the battle she knew how to spare the young and tender.

"When I came here, Mrs Grantly, I little dreamed what a depth of wickedness might be found in the very close of a cathedral city," said Mrs Proudie.

"Then, for dear Olivia's sake, pray do not bring poor Mr Tickler to Barchester."

"Mr Tickler, Mrs Grantly, is a man of assured morals and of a highly religious tone of thinking. I wish everyone could be so safe as regards their daughters' future prospects as I am."

"Yes, I know he has the advantage of being a family man," said Mrs Grantly, getting up. "Good morning, Mrs Proudie; good day, Olivia."

"A great deal better that than——" But the blow fell upon the empty air; for Mrs Grantly had already escaped on to the staircase while Olivia was ringing the bell for the servant to attend the front door.

Mrs Grantly, as she got into her carriage, smiled slightly, thinking of the battle, and as she sat down she gently pressed her daughter's hand. But Mrs Proudie's face was still dark as Acheron when her enemy withdrew, and with angry tone she sent her daughter to her work. "Mr Tickler will have great reason to complain if, in your position, you indulge such habits of idleness," she said. Therefore I conceive that I am justified in saying that in that encounter Mrs Grantly was the conqueror.

F. P.

WHAT IS TRUTH?

We English gentlemen hate the name of a lie; but how often do we find public men who believe each other's words?

B. T.

Bailiffs at Framley

"If you please, your reverence, there are two men outside," said the footman. Two men! Mark knew well enough what men they were, but he could hardly take the coming of two such men to his quiet country parsonage quite as a matter of course.

"Who are they, John?" said he, not wishing any answer, but because the question was forced upon him.

"I'm afeared they're—bailiffs, sir."

"Very well, John; that will do; of course they must do what they please about the place." And then, when the servant left him, he still stood without moving, exactly as he had stood before. There he remained for ten minutes, but the time went by very slowly. When about noon some circumstance told him what was the hour, he was surprised to find that the day had not nearly passed away. And then another tap was struck on the door—a sound which he well recognized—and his wife crept silently into the room. She came close up to him before she spoke, and put her arm within his,

"Mark," she said, "the men are here; they are in the yard."

"I know it," he answered gruffly.

"Will it be better that you should see them, dearest?"

"See them; no; what good can I do by seeing them? But I shall see them soon enough; they will be here, I suppose, in a few minutes."

"They are taking an inventory, cook says; they are in the stable now."

"Very well; they must do as they please; I cannot help them."

"Cook says that if they are allowed their meals and some beer, and if nobody takes anything away, they will be quite civil."

"Civil! But what does it matter? Let them eat and drink what they please, as long as the food lasts. I don't suppose the butcher will send you more."

"But, Mark, there's nothing due to the butcher—only the regular monthly bill."

"Very well; you'll see."

"Oh, Mark, don't look at me in that way. Do not turn away from me. What is to comfort us if we do not cling to each other now?"

"Comfort us! God help you! I wonder, Fanny, that you can bear to stay in the room with me."

"Mark, dearest Mark, my own dear, dearest husband! who is to be true to you, if I am not? You shall not turn from me. How can anything like this make a difference between you and me?" And then she threw her arms round his neck and embraced him. It was a terrible morning to him, and one of which every incident will dwell on his memory to the last day of his life. He had been so proud in his position—had assumed to himself so prominent a standing—had contrived, by some trick which he had acquired, to carry his head so high above the heads of neighbouring parsons. It was this that had taken him among great people, had introduced him to the Duke of Omnium, had procured for him the stall at Barchester. But how was he to carry his head now? What would the Arabins and Grantlys say? How would the bishop sneer at him, and Mrs Proudie and her daughters tell of him in all their quarters? How would Crawley look at him—Crawley, who had already once had him on the hip? The stern severity of Crawley's face loomed upon him now. Crawley, with his children half naked, and his wife a drudge, and himself half starved, had never had a bailiff in his house at Hogglestock. And then his own curate, Evans, whom he had patronized, and treated almost as a dependant—how was he to look his curate in the face and arrange with him for the sacred duties of the next Sunday? His wife still stood by him, gazing into his face; and as he looked at her and thought of her misery, he could not control his heart with reference to the wrongs which Sowerby had heaped on him. It was Sowerby's falsehood and Sowerby's fraud which had brought upon him and his wife this terrible anguish.

"If there be justice on earth he will suffer for it yet," he said at last, not speaking intentionally to his wife, but unable to repress his feelings.

"Do not wish him evil, Mark; you may be sure he has his own sorrows."

"His own sorrows! No; he is callous to such misery as this. He has become so hardened in dishonesty that all this is mirth to him. If there be punishment in heaven for falsehood——"

"Oh, Mark, do not curse him!"

"How am I to keep myself from cursing when I see what he has brought upon you?"

" 'Vengeance is mine, saith the Lord,' " answered the young wife, not with solemn, preaching accent, as though bent on reproof, but

with the softest whisper into his ear. "Leave that to Him, Mark; and for us, let us pray that He may soften the hearts of us all—of him who has caused us to suffer, and of our own." Mark was not called upon to reply to this, for he was again disturbed by a servant at the door. It was the cook this time herself, who had come with a message from the men of the law. And she had come, be it remembered, not from any necessity that she as cook should do this line of work; for the footman, or Mrs Robarts' maid, might have come as well as she. But when things are out of course, servants are always out of course also. As a rule, nothing will induce a butler to go into a stable, or persuade a house-maid to put her hand to a frying-pan. But now that this new excitement had come upon the household— seeing that the bailiffs were in possession, and that the chattels were being entered in a catalogue, everybody was willing to do everything—everything but his or her own work. The gardener was looking after the dear children; the nurse was doing the rooms before the bailiffs should reach them; the groom had gone into the kitchen to get their lunch ready for them; and the cook was walking about with an inkstand, obeying all the orders of these great potentates. As far as the servants were concerned, it may be a question whether the coming of the bailiffs had not hitherto been regarded as a treat.

"If you please, ma'am," said Jemima cook, "they wishes to know in which room you'd be pleased to have the inmin-tory took fust. 'Cause, ma'am, they wouldn't disturb you nor master more than can be avoided. For their line of life, ma'am, they is very civil—very civil indeed."

"I suppose they may go into the drawing-room," said Mrs Robarts, in a sad low voice. All nice women are proud of their drawing-rooms, and she was very proud of hers. It had been furnished when money was plenty with them, immediately after their marriage, and everything in it was pretty, good, and dear to her. O ladies, who have drawing-rooms in which the things are pretty, good, and dear to you, think of what it would be to have two bailiffs rummaging among them with pen and ink-horn, making a catalogue preparatory to a sheriff's auction; and all without fault or extravagance of your own! There were things there that had been given to her by Lady Lufton, by Lady Meredith, and other friends, and the idea did occur to her that it might be possible to save them from contamination; but she would not say a word, lest by so saying she might add to Mark's misery.

"And then the dining-room," said Jemima cook, in a tone almost of elation.

"Yes; if they please."

"And then the master's book-room here; or perhaps the bed-rooms, if you and master be still here."

"Any way they please, cook; it does not much signify," said Mrs Robarts. But for some days after that Jemima was by no means a favourite with her.

The cook was hardly out of the room before a quick footstep was heard on the gravel before the window, and the hall door was immediately opened.

"Where is your master?" said the well-known voice of Lord Lufton; and then in half a minute he also was in the book-room.

"Mark, my dear fellow, what's all this?" said he, in a cheery tone and with a pleasant face. "Did not you know that I was here? I came down yesterday; landed from Hamburg only yesterday morning. How do you do, Mrs Robarts? This is a terrible bore, isn't it?" Robarts, at the first moment, hardly knew how to speak to his old friend. He was struck dumb by the disgrace of his position; the more so as his misfortune was one which it was partly in the power of Lord Lufton to remedy. He had never yet borrowed money since he had filled a man's position, but he had had words about money with the young peer, in which he knew that his friend had wronged him; and for this double reason he was now speechless.

"Mr Sowerby has betrayed him," said Mrs Robarts, wiping the tears from her eyes. Hitherto she had said no word against Sowerby, but now it was necessary to defend her husband.

"No doubt about it. I believe he has always betrayed every one who has ever trusted him. I told you what he was, some time since;

did I not? But, Mark, why on earth have you let it go as far as this? Would not Forrest help you?"

"Mr Forrest wanted him to sign more bills, and he would not do that," said Mrs Robarts, sobbing.

"Bills are like dram-drinking," said the discreet young lord: "when one once begins, it is very hard to leave off. Is it true that the men are here now, Mark?"

"Yes, they are in the next room."

"What, in the drawing-room?"

"They are making out a list of the things," said Mrs Robarts.

"We must stop that at any rate," said his lordship, walking off towards the scene of the operations; and as he left the room Mrs Robarts followed him, leaving her husband by himself.

"Why did you not send down to my mother?" said he, speaking hardly above a whisper, as they stood together in the hall.

"He would not let me."

"But why not go yourself? or why not have written to me—considering how intimate we are?" Mrs Robarts could not explain to him that the peculiar intimacy between him and Lucy must have hindered her from doing so, even if otherwise it might have been possible; but she felt such was the case.

"Well, my men, this is bad work you're doing here," said he, walking into the drawing-room. Whereupon the cook curtseyed low, and the bailiffs, knowing his lordship, stopped from their business and put their hands to their foreheads. "You must stop this, if you please—at once. Come, let's go out into the kitchen, or some place outside. I don't like to see you here with your big boots and the pen and ink among the furniture."

"We ain't a-done no harm, my lord, so please your lordship," said Jemima cook.

"And we is only a-doing our bounden dooties," said one of the bailiffs.

"As we is sworn to do, so please your lordship," said the other.

"And is wery sorry to be unconwenient, my lord, to any gen'leman or lady. But accidents will happen, and then what can the likes of us do?" said the first.

"Because we is sworn, my lord," said the second. But, nevertheless, in spite of their oaths, and in spite also of the stern necessity which they pleaded, they ceased their operations at the instance of the peer. For the name of a lord is still great in England.

"And now leave this, and let Mrs Robarts go into her drawing-room."

"And, please your lordship, what is we to do? Who is we to look to?" In satisfying them absolutely on this point Lord Lufton had to use more than his influence as a peer. It was necessary that he should have pen and paper. But with pen and paper he did satisfy them—satisfy them so far that they agreed to return to Stubb's room, the former hospital, due stipulation having been made for the meals and beer, and there await the order to evacuate the premises which would no doubt, under his lordship's influence, reach them on the following day. The meaning of all which was that Lord Lufton had undertaken to bear upon his own shoulder the whole debt due by Mr Robarts. And then he returned to the book-room, where Mark was still standing almost on the same spot in which he had placed himself immediately after breakfast. Mrs Robarts did not return, but went up among the children to counter-order such directions as she had given for the preparation of the nursery for the Philistines. "Mark," he said, "do not trouble yourself about this more than you can help. The men have ceased doing anything, and they shall leave the place to-morrow morning."

"And how will the money—be paid?" said the poor clergyman.

"Do not bother yourself about that at present. It shall so be managed that the burden shall fall ultimately on yourself—not on anyone else. But I am sure it must be a comfort to you to know that your wife need not be driven out of her drawing-room."

"But, Lufton, I cannot allow you—after what has passed—and at the present moment——"

"My dear fellow, I know all about it, and I am coming to that just now. You have employed Curling, and he shall settle it; and upon my word, Mark, you shall pay the bill. But, for the present emergency, the money is at my banker's."

"But, Lufton,——"

"And to deal honestly, about Curling's bill I mean, it ought to be as much my affair as your own. It was I that brought you into this mess with Sowerby, and I know now how unjust about it I was to you up in London. But the truth is that Sowerby's treachery had nearly driven me wild. It has done the same to you since, I have no doubt."

"He has ruined me," said Robarts.

"No, he has not done that. No thanks to him though; he would not have scrupled to do it had it come in his way. The fact is, Mark, that you and I cannot conceive the depth of fraud in such a man as that. He is always looking for money; I believe that in all his hours of most friendly intercourse—when he is sitting with you over your wine, and riding beside you in the field—he is still thinking how he can make use of you to tide him over some difficulty. He has lived in that way till he has a pleasure in cheating, and has become so clever in his line of life that if you or I were with him again to-morrow he would again get the better of us. He is a man that must be absolutely avoided; I, at any rate, have learned to know so much." In the expression of which opinion Lord Lufton was too hard upon poor Sowerby; as indeed we are all apt to be too hard in forming an opinion upon the rogues of the world. That Mr Sowerby had been a rogue, I cannot deny. It is roguish to lie, and he had been a great liar. It is roguish to make promises which the promiser knows he cannot perform, and such had been Mr Sowerby's daily practice. It is roguish to live on other men's money, and Mr Sowerby had long been doing so. It is roguish, at least so I would hold it, to deal willingly with rogues; and Mr Sowerby had been constant in such dealings. I do not know whether he had not at times fallen even into more palpable roguery than is proved by such practices as those enumerated. Though I have for him some tender feelings, knowing that there was still a touch of gentle bearing round his heart, an abiding taste for better things within him, I cannot acquit him from the great accusation. But, for all that, in spite of his acknowledged roguery, Lord Lufton was too hard upon him in his judgment. There was yet within him the means of repentance, could a locus penitentiae have

168

been supplied to him. He grieved bitterly over his own ill doings, and knew well what changes gentlehood would have demanded from him. Whether or no he had gone too far for all changes—whether the *locus penitentiae* was for him still a possibility—that was between him and a higher power.

"I have no one to blame but myself," said Mark, still speaking in the same heart-broken tone and with his face averted from his friend.

The debt would now be paid, and the bailiffs would be expelled; but that would not set him right before the world. It would be known to all men—to all clergymen in the diocese, that the sheriff's officers had been in charge of Framley Parsonage, and he could never again hold up his head in the close of Barchester. "My dear fellow, if we were all to make ourselves miserable for such a trifle as this——" said Lord Lufton, putting his arm affectionately on his friend's shoulder.

"But we are not all clergymen," said Mark, and as he spoke he turned away to the window, and Lord Lufton knew that the tears were on his cheek.

Nothing was then said between them for some moments, after which Lord Lufton again spoke:

"Mark, my dear fellow!"

"Well?" said Mark, with his face still turned towards the window.

"You must remember one thing; in helping you over this stile, which will be really a matter of no inconvenience to me, I have a better right than that even of an old friend; I look upon you now as my brother-in-law." Mark turned slowly round, plainly showing the tears upon his face.

"Do you mean", said he, "that anything more has taken place?"

"I mean to make your sister my wife; she sent me word by you to say that she loved me, and I am not going to stand upon any nonsense after that. If she and I are both willing no one alive has a right to stand between us, and, by heavens, no one shall. I will do nothing secretly, so I tell you that, exactly as I have told her ladyship."

"But what does she say?"

"She says nothing; but it cannot go on like that. My mother and

I cannot live here together if she opposes me in this way. I do not want to frighten your sister by going over to her at Hogglestock, but I expect you to tell her so much as I now tell you, as coming from me; otherwise she will think that I have forgotten her."

"She will not think that."

"She need not; good-bye, old fellow. I'll make it all right between you and her ladyship about this affair of Sowerby's." And then he took his leave, and walked off to settle about the payment of the money.

"Mother," said he to Lady Lufton that evening, "you must not bring this affair of the bailiffs up against Robarts. It has been more my fault than his."

Hitherto not a word had been spoken between Lady Lufton and her son on the subject. She had heard with terrible dismay of what had happened, and had heard also that Lord Lufton had immediately gone to the parsonage. It was impossible, therefore, that she should now interfere. That the necessary money would be forthcoming she was aware, but that would not wipe out the terrible disgrace attached to an execution in a clergyman's house. And then, too, he was her clergyman—her own clergyman, selected and appointed, and brought to Framley by herself, endowed with a wife of her own choosing, filled with good things by her own hand! It was a terrible misadventure, and she began to repent that she had ever heard the name of Robarts. She would not, however, have been slow to put forth the hand to lessen the evil by giving her own money, had this been either necessary or possible. But how could she interfere between Robarts and her son, especially when she remembered the proposed connection between Lucy and Lord Lufton?

"Your fault, Ludovic?"

"Yes, mother. It was I who introduced him to Mr Sowerby; and, to tell the truth, I do not think he would ever have been intimate with Sowerby if I had not given him some sort of a commission with reference to money matters then pending between Mr Sowerby and me. They are all over now—thanks to you, indeed."

"Mr Robarts' character as a clergyman should have kept him from such troubles, if no other feeling did so."

"At any rate, mother, oblige me by letting it pass by."

"Oh, I shall say nothing to him."

"You had better say something to her, or otherwise it will be strange; and even to him I would say a word or two—a word in kindness, as you well know how. It will be easier to him in that way, than if you were to be altogether silent."

No further conversation took place between them at the time, but later in the evening she brushed her hand across her son's forehead, sweeping the long silken hairs into their place, as she was wont to do when moved by any special feeling of love. "Ludovic," she said, "no one, I think, has so good a heart as you. I will do exactly as you would have me about this affair of Mr Robarts and the money." And then there was nothing more said about it.

F. P.

FAMILIARITY

That feeling of overdue bills, of bills coming due, of accounts overdrawn, of tradesmen unpaid, of general money cares, is very dreadful at first; but it is astonishing how soon men get used to it. A load which would crush a man at first becomes, by habit, not only endurable, but easy and comfortable to the bearer. The habitual debtor goes along jaunty and with elastic step, almost enjoying the excitement of his embarrassments.

F. P.

Johnny Eames does well

T he eyes of the two met, and Crosbie made a slight inclination of the head. To this Eames gave no acknowledgment whatever, but looked straight into the other's face. Crosbie immediately saw that they were not to know each other, and was well contented that it should be so. Among all his many troubles, the enmity of John Eames did not go for much. He showed no appearance of being disconcerted, though our friend had shown much. He opened his bag, and taking out a book was soon deeply engaged in it, pursuing his studies as though the man opposite was quite unknown to him. I will not say that his mind did not run away from his book, for indeed there were many things of which he found it impossible not to think; but it did not revert to John Eames. Indeed, when the carriages reached Paddington, he had in truth all but forgotten him; and as he stepped out of the carriage, with his bag in his hand, was quite free from any remotest trouble on his account.

But it had not been so with Eames himself. Every moment of the journey had for him been crowded with thought as to what he would do now that chance had brought his enemy within his reach. He had been made quite wretched by the intensity of his thinking; and yet, when the carriages stopped, he had not made up his mind. His face had been covered with perspiration ever since Crosbie had come across him, and his limbs had hardly been under his own command. Here had come to him a great opportunity, and he felt so little confidence in himself that he almost knew that he would not use it properly. Twice and thrice he had almost flown at Crosbie's throat in the carriage, but he was restrained by an idea that the world and the police would be against him if he did such a thing in the presence of that old lady.

But when Crosbie turned his back upon him, and walked out, it was absolutely necessary that he should do something. He was not going to let the man escape, after all that he had said as to the expediency of thrashing him. Any other disgrace would be preferable to that. Fearing, therefore, lest his enemy should be too quick for him, he hurried out after him, and only just gave Crosbie time to turn round and face the carriages before he was upon him. "You confounded scoundrel!" he screamed out. "You confounded scoundrel!" and seized him by the throat, throwing himself upon him, and almost devouring him by the fury of his eyes.

The crowd upon the platform was not very dense, but there were quite enough of people to make a very respectable audience for this little play. Crosbie, in his dismay, retreated a step or two, and his retreat was much accelerated by the weight of Eames' attack. He endeavoured to free his throat from his foe's grasp; but in that he failed entirely. For the minute, however, he did manage to escape any positive blow, owing his safety in that respect rather to Eames' awkwardness than to his own efforts. Something about the police he was just able to utter, and there was, as a matter of course, an immediate call for a supply of those functionaries. In about three minutes three policemen, assisted by six porters, had captured our poor friend Johnny; but this had not been done quick enough for Crosbie's purposes. The bystanders, taken by surprise, had allowed the combatants to fall back upon Mr Smith's bookstall, and there Eames laid his foe prostrate among the newspapers, falling himself into the yellow shilling-novel depot by the over-fury of his own energy; but as he fell, he contrived to lodge one blow with his fist in Crosbie's right eye—one telling blow; and Crosbie had, to all intents and purposes, been thrashed.

"Con—founded scoundrel, rascal, blackguard!" shouted Johnny, with what remnants of voice were left to him, as the police dragged him off. "If you only knew—what he's—done." But in the meantime the policemen held him fast.

As a matter of course the first burst of public sympathy went with Crosbie. He had been assaulted, and the assault had come from

Eames. In the British bosom there is so firm a love of well-constituted order, that these facts alone were sufficient to bring twenty knights to the assistance of the three policemen and the six porters; so that for Eames, even had he desired it, there was no possible chance of escape. But he did not desire it. One only sorrow consumed him at present. He had, as he felt, attacked Crosbie, but had attacked him in vain. He had had his opportunity, and had misused it. He was perfectly unconscious of that happy blow, and was in absolute ignorance of the great fact that his enemy's eye was already swollen and closed, and that in another hour it would be black as his hat.

"He is a con—founded rascal!" ejaculated Eames, as the policemen and porters hauled him about. "You don't know what he's done."

"No, we don't," said the senior constable; "but we know what you have done. I say, Bushers, where's that gentleman? He'd better come along with us."

Crosbie had been picked up from among the newspapers by another policeman and two or three other porters, and was attended also by the guard of the train, who knew him, and knew that he had come up from Courcy Castle. Three or four hangers-on were standing also around him, together with a benevolent medical man who was proposing to him an immediate application of leeches. If he could have done as he wished, he would have gone his way quietly, allowing Eames to do the same. A great evil had befallen him, but he could in no way mitigate that evil by taking the law of the man who had attacked him. To have the thing as little talked about as possible should be his endeavour. What though he should have Eames locked up and fined, and scolded by a police magistrate? That would not in any degree lessen his calamity. If he could have parried the attack, and got the better of his foe; if he could have administered the black eye instead of receiving it, then indeed he could have laughed the matter off at his club, and his original crime would have been somewhat glozed over by his success in arms. But such good fortune had not been his. He was forced, however, on the moment to decide as to what he would do.

"We've got him here in custody, sir," said Bushers, touching his hat. It had become known from the guard that Crosbie was some-what of a big man, a frequent guest at Courcy Castle, and of repute and station in the higher regions of the Metropolitan world. "The magistrates will be sitting at Paddington now, sir—or will be by the time we get there."

By this time some mighty railway authority had come upon the scene and made himself cognisant of the facts of the row—a stern official who seemed to carry the weight of many engines on his brow; one at the very sight of whom smokers would drop their cigars, and porters close their fists against sixpences; a great man with an erect chin, a quick step, and a well-brushed hat powerful with an elaborately upturned brim. This was the platform-superintendent, dominant even over the policemen.

"Step into my room, Mr Crosbie," he said. "Stubbs, bring that man in with you." And then, before Crosbie had been able to make up his mind as to any other line of conduct, he found himself in the superintendent's room, accompanied by the guard, and by the two policemen who conducted Johnny Eames between them.

"What's all this?" said the superintendent, still keeping on his hat, for he was aware how much of the excellence of his personal dignity was owing to the arrangement of that article; and as he spoke he frowned upon the culprit with his utmost severity. "Mr Crosbie, I am very sorry that you should have been exposed to such brutality on our platform."

"You don't know what he has done," said Johnny. "He is the most confounded scoundrel living. He has broken——" But then he stopped himself. He was going to tell the superintendent that the confounded scoundrel had broken a beautiful young lady's heart; but he bethought himself that he would not allude more specially to Lily Dale in that hearing.

"Do you know who he is, Mr Crosbie?" said the superintendent.

"Oh, yes," said Crosbie, whose eye was already becoming blue. "He is a clerk in the Income-tax Office, and his name is Eames. I believe you had better leave him to me."

But the superintendent at once wrote down the words "Income-tax Office—Eames" on his tablet. "We can't allow a row like that to take place on our platform and not notice it. I shall bring it before the directors. It's a most disgraceful affair, Mr Eames—most disgraceful."

But Johnny by this time had perceived that Crosbie's eye was in a state which proved satisfactorily that his morning's work had not been thrown away, and his spirits were rising accordingly. He did not care two straws for the superintendent or even for the policemen, if only the story could be made to tell well for himself hereafter. It was his object to have thrashed Crosbie, and now, as he looked at his enemy's face, he acknowledged that Providence had been good to him.

"That's your opinion," said Johnny.

"Yes, sir, it is," said the superintendent; "and I shall know how to represent the matter to your superiors, young man."

"You don't know all about it," said Eames; "and I don't suppose you ever will. I had made up my mind what I'd do the first time I saw that scoundrel there; and now I've done it. He'd have got much worse in the railway carriage, only there was a lady there."

"Mr Crosbie, I really think we had better take him before the magistrates."

To this, however, Crosbie objected. He assured the superintendent that he would himself know how to deal with the matter—which, however, was exactly what he did not know. Would the superintendent allow one of the railway servants to get a cab for him, and to find his luggage? He was very anxious to get home without being subject to any more of Mr Eames' insolence.

"You haven't done with Mr Eames' insolence yet, I can tell you. All London shall hear of it, and shall know why. If you have any shame in you, you shall be ashamed to show your face."

Unfortunate man! Who can say that punishment—adequate punishment—had not overtaken him? For the present, he had to sneak home with a black eye, with the knowledge inside him that he had been whipped by a clerk in the Income-tax Office; and for the future—he was bound over to marry Lady Alexandrina de Courcy!

He got himself smuggled off in a cab, without being forced to go again upon the platform—his luggage being brought to him by two assiduous porters. But in all this there was very little balm for his hurt pride. As he ordered the cabman to drive to Mount Street, he felt that he had ruined himself by that step in life which he had taken at Courcy Castle. Whichever way he looked he had no comfort. "D—— the fellow!" he said, almost out loud in the cab; but though he did with his outward voice allude to Eames, the curse in his inner thoughts was uttered against himself.

Johnny was allowed to make his way down to the platform, and there find his own carpet-bag. One young porter, however, came up and fraternised with him.

"You guve it him tidy just at that last moment, sir. But, laws, sir, you should have let out at him at fust. What's the use of clawing a man's neck-collar?"

It was then a quarter past eleven, but, nevertheless, Eames appeared at his office precisely at twelve.

S. H. A.

MISPLACED SYMPATHY

If you, my reader, ever chanced to slip into the gutter on a wet day, did you not find that the sympathy of the bystanders was by far the severest part of your misfortune?

S. H. A.

A GENTLEMANLY DON JUAN

. . . the hobbledehoy, though he blushes when women address him, and is uneasy even when he is near them, though he is not master of his limbs in a ball-room, and is hardly master of his tongue at any time, is the most eloquent of beings, and especially eloquent among beautiful women. He enjoys all the triumphs of a Don Juan, without any of Don Juan's heartlessness, and is able to conquer in all encounters, through the force of his wit and the sweetness of his voice. But this eloquence is heard only by his own inner ears, and these triumphs are the triumphs of his imagination.

S. H. A.

Crosbie starts his Honeymoon

And now that she was his wife, what was he to say to her? They two had commenced a partnership which was to make of them for the remaining term of their lives one body and one flesh. They were to be all-in-all to each other. But how was he to begin this all-in partnership? Had the priest, with his blessing, done it so sufficiently that no other doing on Crosbie's own part was necessary? There she was, opposite to him, his very actual wife— bone of his bone; and what was he to say to her? As he settled himself on his seat, taking over his own knees a part of a fine fur rug trimmed with scarlet, with which he had covered her other mufflings, he bethought himself how much easier it would have been to talk to Lily. And Lily would have been ready with all her ears, and all her mind, and all her wit, to enter quickly upon whatever thoughts had occurred to him. In that respect Lily would have been a wife indeed —a wife that would have transferred herself with quick mental activity into her husband's mental sphere. Had he begun about his office Lily would have been ready for him, but Alexandrina had never yet asked him a single question about his official life. Had he been prepared with a plan for to-morrow's happiness Lily would have taken it up eagerly, but Alexandrina never cared for such trifles.

"Are you quite comfortable?" he said, at last.

"Oh, yes, quite, thank you. By-the-by, what did you do with my dressing-case?"

And that question she did ask with some energy.

"It is under you. You can have it as foot-stool if you like it."

"Oh, no; I should scratch it. I was afraid that if Hannah had it, it might be lost." Then again there was silence, and Crosbie again considered as to what he would next say to his wife.

178

We all know the advice given us of old as to what we should do under such circumstances; and who can be so thoroughly justified in following that advice as a newly-married husband? So he put out his hand for hers and drew her closer to him.

"Take care of my bonnet," she said, as she felt the motion of the railway carriage when he kissed her. I don't think he kissed her again till he had landed her and her bonnet safely at Folkestone. How often would he have kissed Lily, and how pretty would her bonnet have been when she reached the end of her journey, and how delightfully happy would she have looked when she scolded him for bending! But Alexandrina was quite in earnest about her bonnet; by far too much in earnest for any appearance of happiness.

So he sat without speaking, till the train came to the tunnel.

"I do so hate tunnels," said Alexandrina.

He had half intended to put out his hand again, under some mistaken idea that the tunnel afforded him an opportunity. The whole journey was one long opportunity, had he desired it; but his wife hated tunnels, and so he drew his hand back again. Lily's little fingers would have been ready for his touch. He thought of this, and could not help thinking of it.

He had *The Times* newspaper in his dressing-bag. She also had a novel with her. Would she be offended if he took out the paper and read it? The miles seemed to pass by very slowly, and there was still another hour down to Folkestone. He longed for his *Times*, but resolved at last, that he would not read unless she read first. She also had remembered her novel; but by nature she was more patient than he, and she thought that on such a journey any reading might perhaps be almost improper. So she sat tranquilly, with her eyes fixed on the netting over her husband's head.

At last he could stand it no longer, and he dashed off into a conversation, intended to be most affectionate and serious.

"Alexandrina," he said, and his voice was well-tuned for the tender serious manner, had her ears been alive to such tuning. "Alexandrina this is a very important step that you and I have taken to-day."

"Yes; it is, indeed," said she.

"I trust we shall succeed in making each other happy."

"Yes; I hope we shall."

"If we both think seriously of it, and remember that that is our chief duty, we shall do so."

"Yes, I suppose we shall. I only hope we shan't find the house very cold. It is so new, and I am so subject to colds in my head. Amelia says we shall find it very cold; but then she was always against our going there."

"The house will do very well," said Crosbie. And Alexandrina could perceive that there was something of the master in his tone as he spoke.

"I am only telling you what Amelia said," she replied.

Had Lily been his bride, and had he spoken to her of their future life and mutual duties, how she would have kindled to the theme! She would have knelt at his feet on the floor of the carriage, and, looking up into his face, would have promised him to do her best—

her best—her very best. And with what an eagerness of inward resolution would she have determined to keep her promise. He thought of all this now, but he knew that he ought not to think of it. Then, for some quarter of an hour, he did take out his newspaper, and she, when she saw him do so, did take out her novel.

He took out his newspaper, but he could not fix his mind upon the politics of the day. Had he not made a terrible mistake? Of what use to him in life would be that thing of a woman that sat opposite to him? Had not a great punishment come upon him, and had he not deserved the punishment? In truth, a great punishment had come upon him. It was not only that he had married a woman incapable of understanding the higher duties of married life, but that he himself would have been capable of appreciating the value of a woman who did understand them. He would have been happy with Lily Dale; and therefore we may surmise that his unhappiness with Lady Alexandrina would be the greater. There are men who, in marrying such as Lady Alexandrina de Courcy, would get the article best suited to them, as Mortimer Gazebee had done in marrying her sister. Miss Griselda Grantly, who had become Lady Dumbello, though somewhat colder and somewhat cleverer than Lady Alexandrina, had been of the same sort. But in marrying her Lord Dumbello had got the article best suited to him—if only the ill-natured world would allow him to keep the article. It was in this that Crosbie's failure had been so grievous—that he had seen and approved the better course, but had chosen for himself to walk in that which was worse. During that week at Courcy Castle—the week which he passed there immediately after his second visit to Allington—he had deliberately made up his mind that he was more fit for the bad course than for the good one. The course was now before him, and he had no choice but to walk in it.

It was very cold when they got to Folkestone, and Lady Alexandrina shivered as she stepped into the private-looking carriage which had been sent to the station for her use.

"We shall find a good fire in the parlour at the hotel," said Crosbie.

"Oh, I hope so," said Alexandrina, "and in the bedroom too."

The young husband felt himself to be offended, but he hardly knew why. He felt himself to be offended, and with difficulty induced himself to go through all those little ceremonies the absence of which would have been remarked by everybody. He did his work, however, seeing to all her shawls and wrappings, speaking with good-nature to Hannah, and paying special attention to the dressing-case.

"What time would you like to dine?" he asked, as he prepared to leave her alone with Hannah in the bedroom.

"Whenever you please; only I should like some tea and bread-and-butter presently."

Crosbie went into the sitting-room, ordered the tea and bread-and-butter, ordered also the dinner, and then stood himself up with his back to the fire, in order that he might think a little of his future career.

He was a man who had long since resolved that his life should be a success. It would seem that all men would so resolve, if the matter were simply one of resolution. But the majority of men, as I take it, make no such resolution, and very many men resolve that they will be unsuccessful. Crosbie, however, had resolved on success, and had done much towards carrying out his purpose. He had made a name for himself, and had acquired a certain fame. That, however, was, as he acknowledged to himself, departing from him. He looked the matter straight in the face, and told himself that his fashion must be abandoned; but the office remained to him. He might still rule over Mr Optimist, and make a subservient slave of Butterwell. That must be his line in life now, and to that line he would endeavour to be true. As to his wife and his home—he would look to them for his breakfast, and perhaps his dinner. He would have a comfortable armchair, and if Alexandrina should become a mother, he would endeavour to love his children; but above all things he would never think of Lily. After that he stood and thought of her for half an hour.

"If you please, sir, my lady wants to know at what time you have ordered dinner."

"At seven, Hannah."

"My lady says she is very tired, and will lie down till dinner-time."

"Very well, Hannah. I will go into her room when it is time to dress. I hope they are making you comfortable down-stairs?"

Then Crosbie strolled out on the pier in the dusk of the cold winter evening.

S. H. A.

HOLY WEDLOCK (I)

Happy marriages, men say, are made in heaven, and I believe it. Most marriages are fairly happy. . . .

F. P.

HOLY WEDLOCK (II)

There is an aroma of love, an undefinable delicacy of flavour, which escapes and is gone before the church portal is left, vanishing with the maiden name, and incompatible with the solid comfort appertaining to the rank of wife.

F. P.

HOLY WEDLOCK (III)

"Marriage means tyranny on one side, and deceit on the other. I say that a man is a fool to sacrifice his interests for such a bargain. A woman, too generally, has no other way of living."—*Signora Madeline Neroni*

B. T.

On the Press, Art, and Dickens

A Great Paper

What the Czar is in Russia, or the mob in America, that the Jupiter is in England.

W.

Infallibility

It is a fact amazing to ordinary mortals that the Jupiter is never wrong.

W.

A Fiery Journalist

. . . with amazing chemisty, Tom Towers compounded thunder-bolts for the destruction of all that is evil, and for the furtherance of all that is good, in this and other hemispheres.

W.

On Art

Our modern artists, whom we style Prae-Raffaellites, have delighted to go back, not only to the finish and peculiar manner, but also to the subjects of the early painters . . . but the lady with the stiff back, and bent back, who looks at her flower, and is still looking from hour to hour, gives us an idea of pain without grace, and abstraction without a cause.

W.

ON DICKENS

It is incredible the number of evil practices he has put down: it is to be feared he will soon lack subjects, and that when he has made the working classes comfortable, and got bitter beer put into proper-sized bottles, there will be nothing further for him to do.

W.

Josiah Crawley
charged with theft

———◆———

O n the Thursday morning, at about ten o'clock, a fly stopped
at the gate of the Hogglestock Parsonage, and out of it
there came two men. One was dressed in ordinary black
clothes, and seemed from his bearing to be a respectable man of the
middle class of life. He was, however, the superintendent of police
for the Silverbridge district. The other man was a policeman, pure
and simple, with the helmet-looking hat which has lately become
common, and all the ordinary half-military and wholly disagreeable
outward adjuncts of the profession. "Wilkins," said the superintendent, "likely enough I shall want you, for they tell me the gent is
uncommon strange. But if I don't call you when I come out, just
open the door like a servant, and mount upon the box when we're in.
And don't speak nor say nothing." Then the senior policeman
entered the house.

He found Mrs Crawley sitting in the parlour with her bonnet and
shawl on, and Mr Crawley in the arm-chair, leaning over the fire. "I
suppose we had better go with you," said Mrs Crawley directly the
door was opened; for of course she had seen the arrival of the fly
from the window.

"The gentleman had better come with us if he'll be so kind," said
Thompson. "I've brought a close carriage for him."

"But may I go with him?" said the wife, with frightened voice.
"I may accompany my husband. He is not well, sir, and wants
assistance."

Thompson thought about it for a moment before he spoke. There
was room in the fly for only two, or if for three, still he knew his

place better than to thrust himself inside together with his prisoner and his prisoner's wife. He had been specially asked by Mr Walker to be very civil. Only one could sit on the box with the driver, and if the request was conceded the poor policeman must walk back. The walk, however, would not kill the policeman. "All right, ma'am," said Thompson—"that is, if the gentleman will just pass his word not to get out till I ask him."

"He will not! He will not!" said Mrs Crawley.

"I will pass my word for nothing," said Mr Crawley.

Upon hearing this, Thompson assumed a very long face, and shook his head as he turned his eyes first towards the husband and then towards the wife, and shrugged his shoulders, and compressing his lips, blew out his breath, as though in this way he might blow off some of the mingled sorrow and indignation with which the gentleman's words afflicted him.

Mrs Crawley rose and came close to him. "You may take my word for it, he will not stir. You may indeed. He thinks it incumbent on him not to give any undertaking himself, because he feels himself to be so harshly used."

"I don't know about harshness," said Thompson, brindling up. "A close carriage brought, and——"

"I will walk. If I am made to go, I will walk," shouted Mr Crawley.

"I did not allude to you—or to Mr Walker," said the poor wife. "I know you have been most kind. I mean the harshness of the circumstances. Of course he is innocent, and you must feel for him."

"Yes, I feel for him, and for you too, ma'am."

"That is all I meant. He knows his own innocence, and therefore he is unwilling to give way in anything."

"Of course he knows hisself, that's certain. But he'd better come in the carriage, if only because of the dirt and slush."

"He will go in the carriage; and I will go with him. There will be room there for you, sir."

Thompson looked up at the rain, and told himself that it was very cold. Then he remembered Mr Walker's injunction, and bethought himself that Mrs Crawley, in spite of her poverty, was a lady. He conceived even unconsciously the idea that something was due to her because of her poverty. "I'll go with the driver," said he, "but he'll only give hisself a deal of trouble if he attempts to get out."

"He won't; he won't," said Mrs Crawley. "And I thank you with all my heart."

"Come along, then," said Thompson.

She went up to her husband, hat in hand, and looking round to see that she was not watched, put the hat on his head, and then lifted him as it were from his chair. He did not refuse to be led, and allowed her to throw round his shoulders the old cloak which was hanging in the passage, and then he passed out, and was the first to seat himself in the Silverbridge fly. His wife followed him, and did not hear the blandishments with which Thompson instructed his myrmidon to follow through the mud on foot. Slowly they made their way through the lanes, and it was nearly twelve when the fly was driven into the yard of the "George and Vulture" at Silverbridge.

Silverbridge, though it was blessed with a mayor and corporation, and was blessed also with a Member of Parliament all to itself, was not blessed with any court-house. The magistrates were therefore compelled to sit in the big room at the "George and Vulture", in which the county balls were celebrated, and the meeting of the West Barsetshire freemasons was held. That part of the country was, no doubt, very much ashamed of its backwardness in this respect, but as yet nothing had been done to remedy the evil. Thompson and his fly were therefore driven into the yard of the Inn, and Mr and Mrs Crawley were ushered by him into a little bed-chamber close adjoining to the big room in which the magistrates were already assembled. "There's a bit of fire here," said Thompson, "and you can make yourselves a little warm." He himself was shivering with the cold. "When the gents is ready in there, I'll just come and fetch you."

"I may go in with him?" said Mrs Crawley.

"I'll have a chair for you at the end of the table, just nigh to him," said Thompson. "You can slip into it and saying nothing to nobody." Then he left them and went away to the magistrates.

Mr Crawley had not spoken a word since he had entered the vehicle. Nor had she said much to him, but had sat with him holding his hand in hers. Now he spoke to her, "Where is it that we are?" he asked.

"At Silverbridge, dearest."

"But what is this chamber? And why are we here?"

"We are to wait here till the magistrates are ready. They are in the next room."

"But this is the Inn?"

"Yes, dear, it is the Inn."

"And I see crowds of people about." There were crowds of people about. There had been men in the yard, and others standing about on the stairs, and the public room was full of men who were curious to see the clergyman who had stolen twenty pounds, and to hear what would be the result of the case before the magistrates. He must be committed; so, at least, said everybody; but then there would be the question of bail. Would the magistrates let him out on bail, and who would be the bailsmen?

"Why are the people here?" said Mr Crawley.

"I suppose it is the custom when the magistrates are sitting," said his wife.

"They have come to see the degradation of a clergyman," said he; "and they will not be disappointed."

"Nothing can degrade but guilt," said his wife.

"Yes—misfortune can degrade, and poverty. A man is degraded when the cares of the world press so heavily upon him that he cannot rouse himself. They have come to look at me as though I were a hunted beast."

"It is but their custom always on such days."

"They have not always a clergyman before them as a criminal." Then he was silent for a while, while she was chafing his cold hands. "Would that I were dead, before they had brought me to this! Would that I were dead!"

"Is it not right, dear, that we should all bear what He sends us?"

"Would that I were dead!" he repeated. "The load is too heavy for me to bear, and I would that I were dead!"

The time seemed to be very long before Thompson returned and asked them to accompany him into the big room. When he did so, Mr Crawley grasped hold of his chair as though he had resolved that he would not go. But his wife whispered a word to him, and he obeyed her. "He will follow me," she said to the policeman. And in that way they went from the small room into the large one. Thompson went first; Mrs Crawley with her veil down came next; and the wretched man followed his wife, with his eyes fixed upon the ground and his hands clasped together upon his breast. He could at first have seen nothing, and could hardly have known where he was when they placed him in a chair. She, with a better courage, contrived to look round through her veil, and saw that there was a long board or table covered with green cloth, and that six or seven gentlemen were sitting at one end of it, while there seemed to be a crowd standing along the sides and about the room. Her husband was seated at the other end of the table, near the corner, and round the corner—so that she might be close to him—her chair had been placed. On the other side of him there was another chair, now empty, intended for any professional gentleman whom he might choose to employ.

There were five magistrates sitting there. Lord Lufton from Framley was in the chair—a handsome man, still young, who was very popular in the county. The cheque which had been cashed had borne his signature, and he had consequently expressed his intention of not sitting on the board; but Mr Walker, desirous of having him there, had overruled him, showing him that the loss was not his loss. The cheque, if stolen, had not been stolen from him. He was not the prosecutor. "No, by Jove," said Lord Lufton, "if I could quash the whole thing, I'd do it at once!"

"You can't do that, my lord, but you may help us at the board," said Mr Walker.

Then there was the Hon. George De Courcy, Lord De Courcy's brother, from Castle Courcy. Lord De Courcy did not live in the county, but his brother did so, and endeavoured to maintain the glory of the family by the discretion of his conduct. He was not, perhaps, among the wisest of men, but he did very well as a country magistrate, holding his tongue, keeping his eyes open, and, on such occasions as this, obeying Mr Walker in all things. Dr Tempest was also there, the rector of the parish, he being both magistrate and clergyman. There were many in Silverbridge who declared that Dr Tempest would have done far better to stay away when a brother clergyman was thus to be brought before the bench; but it had been long since Dr Tempest had cared what was said about him in Silverbridge. He had become so accustomed to the life he led as to like to be disliked, and to be enamoured of unpopularity. So when Mr Walker had ventured to suggest to him that, perhaps, he might not choose to be there, he had laughed Mr Walker to scorn. "Of course I shall be there," he said. "I am interested in the case—very much interested. Of course I shall be there." And had not Lord Lufton been present he would have made himself more conspicuous by taking the chair. Mr Fothergill was the fourth. Mr Fothergill was man of business to the Duke of Omnium, who was the great owner of property in and about Silverbridge, and he was the most active magistrate in that part of the county. He was a sharp man, and not at all likely to have any predisposition in favour of a clergyman. The fifth was Dr Thorne, of Chaldicotes, a gentleman whose name has been already mentioned in these pages. He had been for many years a medical man practising in a little village in the further end of the county; but it had come to be his fate, late in life, to marry a great heiress, with whose money the ancient house and domain of Chaldicotes had been purchased from the Sowerbys. Since then Dr Thorne had done his duty well as a country gentleman—not, however, without some little want of smoothness between him and the duke's people.

Chaldicotes lay next to the duke's territory, and the duke had wished to buy Chaldicotes. When Chaldicotes slipped through the duke's fingers and went into the hands of Dr Thorne—or of Dr Thorne's wife—the duke had been very angry with Mr Fothergill. Hence it had come to pass that there had not always been smoothness between the duke's people and the Chaldicotes people. It was now rumoured that Dr Thorne intended to stand for the county on the next vacancy, and that did not tend to make things smoother. On the right hand of Lord Lufton sat Lord George and Mr Fothergill, and beyond Mr Fothergill sat Mr Walker, and beyond Mr Walker sat Mr Walker's clerk. On the left hand of the chairman were Dr Tempest and Dr Thorne, and a little lower down was Mr Zachary Winthrop, who held the situation of clerk to the magistrates. Many people in Silverbridge said that this was all wrong, as Mr Winthrop was partner with Mr Walker, who was always employed before the magistrates if there was any employment going for an attorney. For this, however, Mr Walker cared very little. He had so much of his own way in Silverbridge, that he was supposed to care nothing for anybody.

There were many other gentlemen in the room, and some who knew Mr Crawley with more or less intimacy. He, however, took notice of no one, and when one friend, who had really known him well, came up behind and spoke to him gently leaning over his chair, the poor man hardly recognised his friend.

"I'm sure your husband won't forget me," said Mr Robarts, the clergyman of Framley, as he gave his hand to that lady across the back of Mr Crawley's chair.

"No, Mr Robarts, he does not forget you. But you must excuse him if at this moment he is not quite himself. It is a trying situation for a clergyman."

"I can understand all that; but I'll tell why I have come. I suppose this inquiry will finish the whole affair, and clear up whatever may be the difficulty. But should it not do so, it may be just possible, Mrs Crawley, that something may be said about bail. I don't understand much about it, and I daresay you do not either; but if there should be anything of that sort, let Mr Crawley name me. A brother clergyman will be best, and I'll have some other gentleman with me." Then he left her, not waiting for any answer.

At the same time there was a conversation going on between Mr Walker and another attorney standing behind him, Mr Mason. "I'll go to him", said Walker, "and try to arrange it." So Mr Walker seated himself in the empty chair beside Mr Crawley, and endeavoured to explain to the wretched man, that he would do well to allow Mr Mason to assist him. Mr Crawley seemed to listen to all that was said, and then turned upon the speaker sharply: "I will have no one to assist me," he said so loudly that everyone in the room heard the words. "I am innocent. Why should I want assistance? Nor have I money to pay for it." Mr Mason made a quick movement forward, intending to explain that that consideration need offer no impediment, but was stopped by further speech from Mr Crawley. "I will have no one to help me," said he, standing upright, and for the first time removing his hat from his head. "Go on, and

do what it is you have to do." After that he did not sit down till the proceedings were nearly over, though he was invited more than once by Lord Lufton to do so.

We need not go through all the evidence that was brought to bear upon the question. It was proved that money for the cheque was paid to Mr Crawley's messenger, and that this money was given to Mr Crawley. When there occurred some little delay in the chain of evidence necessary to show that Mr Crawley had signed and sent the cheque and got the money, he became impatient. "Why do you trouble the man?" he said. "I had the cheque, and I sent him; I got the money. Has anyone denied it, that you should strive to drive a poor man like that beyond his wits?" Then Mr Soames and the manager of the bank showed what inquiry had been made as soon as the cheque came back from the London bank; how at first they had both thought that Mr Crawley could of course explain the matter, and how he had explained it by a statement which was manifestly untrue. Then there was evidence to prove that the cheque could not have been paid to him by Mr Soames, and as this was given, Mr Crawley shook his head and again became impatient. "I erred in that," he exclaimed. "Of course I erred. In my haste I thought it was so, and in my haste I said so. I am not good at reckoning money and remembering sums; but I saw that I had been wrong when my error was shown to me, and I acknowledged at once that I had been wrong."

Up to this point he had behaved not only with so much spirit, but with so much reason, that his wife began to hope that the importance of the occasion had brought back the clearness of his mind, and that he would, even now, be able to place himself right as the inquiry went on. Then it was explained that Mr Crawley had stated that the cheque had been given to him by Dean Arabin, as soon as it was shown that it could not have been given to him by Mr Soames. In reference to this, Mr Walker was obliged to explain that application had been made to the dean, who was abroad, and that the dean had stated that he had given fifty pounds to his friend. Mr Walker explained also that the very notes of which this fifty pounds had consisted had been traced back to Mr Crawley, and that they had

had no connection with the cheque or with money which had been given for the cheque at the bank.

Mr Soames stated that he had lost the cheque with a pocket-book; that he had certainly lost it on the day on which he had called on Mr Crawley at Hogglestock; and that he missed his pocket-book on his journey back from Hogglestock to Barchester. At the moment of missing it he remembered that he had taken the book out from his pocket in Mr Crawley's room, and, at that moment, he had not doubted but that he had left it in Mr Crawley's house. He had written and sent to Mr Crawley to inquire, but had been assured that nothing had been found. There had been no other property of value in the pocket-book—nothing but a few visiting cards and a memorandum, and he had therefore stopped the cheque at the London bank, and thought no more about it.

Mr Crawley was then asked to explain in what way he came possessed of the cheque. The question was first put by Lord Lufton; but it soon fell into Mr Walker's hands, who certainly asked it with all the kindness with which such an inquiry could be made. Could Mr Crawley at all remember by what means that bit of paper had come into his possession, or how long he had had it? He answered the last question first. "It had been with him for months." And why had he kept it? He looked round the room sternly, almost savagely, before he answered, fixing his eyes for a moment upon almost every face around him as he did so. Then he spoke, "I was driven by shame to keep it—and then by shame to use it." That this statement was true, no one in the room doubted.

And then the other question was pressed upon him; and he lifted up his hands, and raised his voice, and swore by the Saviour in whom he trusted, that he knew not from whence the money had come to him. Why then had he said that it had come from the dean? He had thought so. The dean had given him money, covered up, in an enclosure, "so that the touch of the coin might not add to my disgrace in taking his alms," said the wretched man, thus speaking openly and freely in his agony of the shame which he had striven so persistently to hide. He had not seen the dean's monies as they had been given, and he had thought that the cheque had been with them. Beyond that he could tell them nothing.

Then there was a conference between the magistrates and Mr Walker in which Mr Walker submitted that the magistrates had no alternative but to commit the gentleman. To this Lord Lufton demurred, and with him Dr Thorne.

"I believe, as I am sitting here," said Lord Lufton, "that he has told the truth, and that he does not know any more than I do from whence the cheque came."

"I am quite sure he does not," said Dr Thorne.

Lord George remarked that it was the "queerest go he had ever come across". Dr Tempest merely shook his head. Mr Fothergill pointed out that even supposing the gentleman's statement to be true, it by no means went towards establishing the gentleman's innocence. The cheque had been traced to the gentleman's hands, and the gentleman was bound to show how it had come into his possession. Even supposing that the gentleman had found the cheque in his house, which was likely enough, he was not thereby justified in changing it, and applying the proceeds to his own purposes. Mr Walker told them that Mr Fothergill was right, and that the only excuse to be made for Mr Crawley was that he was out of his senses.

"I don't see it," said Lord Lufton. "I might have a lot of paper money by me, and not know from Adam where I got it."

"But you would have to show where you got it, my lord, when inquiry was made," said Mr Fothergill.

Lord Lufton, who was not particularly fond of Mr Fothergill, and was very unwilling to be instructed by him in any of the duties of a magistrate, turned his back at once upon the duke's agent; but within three minutes afterwards he had submitted to the same instructions from Mr Walker.

Mr Crawley had again seated himself, and during this period of the affair was leaning over the table with his face buried on his arms. Mrs Crawley sat by his side, utterly impotent as to any assistance, just touching him with her hand, and waiting behind her veil till she should be made to understand what was the decision of the magistrates. This was at last communicated to her—and to him—in a whisper by Mr Walker. Mr Crawley must understand that he was committed to take his trial at Barchester, at the next assizes, which would be held in April, but that bail would be taken—his own bail in five hundred pounds, and that of two others in two hundred and fifty pounds each. And Mr Walker explained further that he and the bailmen were ready, and that the bail-bond was prepared. The bailmen were to be the Rev Mr Robarts, and Major Grantly. In five minutes the bond was signed and Mr Crawley was at liberty to go away, a free man—till the Barchester Assizes should come round in April.

Of all that was going on at this time Mr Crawley knew little or nothing, and Mrs Crawley did not know much. She did say a word of thanks to Mr Robarts, and begged that the same might be said to—the other gentleman. If she had heard the major's name she did not remember it. Then they were led out back into the bedroom, where Mrs Walker was found, anxious to do something, if she only knew what, to comfort the wretched husband and the wretched wife. But what comfort or consolation could there be within their reach? There was tea made ready for them, and sandwiches cut from the Inn larder. And there was sherry in the Inn decanter. But no such comfort as that was possible for either of them.

They were taken home again in the fly, returning without the escort of Mr Thompson, and as they went some few words were spoken by Mrs Crawley. "Josiah," she said, "there will be a way out of this, even yet, if you will only hold up your head and trust."

"There is a way out of it," he said. "There is a way. There is but one way." When he had so spoken she said no more, but resolved that her eye should never be off him, no—not for a moment. Then, when she had gotten him once more into that front parlour, she threw her arms round him and kissed him.

L. C.

CYNICISM

"Did ye ever know a poor man yet was the better for law, or for a lawyer?"—*Mr Bunce*

W.

The Bishop sends his Inhibition

Tidings of Mr Crawley's fate reached the palace at Barchester on the afternoon of the day on which the magistrates had committed him. All such tidings travel very quickly, conveyed by imperceptible wires, and distributed by indefatigable message boys whom Rumour seems to supply for the purpose. Barchester is twenty miles from Silverbridge by road, and more than forty by railway. I doubt whether anyone was commissioned to send the news along the actual telegraph, and yet Mrs Proudie knew it before four o'clock. But she did not know it quite accurately. "Bishop," she said, standing at her husband's study door. "They have committed that man to gaol. There was no help for them unless they had forsworn themselves."

"Not forsworn themselves, my dear," said the bishop, striving, as was usual with him, by some meek and ineffectual word to teach his wife that she was occasionally led by her energy into error. He never persisted in the lessons when he found, as was usual, that they were taken amiss.

"I say forsworn themselves!" said Mrs Proudie; "and now what do you mean to do? This is Thursday, and of course the man must not be allowed to desecrate the church of Hogglestock by performing the Sunday services."

"If he has been committed, my dear, and is in prison——"

"I said nothing about prison, bishop."

"Gaol, my dear."

"I say they have committed him to gaol. So my informant tells me. But of course all the Plumstead and Framley set will move heaven and earth to get him out, so that he may be there as a disgrace to the diocese. I wonder how the dean will feel when he hears of it!

I do, indeed. For the dean, though he is an idle, useless man, with no church principles, and no real piety, still he has a conscience. I think he has a conscience."

"I'm sure he has, my dear."

"Well—let us hope so. And if he has a conscience, what must be his feelings when he hears that this creature whom he brought into the diocese has been committed to gaol along with common felons."

"Not with felons, my dear; at least, I should think not."

"I say with common felons! A downright robbery of twenty pounds, just as though he had broken into the bank! And so he did, with sly artifice, which is worse in such hands than a crowbar. And now what are we to do? Here is Thursday, and something must be done before Sunday for the souls of those poor benighted creatures at Hogglestock." Mrs Proudie was ready for the battle, and was even now sniffing the blood afar-off. "I believe it's a hundred and thirty pounds a year," she said, before the bishop had collected his thoughts sufficiently for a reply.

"I think we must find out, first of all, whether he is really to be shut up in prison," said the bishop.

"And suppose he is not to be shut up. Suppose they have been weak, or untrue to their duty—and from what we know of the magistrates of Barsetshire, there is too much reason to suppose that they will have been so; suppose they have let him out, is he to go about like a roaring lion—among the souls of the people?"

The bishop shook in his shoes. When Mrs Proudie began to talk of the souls of the people he always shook in his shoes. She had an eloquent way of raising her voice over the word souls that was qualified to make any ordinary man shake in his shoes. The bishop was a conscientious man, and well knew that poor Mr Crawley, even though he might have become a thief under terrible temptation, would not roar at Hogglestock to the injury of any man's soul. He was aware that this poor clergyman had done his duty laboriously and efficiently, and he was also aware that though he might have been committed by the magistrates, and then let out upon bail, he should not be regarded, now, in these days before his trial, as a convicted thief. But to explain all this to Mrs Proudie was beyond his power. He knew well that she would not hear a word in mitigation of Mr Crawley's presumed offence. Mr Crawley belonged to the other party, and Mrs Proudie was a thorough-going partisan. I know a man—an excellent fellow, who, being himself a strong politician, constantly expresses a belief that all politicians opposed to him are thieves, child-murderers, parricides, lovers of incest, demons upon the earth. He is a strong partisan, but not, I think, so strong as Mrs Proudie. He says that he believes all evil of his opponents; but she really believed the evil. The archdeacon had called Mrs Proudie a she-Beelzebub; but that was a simple ebullition of mortal hatred. He believed her to be simply a vulgar, interfering, brazen-faced virago. Mrs Proudie in truth believed that the archdeacon was an actual emanation from Satan, sent to those parts to devour souls—as she would call it—and that she herself was an emanation of another sort, sent from another source expressly to Barchester, to prevent such devouring, as far as it might possibly be prevented by a mortal agency. The bishop knew it all—understood it all. He regarded the archdeacon as a clergyman belonging to a party opposed to his party, and he disliked the man. He knew that from his first coming into the diocese he had been encountered with enmity by the archdeacon and the archdeacon's friends. If left to himself he could feel and to a certain extent resent such enmity. But he had no faith in his wife's doctrine of emanations. He had no faith in many things which she believed religiously—and yet what could he do? If he attempted to explain, she would stop him before he had got through the first half of his first sentence.

"If he is out on bail——", commenced the bishop.

"Of course he will be out on bail."

"Then I think he should feel——"

"Feel! such men never feel! What feeling can one expect from a convicted thief?"

"Not convicted as yet, my dear," said the bishop.

"A convicted thief," repeated Mrs Proudie; and she vociferated the words in such a tone that the bishop resolved that he would for the future let the word convicted pass without notice. After all she was only using the phrase in a peculiar sense given to it by herself.

"It won't be proper, certainly, that he should do the services," suggested the bishop.

"Proper! It would be a scandal to the whole diocese. How could he raise his head as he pronounced the eighth commandment? That must be at least prevented."

The bishop, who was seated, fretted himself in his chair, moving about with little movements. He knew that there was a misery coming upon him; and, as far as he could see, it might become a great misery —a huge blistering sore upon him. When miseries came to him, as they did not unfrequently, he would unconsciously endeavour to fathom them and weigh them, and then, with some gallantry, resolve to bear them, if he could find that their depth and weight were not too great for his powers of endurance. He would let the cold wind whistle by him, putting up the collar of his coat, and would encounter the winter weather without complaint. And he would be patient under the hot sun, knowing well that tranquillity is best for those who have to bear tropical heat. But when the storm threatened to knock him off his legs, when the earth beneath him became too hot for his poor tender feet—what could he do then? There had been with him such periods of misery, during which he had wailed inwardly and had confessed to himself that the wife of his bosom was too much for him. Now the storm seemed to be coming very roughly. It would be demanded of him that he should exercise certain episcopal authority which he knew did not belong to him. Now, episcopal authority admits of being stretched or contracted according to the character of the bishop who uses it. It is not always easy for a bishop himself to know what he may do, and what he may not do. He may certainly give advice to any clergyman in his diocese, and he may give it in such form that it will have in it something of authority. Such advice coming from a dominant bishop to a clergyman with a submissive mind, has in it very much of authority. But Bishop Proudie knew that Mr Crawley was not a clergyman with a submissive mind, and he feared that he himself, as regarded from Mr

Crawley's point of view, was not a dominant bishop. And yet he could only act by advice. "I will write to him," said the bishop, "and will explain to him that as he is circumstanced he should not appear in the reading desk."

"Of course he must not appear in the reading desk. That scandal must at any rate be inhibited." Now the bishop did not at all like the use of the word inhibited, understanding well that Mrs Proudie intended it to be understood as implying some episcopal command against which there should be no appeal—but he let it pass.

"I will write to him, my dear, to-night."

"And Mr Thumble can go over with the letter the first thing in the morning."

"Will not the post be better?"

"No, bishop; certainly not."

"He would get it sooner, if I write to-night, my dear."

"In either case he will get it to-morrow morning. An hour or two will not signify, and if Mr Thumble takes it himself we shall know how it is received. It will be well that Thumble should be there in person as he will want to look for lodgings in the parish."

"But, my dear——"

"Well, bishop?"

"About lodgings? I hardly think that Mr Thumble, if we decide that Mr Thumble shall undertake the duty——"

"We have decided that Mr Thumble should undertake the duty. That is decided."

"But I do not think he should trouble himself to look for lodgings at Hogglestock. He can go over on the Sundays."

"And who is to do the parish work? Would you have that man, a convicted thief, to look after the schools, and visit the sick, and perhaps attend the dying?"

"There will be a great difficulty; there will indeed," said the bishop, becoming very unhappy, and feeling that he was driven by circumstances either to assert his own knowledge or teach his wife something of the law with reference to his position as a bishop. "Who is to pay Mr Thumble?"

"The income of the parish must be sequestrated, and he must be paid out of that. Of course he must have the income while he does the work."

"But, my dear, I cannot sequestrate the man's income."

"I don't believe it, bishop. If the bishop cannot sequestrate, who can? But you are always timid in exercising the authority put into your hands for wise purposes. Not sequestrate the income of a man who has been proved to be a thief! You leave that to us, and we will manage it." The "us" here named comprised Mrs Proudie and the bishop's managing chaplain.

Then the bishop was left alone for an hour to write the letter which Mr Thumble was to carry over to Mr Crawley—and after a while he did write it. Before he commenced the task, however, he sat for some moments in his arm-chair close by the fire-side, asking himself whether it might not be possible for him to overcome his enemy in this matter. How would it go with him to suppose he were to leave the letter unwritten, and send a message by his chaplain to Mrs Proudie, saying that as Mr Crawley was out on bail, the parish might be left for the present without episcopal interference? She could not make him interfere. She could not force him to write the letter. So, at least, he said to himself. But as he said it, he almost thought that she could do these things. In the last thirty years, or more, she had ever contrived by some power latent in her to have her will effected. But what would happen if now, even now, he were to rebel? That he would personally become very uncomfortable, he was well aware, but he thought that he could bear that. The food would become bad—mere ashes between his teeth, the daily modicum of wine would lose its flavour, the chimneys would all smoke, the wind would come from the east, and the servants would not answer the bell. Little miseries of that kind would crowd upon him. He had arrived at a time of life in which such miseries make such men very miserable; but yet he thought that he could endure them. And what other wretchedness would come to him? She would scold him—frightfully, loudly, scornfully, and worse than all, continually. But of this he had so much habitually, that anything

203

added might be borne also—if only he could be sure that the scoldings should go on in private, that the world of the palace should not be allowed to hear the revilings to which he would be subjected. But to be scolded publicly was the great evil which he dreaded beyond all evils. He was well aware that the palace would know his misfortune, that it was known, and freely discussed by all, from the examining chaplain down to the palace boot-boy—nay, that it was known to all the diocese; but yet he could smile upon those around him, and look as though he held his own like other men—unless when open violence was displayed. But when that voice was heard aloud along the corridors of the palace, and when he was summoned imperiously by the woman, calling for her bishop, so that all Barchester heard it, and when he was compelled to creep forth from his study, at the sound of that summons, with distressed face, and shaking hands, and short hurrying steps—then, at such moments as that, he would feel that any submission was better than the misery which he suffered. And he well knew that should he now rebel, the whole house would be in a turmoil. He would be bishoped here, and bishoped there, before the eyes of all palatial men and women, till life would be a burden to him. So he got up from his seat over the fire, and went to his desk and wrote the letter. The letter was as follows:

"The Palace, Barchester, —— December, 186–.

"Reverend Sir,—(he left out the dear, because he knew that if he inserted it he would be compelled to write the letter over again.)

"I have heard to-day with the greatest trouble of spirit, that you have been taken before a bench of magistrates assembled at Silverbridge, having been previously arrested by the police in your parsonage house at Hogglestock, and that the magistrates of Silverbridge have committed you to take your trial at the next assizes at Barchester, on a charge of theft.

"Far be it from me to prejudge the case. You will understand, reverend sir, that I express no opinion whatever as to your guilt or innocence in this matter. If you have been guilty, may the Lord give you grace to repent of your great sin and to make such amends as may come from immediate acknowledgment and confession. If you are innocent, may He protect you, and make your innocence to shine before all men. In either case may the Lord be with you and keep your feet from further stumbling.

"But I write to you now as your bishop, to explain to you that circumstanced as you are, you cannot with decency perform the church services of your parish. I have that confidence in you that I doubt not you will agree with me in this, and will be grateful to me for relieving you so far from the immediate perplexities of your position. I have, therefore, appointed the Rev. Caleb Thumble to perform the duties of incumbent of Hogglestock till such time as a jury shall have decided upon your case at Barchester; and in order that you may at once become acquainted with Mr Thumble, as will be most convenient that you should do, I will commission him to deliver this letter into your hand personally to-morrow, trusting that you will receive him with that brotherly spirit in which he is sent upon this painful mission.

"Touching the remuneration to which Mr Thumble will become entitled for his temporary ministrations in the parish of Hogglestock, I do not at present lay down any strict injunction. He must, at any rate, be paid at a rate not less than that ordinarily afforded for a curate.

"I will once again express my fervent hope that the Lord may bring you to see the true state of your own soul, and that He may fill you with the grace of repentance, so that the bitter waters of the present hour may not pass over your head and destroy you.

I have the honour to be,

Reverend Sir,

Your faithful servant in Christ,

T. Barnum."[1]

The bishop had hardly finished his letter when Mrs Proudie

---

[1] Baronum Castrum having been the old Roman name from which the modern Barchester is derived, the bishops of the diocese have always signed themselves Barnum.

returned to the study, followed by the Rev. Caleb Thumble. Mr Thumble was a little man, about forty years of age, who had a wife and children living in Barchester, and who existed on such chance clerical crumbs as might fall from the table of the bishop's patronage. People in Barchester said that Mrs Thumble was a cousin of Mrs Proudie's; but as Mrs Proudie stoutly denied the connection, it may be supposed that the people of Barchester were wrong. And, had Mr Thumble's wife in truth been a cousin, Mrs Proudie would surely have provided for him during the many years in which the diocese had been in her hands. No such provision had been made, and Mr Thumble, who had now been living in the diocese for three years, had received nothing else from the bishop than such chance employment as this which he was now to undertake at Hogglestock. He was a humble, mild-voiced man, when within the palace precincts, and had so far succeeded in making his way among his brethren in the cathedral city as to be employed not unfrequently for absent minor canons in chanting the week-day services, being remunerated for his work at the rate of about two shillings and sixpence a service.

The bishop handed his letter to his wife, observing in an off-hand kind of way that she might as well see what he said. "Of course I shall read it," said Mrs Proudie. And the bishop winced visibly, because Mr Thumble was present. "Quite right," said Mrs Proudie, "quite right to let him know that you knew that he had been arrested —actually arrested by the police."

"I thought it proper to mention that, because of the scandal," said the bishop.

"Oh, it has been terrible in the city," said Mr Thumble.

"Never mind, Mr Thumble," said Mrs Proudie. "Never mind that at present." Then she continued to read the letter. "What's this? Confession! That must come out, bishop. It will never do that you should recommend confession to anybody, under any circumstances."

"But, my dear ——"

"It must come out, bishop."

"My lord has not meant auricular confession," suggested Mr

Thumble. Then Mrs Proudie turned round and looked at Mr Thumble, and Mr Thumble nearly sank amidst the tables and chairs. "I beg your pardon, Mrs Proudie," he said. "I didn't mean to intrude."

"The word must come out, bishop," repeated Mrs Proudie. "There should be no stumbling-blocks prepared for feet that are only too ready to fall." And the word did come out.

"Now, Mr Thumble," said the lady, as she gave the letter to her satellite, "the bishop and I wish you to be at Hogglestock early to-morrow. You should be there not later than ten, certainly." Then she paused until Mr Thumble had given the required promise. "And we request that you will be very firm in the mission which is confided to you, a mission which, as of course you see, is of a very delicate and important nature. You must be firm."

"I will endeavour," said Mr Thumble.

"The bishop and I both feel that this most unfortunate man must not under any circumstances be allowed to perform the services of the Church while this charge is hanging over him—a charge as to the truth of which no sane man can entertain a doubt."

"I'm afraid not, Mrs Proudie," said Mr Thumble.

"The bishop and I therefore are most anxious that you should make Mr Crawley understand at once—at once," and the lady, as she spoke, lifted up her left hand with an eloquent violence which had its effect upon Mr Thumble, "that he is inhibited"—the bishop shook in his shoes—"inhibited from the performance of any of his sacred duties." Thereupon, Mr Thumble promised obedience and went his way.

L. C.

MARRIED COMFORT

Oh, husbands, oh, my marital friends, what great comfort is there to be derived from a wife well obeyed!

B. T.

Caleb Thumble returns to Barchester

It was nearly nine before Mr Crawley got back to his house, and found his wife and daughter waiting breakfast for him. "I should not wonder if Grace were over here to-day," said Mrs Crawley. "She'd better remain where she is," said he. After this the meal passed almost without a word. When it was over, Jane, at a sign

from her mother, went up to her father and asked him whether she should read with him. "Not now," he said, "not just now. I must rest my brain before it be fit for any work." Then he got into the chair over the fire, and his wife began to fear that he would remain there all the day.

But the morning was not far advanced, when there came a visitor who disturbed him, and by disturbing him did him real service. Just at ten there arrived at the little gate before the house a man on a pony, whom Jane espied, standing there by the pony's head and looking about for some one to relieve him from the charge of his steed. This was Mr Thumble, who had ridden over to Hogglestock on a poor spavined brute belonging to the bishop's stable, and which had once been the bishop's cob. Now it was the vehicle by which Mrs Proudie's episcopal messages were sent backwards and forwards through a twelve-mile ride round Barchester; and so many were the lady's requirements, that the poor animal by no means ate the hay of idleness. Mr Thumble had suggested to Mrs Proudie, after their interview with the bishop and the giving up of the letter to the clerical messenger's charge, that before hiring a gig from the Dragon of Wantley, he should be glad to know—looking as he always did to "Mary Anne and the children"—whence the price of the gig was to be returned to him. Mrs Proudie had frowned at him—not with all the austerity of frowning which she could use when really angered, but simply with a frown which gave her some little time for thought, and would enable her to continue the rebuke if, after thinking, she should find that rebuke was needed. But mature consideration showed her that Mr Thumble's caution was not without reason. Were the bishop energetic—or even the bishop's managing chaplain as energetic as he should be, Mr Crawley might, as Mrs Proudie felt assured, be made in some way to pay for a conveyance for Mr Thumble. But the energy was lacking, and the price of the gig, if the gig were ordered, would certainly fall ultimately upon the bishop's shoulders. This was very sad. Mrs Proudie had often grieved over the necessary expenditure of episcopal surveillance, and had been heard to declare her opinion that a liberal allowance for secret service should be made in every diocese. What better could the Ecclesiastical Commissioners do with all those rich revenues which they had stolen from the bishops? But there was no such liberal allowance at present, and, therefore, Mrs Proudie, after having frowned at Mr Thumble for some seconds, desired him to take the grey cob. Now, Mr Thumble had ridden the grey cob before, and would have much preferred a gig. But even the grey cob was better than a gig at his own cost.

"Mamma, there's a man at the gate wanting to come in," said Jane. "I think he's a clergyman."

Mr Crawley immediately raised his head, though he did not at once leave his chair. Mrs Crawley went to the window, and recognized the reverend visitor. "My dear, it is that Mr Thumble, who is so much with the bishop."

"What does Mr Thumble want with me?"

"Nay, my dear; he will tell you that himself." But Mrs Crawley, though she answered him with a voice intended to be cheerful, greatly feared the coming of this messenger from the palace. She perceived at once that the bishop was about to interfere with her husband in consequence of that which the magistrates had done yesterday.

"Mamma, he doesn't know what to do with his pony," said Jane.

"Tell him to tie it to the rail," said Mr Crawley. "If he has expected to find menials here, as he has them at the palace, he will be wrong. If he wants to come in here, let him tie the beast to the rail."

So Jane went out and sent a message to Mr Thumble by the girl, and Mr Thumble did tie the pony to the rail, and followed the girl into the house. Jane in the meantime had retired out by the back door to the school, but Mrs Crawley kept her ground. She kept her ground although she almost believed that her husband would prefer to have the field to himself. As Mr Thumble did not at once enter the room, Mr Crawley stalked to the door, and stood with it open in his hand. Though he knew Mr Thumble's person, he was not acquainted with him, and therefore he simply bowed to the visitor, bowing more than once or twice with a cold courtesy, which did not put Mr Thumble altogether at his ease. "My name is Mr Thumble," said the visitor—"The Reverend Caleb Thumble," and he held the bishop's letter in his hand. Mr Crawley seemed to take no notice of the letter, but motioned Mr Thumble with his hand into the room.

"I suppose you have come over from Barchester this morning?" said Mrs Crawley.

"Yes, madam—from the palace." Mr Thumble, though a humble man in positions in which he felt that humility would become him— a humble man to his betters, as he himself would have expressed it— had still about him something of that pride which naturally belonged to those clergymen who were closely attached to the palace at Barchester. Had he been sent on a message to Plumstead—could any such message from Barchester palace have been possible, he would have been properly humble in his demeanour to the archdeacon, or to Mrs Grantly had he been admitted to the august presence of that lady; but he was aware that humility would not become him on his present mission; he had been expressly ordered to be firm by Mrs Proudie, and firm he meant to be; and therefore, in communicating to Mrs Crawley the fact that he had come from the palace, he did load the tone of his voice with something of dignity which Mr Crawley might perhaps be excused for regarding as arrogance.

"And what does the 'palace' want with me?" said Mr Crawley. Mrs Crawley knew at once that there was to be a battle. Nay, the battle had begun. Nor was she altogether sorry; for though she could not trust her husband to sit alone all day in his arm-chair over the fire, she could trust him to carry on a disputation with any other clergyman on any subject whatever. "What does the palace want with me?" And as Mr Crawley asked the question he stood erect, and looked Mr Thumble full in the face. Mr Thumble called to mind the fact that Mr Crawley was a very poor man indeed—so poor that he owed money all round the country to butchers and bakers, and the other fact that he, Mr Thumble himself, did not owe any money to anyone, his wife luckily having a little income of her own; and, strengthened by these remembrances, he endeavoured to bear Mr Crawley's attack with gallantry.

"Of course, Mr Crawley, you are aware that this unfortunate affair at Silverbridge ——"

"I am not prepared, sir, to discuss the unfortunate affair at Silverbridge with a stranger. If you are the bearer of any message to me from the Bishop of Barchester, perhaps you will deliver it."

"I have brought a letter," said Mr Thumble. Then Mr Crawley stretched out his hand without a word, and taking the letter with him to the window, read it very slowly. When he had made himself master of its contents, he refolded the letter, placed it again in the envelope, and returned to the spot where Mr Thumble was standing. "I will answer the bishop's letter," he said; "I will answer it of course, as it is fitting that I should do. Shall I ask you to wait for my reply, or shall I send it by course of post?"

"I think, Mr Crawley, as the bishop wishes me to undertake the duty ——"

"You will not undertake the duty, Mr Thumble. You need not trouble yourself, for I shall not surrender my pulpit to you."

"But the bishop ——"

"I care nothing for the bishop in this matter." So much he spoke in anger, and then he corrected himself. "I crave the bishop's pardon, and yours as his messenger, if in the heat occasioned by my strong feelings I have said aught which may savour of irreverence towards his lordship's office. I respect his lordship's high position as bishop of this diocese, and I bow to his commands in all things lawful. But I must not bow to him in things unlawful, nor must I abandon my duty before God at his bidding, unless his bidding be given in accordance with the canons of the Church and the laws of the land. It will be my duty, on the coming Sunday, to lead the prayers of my people in the church of my parish, and to preach to them from my pulpit; and that duty, with God's assistance, I will perform. Nor will I allow any clergyman to interfere with me in the performance of those sacred offices—no, not though the bishop himself should be present with the object of enforcing his illegal command." Mr Crawley spoke these words without hesitation, even with eloquence, standing upright, and with something of a noble anger gleaming over his poor wan face; and, I think, that while speaking them, he was happier than he had been for many a long day.

Mr Thumble listened to him patiently, standing with one foot a little in advance of the other, with one hand folded over the other, with his head rather on one side, and with his eyes fixed on the corner where the wall and ceiling joined each other. He had been told to be firm, and he was considering how he might best display firmness. He thought that he remembered some story of two parsons fighting for one pulpit, and he thought also that he should not himself like to incur the scandal of such a proceeding in the diocese. As to the law in the matter he knew nothing himself; but he presumed that a bishop would probably know the law better than a perpetual curate. That Mrs Proudie was intemperate and imperious, he was aware. Had the message come from her alone, he might have felt that even for her sake he had better give way. But as the despotic arrogance of the lady had been in this case backed by the timid presence and hesitating words of her lord, Mr Thumble thought that he must have the law on his side. "I think you will find, Mr Crawley," said he, "that the bishop's inhibition is strictly legal." He had picked up the powerful word from Mrs Proudie and flattered himself that it might be of use to him in carrying his purpose.

"It is illegal," said Mr Crawley, speaking somewhat louder than before, "and will be absolutely futile. As you pleaded to me that you yourself and your own personal convenience were concerned in this matter, I have made known my intentions to you, which otherwise I should have made known only to the bishop. If you please, we will discuss the subject no further."

"Am I to understand, Mr Crawley, that you refuse to obey the bishop?"

"The bishop has written to me, sir; and I will make known my intention to the bishop by a written answer. As you have been the bearer of the bishop's letter to me, I am bound to ask you whether I shall be indebted to you for carrying back my reply, or whether I shall send it by course of post?" Mr Thumble considered for a moment, and then made up his mind that he had better wait, and carry back the epistle. This was Friday, and the letter could not be delivered by post till the Saturday morning. Mrs Proudie might be angry with him if he should be the cause of loss of time. He did not, however, at all like waiting, having perceived that Mr Crawley, though with language courteously worded, had spoken of him as a mere messenger.

"I think", he said, "that I may, perhaps, best further the object which we must all have in view, that namely of providing properly for the Sunday services of the church of Hogglestock, by taking your reply personally to the bishop."

"That provision is my care and need trouble no one else," said Mr Crawley, in a loud voice. Then, before seating himself at his old desk, he stood awhile, pondering, with his back turned to his visitor. "I have to ask your pardon, sir," said he, looking round for a moment, "because, by reason of the extreme poverty of this house, my wife is unable to offer to you that hospitality which is especially due from one clergyman to another."

"Oh, don't mention it," said Mr Thumble.

"If you will allow me, sir, I would prefer that it should be mentioned." Then he seated himself at his desk, and commenced his letter.

Mr Thumble felt himself to be awkwardly placed. Had there been no third person in the room he could have sat down in Mr Crawley's arm-chair, and waited patiently till the letter should be finished. But Mrs Crawley was there, and of course he was bound to speak to her. In what strain could he do so? Even he, little as he was given to indulge in sentiment, had been touched by the man's appeal to his own poverty, and he felt, moreover, that Mrs Crawley must have been deeply moved by her husband's position with reference to the bishop's order. It was out of the question that he should speak of that, as Mr Crawley would, he was well aware, immediately turn upon him. At last he thought of a subject, and spoke with a voice intended to be pleasant. "That was the school-house I passed, probably, just as I came here?" Mrs Crawley told him that it was the school-house. "Ah, yes, I thought so. Have you a certified teacher here?" Mrs Crawley explained that no Government aid had ever reached Hogglestock. Besides themselves, they had only a young woman whom they themselves had instructed. "Ah, that is a pity," said Mr Thumble.

"I—I am the certified teacher," said Mr Crawley, turning round upon him from his chair.

"Oh, ah, yes," said Mr Thumble; and after that Mr Thumble asked no more questions about the Hogglestock school. Soon afterwards Mrs Crawley left the room, seeing the difficulty under which Mr Thumble was labouring, and feeling sure that her presence would not now be necessary. Mr Crawley's letter was written quickly, though every now and then he would sit for a moment with his pen poised in the air, searching his memory for a word. But the words came to him easily, and before an hour was over he had handed his letter to Mr Thumble. The letter was as follows:

"The Parsonage, Hogglestock, Dec. 186–.

"Right Reverend Lord,

"I have received the letter of yesterday's date which your lordship has done me the honour of sending to me by the hands of the Reverend Mr Thumble, and I avail myself of that gentleman's kindness to return to you an answer by the same means, moved thus to use his patience chiefly by the consideration that in this way my reply to your lordship's injunctions may be in your hands with less delay than would attend the regular course of the mail-post.

"It is with deep regret that I feel myself constrained to inform your lordship that I cannot obey the command which you have laid upon me with reference to the services of my church in this parish. I cannot permit Mr Thumble, or any other delegate from your lordship, to usurp my place in my pulpit. I would not have you to think, if I can possibly dispel such thoughts from your mind, that I disregard your high office, or that I am deficient in that respectful obedience to the bishop set over me, which is due to the authority of the Crown as the head of the church in these realms; but in this, as in all questions of obedience, he who is required to obey must examine the extent of the authority exercised by him who demands obedience. Your lordship might possibly call upon me, using your voice as bishop of the diocese, to abandon altogether the freehold rights which are now mine in this perpetual curacy. The judge of assize, before whom I shall soon stand for my trial, might command me to retire to prison without a verdict given by the jury. The magistrates who committed me so lately as yesterday, upon whose decision in that respect your lordship has taken action against me so quickly, might have equally strained their authority. But in no case, in this land, is he that is subject bound to obey, further than where the law gives authority and exacts obedience. It is not in the power of the Crown itself to inhibit me from the performance of my ordinary duties in this parish by any such missive as that sent to me by your lordship. If your lordship think it right to stop my mouth as a clergyman in your diocese, you must proceed to do so in an ecclesiastical court in accordance with the laws, and will succeed in your object, or fail, in accordance with the evidences as to ministerial fitness or unfitness, which may be produced respecting me before the proper tribunal.

"I will allow that much attention is due from a clergyman to pastoral advice given to him by his bishop. On that head I must first express to your lordship my full understanding that your letter has not been intended to convey advice, but an order—an inhibition, as your messenger, the Reverend Mr Thumble, has expressed it. There might be a case certainly in which I should submit myself to counsel, though I should resist command. No counsel, however, has been given—except indeed that I should receive your messenger in a proper spirit, which I hope I have done. No other advice has been given me, and therefore there is now no such case as that I have imagined. But in this matter, my lord, I could not have accepted advice from living man, no, not though the hands of the apostles themselves had made him bishop who tendered it to me, and had set him over me for my guidance. I am in a terrible strait. Trouble, and sorrow, and danger are upon me and mine. It may well be, as your lordship says, that the bitter waters of the present hour may pass over my head and destroy me. I thank your lordship for telling me whither I am to look for assistance. Truly I know not whether there is any to be found for me on earth. But the deeper my troubles, the greater my sorrow, the more pressing my danger, the stronger is my need that I should carry myself in these days with that outward respect of self which will teach those around me to know that, let who will condemn me, I have not condemned myself. Were I to abandon my pulpit, unless forced to do so by legal means, I should in doing so be putting a plea of guilty against myself upon the record. This, my lord, I will not do.

> I have the honour to be, my lord,
> Your lordship's most obedient servant,
> Josiah Crawley."

When he had finished writing his letter he read it over slowly, and then handed it to Mr Thumble. The act of writing, and the current of the thoughts through his brain, and the feeling that in every word written he was getting the better of the bishop—all this joined to a certain manly delight in warfare against authority, lighted up the man's face and gave to his eyes an expression which had been long wanting to them. His wife at that moment came into the room and he looked at her with an air of triumph as he handed the letter to Mr Thumble. "If you will give that to his lordship with an assurance of my duty to his lordship in all things proper, I will thank you kindly, craving your pardon for the great delay to which you have been subjected."

"As to the delay, that is nothing," said Mr Thumble.

"It has been much; but you as a clergyman will feel that it has been incumbent on me to speak my mind fully."

"Oh, yes; of course." Mr Crawley was standing up, as also was Mrs Crawley. It was evident to Mr Thumble that they both expected that he should go. But he had been specially enjoined to be firm, and he doubted whether hitherto he had been firm enough. As far as this morning's work had as yet gone, it seemed to him that Mr Crawley had had the play all to himself, and that he, Mr Thumble, had not had his innings. He, from the palace, had been, as it were, cowed by this man, who had been forced to plead his own poverty. It was certainly incumbent upon him, before he went, to speak up, not only for the bishop, but for himself also. "Mr Crawley," he said, "hitherto I have listened to you patiently."

"Nay," said Mr Crawley, smiling, "you have indeed been patient, and I thank you; but my words have been written, not spoken."

"You have told me that you intend to disobey the bishop's inhibition."

"I have told the bishop so certainly."

"May I ask you now to listen to me for a few minutes?"

Mr Crawley, still smiling, still having in his eyes the unwonted triumph which had lighted them up, paused a moment, and then answered him. "Reverend sir, you must excuse me if I say no—not on this subject."

"You will not let me speak?"

"No; not on this matter, which is very private to me. What should you think if I went into your house and inquired of you as to those things which were particularly near to you?"

"But the bishop sent me."

"Though ten bishops had sent me—a council of archbishops if you will!" Mr Thumble started back, appalled at the energy of the words used to him. "Shall a man have nothing of his own—no sorrow in his heart, no care in his family, no thought in his breast so private and special to him, but that, if he happen to be a clergyman, the bishop may touch it with his thumb?"

"I am not the bishop's thumb," said Mr Thumble, drawing himself up.

"I intended not to hint anything personally objectionable to yourself. I will regard you as one of the angels of the church." Mr Thumble, when he heard this, began to be sure that Mr Crawley was mad; he knew of no angels that could ride about the Barsetshire lanes on grey ponies. "And as such I will respect you; but I cannot discuss with you the matter of the bishop's message."

"Oh, very well. I will tell his lordship."

"I will pray you to do so."

"And his lordship, should he so decide, will arm me with such power on my next coming as will enable me to carry out his lordship's wishes."

"His lordship will abide by the law, as will you also." In speaking these last words he stood with the door in his hand, and Mr Thumble, not knowing how to increase or even to maintain his firmness, thought it best to pass out, and mount his grey pony and ride away.

"The poor man thought that you were laughing at him when you called him an angel of the church," said Mrs Crawley, coming up to him and smiling on him.

"Had I told him he was simply a messenger, he would have taken it worse—poor fool! When they have rid themselves of me they may put him here, in my church; but not yet—not yet. Where is Jane? Tell her that I am ready to commence the Seven against Thebes with her." Then Jane was immediately sent for out of the school, and the Seven against Thebes was commenced with great energy. Often during the next hour and a half Mrs Crawley from the kitchen would hear him reading out, or rather saying by rote, with sonorous, rolling voice, great passages from some chorus, and she was very thankful to the bishop who had sent over to them a message and a messenger which had been so salutary in their effect upon her husband. "In truth an angel of the church," she said to herself as she chopped up the onions for the mutton-broth; and ever afterwards she regarded Mr Thumble as an "angel".

L. C.

Prophets without Honour

No man reverences a clergyman, as a clergyman, so slightly as a brother clergyman.

L. C.

Realism

"Peace on earth and good-will among men, are like heaven, promises for the future."

B. T.

Josiah Crawley at the Palace

Who inquires why it is that a little greased flour rubbed in among the hair on a footman's head—just one dab here and another there—gives such a tone of high life to the family? And seeing that the thing is so easily done, why do not more people attempt it? The tax on hair-powder is but thirteen shillings a year. It may, indeed, be that the slightest dab in the world justifies the wearer in demanding hot meat three times a day, and wine at any rate on Sundays. I think, however, that a bishop's wife may enjoy the privilege without such heavy attendant expense; otherwise the man who opened the bishop's door to Mr Crawley would hardly have been so ornamented.

The man asked for a card. "My name is Mr Crawley," said our friend. "The bishop has desired me to come to him at this hour. Will you be pleased to tell him that I am here." The man again asked for a card. "I am not bound to carry with me my name printed on a ticket," said Mr Crawley. "If you cannot remember it, give me pen and paper, and I will write it." The servant, somewhat awed by the stranger's manner, brought the pen and paper, and Mr Crawley wrote his name:

"The Rev. Josiah Crawley, M.A.,
Perpetual Curate of Hogglestock."

He was then ushered into a waiting-room, but, to his disappointment, was not kept there waiting long. Within three minutes he was ushered into the bishop's study, and into the presence of the two great luminaries of the diocese. He was at first somewhat disconcerted by finding Mrs Proudie in the room. In the imaginary conversation with the bishop which he had been preparing on the road, he had conceived that the bishop would be attended by a chaplain, and he had suited his words to the joint discomfiture of the bishop and of the lower clergyman—but now the line of his battle must be altered. This was no doubt an injury, but he trusted to his courage and readiness to enable him to surmount it. He had left his hat behind him in the waiting-room, but he kept his old short cloak still upon his shoulders; and when he entered the bishop's room his hands and arms were hid beneath it. There was something lowly in this constrained gait. It showed at least that he had no idea of being asked to shake hands with the august persons he might meet. And his head was somewhat bowed, though his great, bald, broad forehead showed itself so prominent, that neither the bishop nor Mrs Proudie could drop it from their sight during the whole interview. He was a man who when seen could hardly be forgotten. The deep angry remonstrant eyes, the shaggy eyebrows, telling tales of frequent anger—of anger frequent but generally silent—the repressed indignation of the habitual frown, the long nose and large powerful mouth, the deep furrows on the cheek, and the general look of thought and suffering, all combined to make the appearance of the man remarkable, and to describe to the beholders at once his true character. No one ever on seeing Mr Crawley took him to be a happy man, or a weak man, or an ignorant man, or a wise man.

"You are very punctual, Mr Crawley," said the bishop. Mr Crawley simply bowed his head, still keeping his hands beneath his cloak. "Will you not take a chair nearer to the fire?" Mr Crawley had not seated himself, but had placed himself in front of a chair at the extreme end of the room—resolved that he would not use it unless he were duly asked.

"Thank you, my lord," he said. "I am warm with walking, and, if you please, will avoid the fire."

"You have not walked, Mr Crawley?"

"Yes, my lord. I have been walking."

"Not from Hogglestock!"

Now this was a matter which Mr Crawley certainly did not mean to discuss with the bishop. It might be well for the bishop to demand his presence in the palace, but it could be no part of the bishop's duty to inquire how he got there. "That, my lord, is a matter of no moment," said he. "I am glad at any rate that I have been enabled to obey your lordship's order in coming hither on this morning."

Hitherto Mrs Proudie had not said a word. She stood back in the room, near the fire—more backward a good deal than she was accustomed to be when clergymen made their ordinary visits. On such occasions she would come forward and shake hands with them graciously—graciously even, if proudly; but she had felt that she must do nothing of that kind now; there must be no shaking hands with a man who had stolen a cheque for twenty pounds! It might probably be necessary to keep Mr Crawley at a distance, and therefore she had remained in the background. But Mr Crawley seemed to be disposed to keep himself in the background, and therefore she could speak. "I hope your wife and children are well, Mr Crawley," she said.

"Thank you, madam, my children are well, and Mrs Crawley suffers no special ailment at present."

"That is much to be thankful for, Mr Crawley." Whether he were or were not thankful for such mercies as these was no business of the bishop or the bishop's wife. That was between him and his God. So he would not even bow to this civility, but sat with his head erect, and with a great frown on his heavy brow.

Then the bishop rose from his chair to speak, intending to take up a position on the rug. But as he did so Mr Crawley, who had seated himself on the intimation that he was expected to sit down, rose also, and the bishop found that he would thus lose his expected vantage. "Will you not be seated, Mr Crawley?" said the bishop. Mr Crawley smiled, but stood his ground. Then the bishop returned to his armchair, and Mr Crawley also sat down again. "Mr Crawley," began the bishop, "this matter which came the other day before the magistrates at Silverbridge has been a most unfortunate affair. It has given me, I can assure you, the most sincere pain."

Mr Crawley had made up his mind how far the bishop should be allowed to go without a rebuke. He had told himself that it would only be natural, and would not be unbecoming, that the bishop should allude to the meeting of the magistrates and to the alleged theft, and that therefore such allusion should be endured with patient humility. And, moreover, the more rope he gave the bishop, the more likely the bishop would be to entangle himself. It certainly was Mr Crawley's wish that the bishop should entangle himself. He, therefore, replied very meekly, "It has been most unfortunate, my lord."

"I have felt for Mrs Crawley very deeply," said Mrs Proudie. Mr Crawley had now made up his mind that as long as it was possible he would ignore the presence of Mrs Proudie altogether; and, therefore, he made no sign that he had heard the latter remark.

"It has been most unfortunate," continued the bishop. "I have never before had a clergyman in my diocese placed in so distressing a position."

"That is a matter of opinion, my lord," said Mr Crawley, who at that moment thought of a crisis which had come in the life of another clergyman in the diocese of Barchester, with the circumstances of which he had by chance been made acquainted.

"Exactly," said the bishop. "And I am expressing my opinion." Mr Crawley, who understood fighting, did not think that the time had yet come for striking a blow, so he simply bowed again. "A most unfortunate position, Mr Crawley," continued the bishop. "Far be it from me to express an opinion upon the matter, which will have to come before a jury of your countrymen. It is enough for me to know that the magistrates assembled at Silverbridge, gentlemen to whom no doubt you must be known, as most of them live in your neighbourhood, have heard evidence upon the subject ——"

"Most convincing evidence," said Mrs Proudie, interrupting her husband. Mr Crawley's black brow became a little blacker as he heard the word, but still he ignored the woman. He not only did not speak, but did not turn his eye upon her.

"They have heard the evidence on the subject," continued the bishop, "and they have thought it proper to refer the decision as to your innocence or your guilt to a jury of your countrymen."

"And they were right," said Mr Crawley.

"Very possibly. I don't deny it. Probably," said the bishop, whose eloquence was somewhat disturbed by Mr Crawley's ready acquiescence.

"Of course they were right," said Mrs Proudie.

"At any rate it is so," said the bishop. "You are in the position of a man amenable to the criminal laws of the land."

"There are no criminal laws, my lord," said Mr Crawley; "but to such laws as there are we are all amenable—your lordship and I alike."

"But you are so in a very particular way. I do not wish to remind you what might be your condition now, but for the interposition of private friends."

"I should be in the condition of a man not guilty before the law—guiltless, as far as the law goes—but kept in durance, not for faults of his own, but because otherwise, by reason of laches in the police, his presence at the assizes might not be ensured. In such a position a man's reputation is made to hang for awhile on the trust which some friends or neighbours may have in it. I do not say that the test is a good one."

"You would have been put in prison, Mr Crawley, because the magistrates were of opinion that you had taken Mr Soames' cheque," said Mrs Proudie. On this occasion he did look at her. He turned one glance upon her from under his eyebrows, but he did not speak.

"With all that I have nothing to do," said the bishop.

"Nothing whatever, my lord," said Mr Crawley.

"But, bishop, I think that you have," said Mrs Proudie. "The judgment formed by the magistrates as to the conduct of one of your clergymen makes it imperative upon you to act in the matter."

"Yes, my dear, yes; I am coming to that. What Mrs Proudie says is perfectly true. I have been constrained most unwillingly to take action in this matter. It is undoubtedly the fact that you must at the next assizes surrender yourself at the court-house yonder, to be tried for this offence against the laws."

"That is true. If I be alive, my lord, and have strength sufficient, I shall be there."

"You must be there," said Mrs Proudie. "The police will look to that, Mr Crawley." She was becoming very angry in that the man would not answer her a word. On this occasion again he did not even look at her.

"Yes; you will be there," said the bishop. "Now that is, to say the least of it, an unseemly position for a beneficed clergyman."

"You said before, my lord, that it was an unfortunate position, and the word, methinks, was better chosen."

"It is very unseemly, very unseemly indeed," said Mrs Proudie; "nothing could possibly be more unseemly. The bishop might very properly have used a much stronger word."

"Under these circumstances," continued the bishop, "looking to the welfare of your parish, to the welfare of the diocese, and allow me to say, Mr Crawley, to the welfare of yourself also——"

"And especially to the souls of the people," said Mrs Proudie.

The bishop shook his head. It is hard to be impressively eloquent when one is interrupted at every best turned period, even by a supporting voice. "Yes—and looking of course to the religious interests of your people, Mr Crawley, I came to the conclusion that it would be expedient that you should cease your ministrations for awhile." The bishop paused, and Mr Crawley bowed his head. "I, therefore, sent over to you a gentleman with whom I am well acquainted, Mr Thumble, with a letter from myself, in which I endeavoured to impress upon you, without the use of any severe language, what my convictions were."

"Severe words are often the best mercy," said Mrs Proudie. Mr Crawley had raised his hand, with his finger out, preparatory to answering the bishop. But as Mrs Proudie had spoken he dropped his finger and was silent.

"Mr Thumble brought me back your written reply," continued the bishop, "by which I was grieved to find that you were not willing to submit yourself to my counsel in the matter."

"I was most unwilling, my lord. Submission to authority is at times a duty—and at times opposition to authority is a duty also."

"Opposition to a just authority cannot be a duty, Mr Crawley."

"Opposition to usurped authority is an imperative duty," said Mr Crawley.

"And who is to be the judge?" demanded Mrs Proudie. Then there was silence for a while; when, as Mr Crawley made no reply, the lady repeated her question. "Will you be pleased to answer my question, sir? Who, in such a case, is to be the judge?" But Mr Crawley did not please to answer her question. "The man is obstinate," said Mrs Proudie.

"I had better proceed," said the bishop. "Mr Thumble brought me back your reply, which grieved me greatly."

"It was contumacious and indecent," said Mrs Proudie.

The bishop again shook his head and looked so unutterably miserable that a smile came across Mr Crawley's face. After all, others beside himself had their troubles and trials. Mrs Proudie saw and understood the smile, and became more angry than ever. She drew her chair close to the table, and began to fidget with her fingers among the papers. She had never before encountered a clergyman so contumacious, so indecent, so unreverend—so upsetting. She had had to do with men difficult to manage—the archdeacon for instance; but the archdeacon had never been so impertinent to her as this man. She had quarrelled once openly with a chaplain of her husband's, a clergyman whom she herself had introduced to her husband, and who had treated her very badly—but not so badly, not with such unscrupulous violence, as she was now encountering from this ill-clothed beggarly man, this perpetual curate, with his dirty broken boots, this already half-convicted thief! Such was her idea of Mr Crawley's conduct to her, while she was fingering the papers—simply because Mr Crawley would not speak to her.

"I forget where I was," said the bishop. "Oh. Mr Thumble came back, and I received your letter—of course I received it. And I was surprised to learn from that, that in spite of what had occurred at

Silverbridge, you were still anxious to continue the usual Sunday ministrations in your church."

"I was determined that I would do my duty at Hogglestock, as long as I might be left there to do it," said Mr Crawley.

"Duty!" said Mrs Proudie.

"Just a moment, my dear," said the bishop. "When Sunday came, I had no alternative but to send Mr Thumble over again to Hogglestock. It occurred to us—to me and Mrs Proudie——"

"I will tell Mr Crawley just now what has occurred to me," said Mrs Proudie.

"Yes—just so. And I am sure that he will take it in good part. It occurred to me, Mr Crawley, that your first letter might have been written in haste."

"It was written in haste, my lord; your messenger was waiting."

"Yes; just so. Well; so I sent him again, hoping that he might be accepted as a messenger of peace. It was a most disagreeable mission for any gentleman, Mr Crawley."

"Most disagreeable, my lord."

"And you refused him permission to obey the instructions which I had given him! You would not let him read from your desk, or preach from your pulpit."

"Had I been Mr Thumble," said Mrs Proudie, "I would have read from that desk and I would have preached from that pulpit."

Mr Crawley waited a moment, thinking that the bishop might perhaps speak again; but as he did not, but sat expectant as though he had finished his discourse, and now expected a reply, Mr Crawley got up from his seat and drew near to the table. "My lord," he began, "it has all been just as you have said. I did answer your first letter in haste."

"The more shame for you," said Mrs Proudie.

"And therefore, for aught I know, my letter to your lordship may be so worded as to need some apology."

"Of course it needs an apology," said Mrs Proudie.

"But for the matter of it, my lord, no apology can be made, nor is any needed. I did refuse to your messenger permission to perform the services of my church, and if you send twenty more, I shall refuse them all—till the time may come when it will be your lordship's duty, in accordance with the laws of the Church—as borne out and backed by the laws of the land, to provide during my constrained absence for the spiritual wants of those poor people at Hogglestock."

"Poor people, indeed," said Mrs Proudie. "Poor wretches!"

"And, my lord, it may well be, that it shall soon be your lordship's duty to take due and legal steps for depriving me of my benefice at Hogglestock—nay, probably, for silencing me altogether as to the exercise of my sacred profession!"

"Of course it will, sir. Your gown will be taken from you," said Mrs Proudie. The bishop was looking with all his eyes up at the great forehead and great eyebrows of the man, and was so fascinated by the power that was exercised over him by the other man's strength that he hardly now noticed his wife.

"It may well be so," continued Mr Crawley. "The circumstances are strong against me; and, though your lordship has altogether misunderstood the nature of the duty performed by the magistrates in sending my case for trial—although, as it seems to me, you have come to conclusions in this matter in ignorance of the very theory of our laws——"

"Sir!" said Mrs Proudie.

"Yet I can foresee the probability that a jury may discover me to have been guilty of theft."

"Of course the jury will do so," said Mrs Proudie.

"Should such verdict be given, then, my lord, your interference will be legal, proper, and necessary. And you will find that, even if it be within my power to oppose obstacles to your lordship's authority, I will oppose no such obstacle. There is, I believe, no appeal in criminal cases."

"None at all," said Mrs Proudie. "There is no appeal against your bishop. You should have learned that before."

"But till that time shall come, my lord, I shall hold my own at Hogglestock as you hold your own here at Barchester. Nor have you more power to turn me out of my pulpit by your mere voice, than I have to turn you out of your throne by mine. If you doubt me, my lord, your lordship's ecclesiastical court is open to you. Try it there."

"You defy us, then?" said Mrs Proudie.

"My lord, I grant your authority as bishop to be great, but even a bishop can only act as the law allows him."

"God forbid that I should do more," said the bishop.

"Sir, you will find that your wicked threats will fall back upon your own head," said Mrs Proudie.

"Peace, woman," Mr Crawley said, addressing her at last. The bishop jumped out of his chair at hearing the wife of his bosom called a woman. But he jumped rather in admiration than in anger.

He had already begun to perceive that Mr Crawley was a man who had better be left to take care of the souls at Hogglestock, at any rate till the trial should come on.

"Woman!" said Mrs Proudie, rising to her feet as though she really intended some personal encounter.

"Madam," said Mr Crawley, "you should not interfere in these matters. You simply debase your husband's high office. The distaff were more fitting for you. My lord, good morning." And before either of them could speak again, he was out of the room, and through the hall, and beyond the gate, and standing beneath the towers of the cathedral. Yes, he had, he thought, in truth crushed the bishop. He had succeeded in crumpling the bishop up within the clutch of his fist.

He started in a spirit of triumph to walk back on his road towards Hogglestock. He did not think of the long distance before him for the first hour of his journey. He had had his victory, and the remembrance of that braced his nerves and gave elasticity to his sinews, and he went stalking along the road with rapid strides, muttering to himself from time to time as he went along some word about Mrs Proudie and her distaff. Mr Thumble would not, he thought, come to him again—not, at any rate, till the assizes were drawing near. And he had resolved what he would do then. When the day of his trial was near, he would himself write to the bishop, and beg that provision might be made for his church, in the event of the verdict going against him. His friend, Dean Arabin, was to be home before that time, and the idea had occurred to him of asking the dean to see to this; but now the other would be the more independent course and the better. And there was a matter as to which he was not altogether well pleased with the dean, although he was so conscious of his own peculiarities as to know that he could hardly trust himself for a judgment. But, at any rate, he would apply to the bishop—to the bishop whom he had just left prostrate in his palace—when the time of his trial should be close at hand.

Full of such thoughts as these he went along almost gaily, nor felt the fatigue of the road till he had covered the first five miles out of Barchester. It was nearly four o'clock, and the thick gloom of the winter evening was making itself felt. And then he began to be fatigued. He had not as yet eaten since he had left his home in the morning, and he now pulled a crust out of his pocket and leaned against a gate as he crunched it. There were still ten miles before him, and he knew that such an addition to the work he had already done would task him very severely. Farmer Mangle had told him that he would not leave Framley Mill till five, and he had got time to reach Framley Mill by that time. But he had said that he would not return to Framley Mill, and he remembered his suspicion that his wife and farmer Mangle between them had cozened him. No; he would persevere and walk—walk, though he should drop upon the road. He was now nearer fifty than forty years of age, and hardships as well as time had told upon him. He knew that though his strength was good for the commencement of a hard day's work, it would not hold out for him as it used to do. He knew that the last four miles in the dark night would be very sad with him. But still he persevered, endeavouring, as he went, to cherish himself with the remembrance of his triumph.

He passed the turning going down to Framley with courage, but when he came to the further turning, by which the cart would return from Framley to the Hogglestock road, he looked wistfully down the road for farmer Mangle. But farmer Mangle was still at the mill, waiting in expectation that Mr Crawley might come to him. But the poor traveller paused here barely for a minute, and then went on, stumbling through the mud, striking his ill-covered feet against the rough stones in the dark, sweating in his weakness, almost tottering at times, and calculating whether his remaining strength would serve to carry him home. He had almost forgotten the bishop and his wife before at last he grasped the wicket gate leading to his own door.

"Oh, mamma, here is papa!"

"But where is the cart? I did not hear the wheels," said Mrs Crawley.

"Oh, mamma, I think papa is ill." Then the wife took her drooping husband by both arms and strove to look him in the face. "He has walked all the way, and he is ill," said Jane.

"No, my dear, I am very tired, but not ill. Let me sit down, and give me some bread and tea, and I shall recover myself." Then Mrs

Crawley, from some secret hoard, got him a small modicum of spirits, and gave him meat and tea, and he was docile; and, obeying her behests, allowed himself to be taken to his bed.

"I do not think the bishop will send for me again," he said, as she tucked the clothes around him.

L. C.

THE BRITISH BULL-DOG

"It's dogged as does it. It ain't thinking about it."—*Giles Hoggett*

L. C.

Mrs Proudie goes too far

At breakfast on the following morning there was no one present but the bishop, Mrs Proudie, and Dr Tempest. Very little was said at the meal. Mr Crawley's name was not mentioned, but there seemed to be a general feeling among them that there was a task hanging over them which prevented any general conversation. The eggs were eaten and the coffee was drunk, but the eggs and the coffee disappeared almost in silence. When these ceremonies had been altogether completed, and it was clearly necessary that something further should be done, the bishop spoke: "Dr Tempest," he said, "perhaps you will join me in my study at eleven. We can then say a few words to each other about the unfortunate matter on which I shall have to trouble you." Dr Tempest said he would be punctual to his appointment, and then the bishop withdrew, muttering something as to the necessity of looking at his letters. Dr Tempest took a newspaper in his hand, which had been brought in by a servant, and Mrs Proudie did not allow him to read it. "Dr Tempest," she said, "this is a matter of most vital importance. I am quite sure that you feel that it is so."

"What matter, madam?" said the doctor.

"This terrible affair of Mr Crawley's. If something be not done the whole diocese will be disgraced." Then she waited for an answer, but receiving none she was obliged to continue. "Of the poor man's guilt there can, I fear, be no doubt." Then there was another pause, but still the doctor made no answer. "And if he be guilty," said Mrs Proudie, resolving that she would ask a question that must bring forth some reply, "can any experienced clergyman think that he can be fit to preach from the pulpit of a parish church? I am sure that you must agree with me, Dr Tempest? Consider the souls of the people!"

"Mrs Proudie," said he, "I think that we had better not discuss the matter."

"Not discuss it?"

"I think that we had better not do so. If I understand the bishop aright, he wishes that I should take some step in the matter."

"Of course he does."

"And therefore I must decline to make it a matter of common conversation."

"Common conversation, Dr Tempest! I should be the last person in the world to make it a matter of common conversation. I regard this as by no means a common conversation. God forbid that it should be a common conversation. I am speaking now very seriously with reference to the interests of the Church, which I think will be endangered by having among her active servants a man who has been guilty of so base a crime as theft. Think of it, Dr Tempest. Theft! Stealing money! Appropriating to his own use a cheque for twenty pounds which did not belong to him! And then telling such terrible falsehoods about it! Can anything be worse, anything more scandalous, anything more dangerous? Indeed, Dr Tempest, I do not regard this as any common conversation." The whole of this speech was not made at once, fluently, or without a break. From stop to stop Mrs Proudie paused, waiting for her companion's words; but as he would not speak she was obliged to continue. "I am sure that you cannot but agree with me, Dr Tempest?" she said.

"I am quite sure that I shall not discuss it with you," said the doctor, very brusquely.

"And why not? Are you not here to discuss it?"

"Not with you, Mrs Proudie. You must excuse me for saying so, but I am not here to discuss any such matter with you. Were I to do so, I should be guilty of a very great impropriety."

"All these things are in common between me and the bishop," said Mrs Proudie, with an air that was intended to be dignified, but which nevertheless displayed her rising anger.

"As to that I know nothing, but they cannot be in common between you and me. It grieves me much that I should have to speak to you in such a strain, but my duty allows me no alternative. I think, if you will permit me, I will take a turn round the garden before I keep my appointment with his lordship." And so saying he escaped from the lady without hearing her further remonstrance.

It still wanted nearly an hour to the time named by the bishop, and Dr Tempest used it in preparing for his withdrawal from the palace as soon as his interview with the bishop should be over. After what had passed he thought that he would be justified in taking his departure without bidding adieu formally to Mrs Proudie. He would say a word or two, explaining his haste, to the bishop; and then, if he could get out of the house at once, it might be that he would never see Mrs Proudie again. He was rather proud of his success in their late battle, but he felt that, having been so completely victorious, it would be foolish in him to risk his laurels in the chance of another encounter. He would say not a word of what had happened to the bishop, and he thought it probable that neither would Mrs Proudie speak of it—at any rate till after he was gone. Generals who are beaten out of the field are not quick to talk of their own repulses. He, indeed, had not beaten Mrs Proudie out of the field. He had, in fact, himself run away. But he had left his foe silenced; and with such a foe, and in such a contest, that was everything. He put up his port-manteau, therefore, and prepared for his final retreat. Then he rang his bell and desired the servant to show him to the bishop's study. The servant did so, and when he entered the room the first thing he saw was Mrs Proudie sitting in an arm-chair near the window. The bishop was also in the room, sitting with his arms upon the writing-table, and his head upon his hands. It was very evident that Mrs Proudie did not consider herself to have been beaten, and that she was prepared to fight another battle. "Will you sit down, Dr Tempest?" she said, motioning him with her hand to a chair opposite to that occupied by the bishop. Dr Tempest sat down. He felt that at the moment he had nothing else to do, and that he must restrain any remonstrance that he might make till Mr Crawley's name should be mentioned. He was almost lost in admiration of the woman. He had left her, as he thought, utterly vanquished and prostrated by his determined but uncourteous usage of her; and here she was, present again upon the field of battle as though she had never been even wounded. He could see that there had been words between her and the bishop, and that she had carried a point on which the bishop had been very anxious to have his own way. He could perceive at once that the bishop had begged her to absent herself and was greatly chagrined that he should not have prevailed with her. There she was—and as Dr Tempest was resolved that he would neither give advice nor receive instructions respecting Mr Crawley in her pres-ence, he could only draw upon his courage and his strategy for the coming warfare. For a few moments no one said a word. The bishop felt that if Dr Tempest would only begin, the work on hand might be got through, even in his wife's presence. Mrs Proudie was aware that her husband should begin. If he would do so, and if Dr Tempest would listen and then reply, she might gradually make her way into the conversation; and if her words were once accepted then she could say all that she desired to say; then she could play her part and become somebody in the episcopal work. When once she should have been allowed liberty of speech, the enemy would be powerless to stop her. But all this Dr Tempest understood quite as well as she understood it, and had they waited all night he would not have been the first to mention Mr Crawley's name.

The bishop sighed aloud. The sigh might be taken as expressing grief over the sin of the erring brother whose conduct they were then to discuss, and was not amiss. But when the sigh with its attendant murmurs had passed away it was necessary that some initiative step should be taken. "Dr Tempest," said the bishop, "what are we to do about this poor stiff-necked gentleman?" Still Dr Tempest did not speak. "There is no clergyman in the diocese", continued the bishop, "in whose prudence and wisdom I have more confidence than in yours. And I know, too, that you are by no means disposed to severity where severe measures are not necessary. What ought we to do? If he has been guilty, he should not surely return to his pulpit after the expiration of such punishment as the law of his country may award to him."

Dr Tempest looked at Mrs Proudie, thinking that she might perhaps say a word now; but Mrs Proudie knew her part better and was silent. Angry as she was, she contrived to hold her peace. Let the debate once begin and she would be able to creep into it, and then to lead it—and so she would hold her own. But she had met a foe as wary as herself. "My lord," said the doctor, "it will perhaps be well that you should communicate your wishes to me in writing. If it be possible for me to comply with them I will do so."

"Yes—exactly; no doubt—but I thought that perhaps we might better understand each other if we had a few words of quiet conversation upon the subject. I believe you know the steps that I have——"

But here the bishop was interrupted. Dr Tempest rose from his chair, and advancing to the table put both his hands upon it. "My lord," he said, "I feel myself compelled to say that which I would very much rather leave unsaid, were it possible. I feel the difficulty, and I may say delicacy, of my position; but I should be untrue to my conscience and to my feeling of what is right in such matters, if I were to take any part in a discussion on this matter in the presence of—a lady."

"Dr Tempest, what is your objection?" said Mrs Proudie, rising from her chair, and coming also to the table, so that from thence she might confront her opponent; and as she stood opposite to Dr Tempest she also put both her hands upon the table.

"My dear, perhaps you will leave us for a few moments," said the bishop. Poor bishop! Poor weak bishop! As the words came from his mouth he knew that they would be spoken in vain, and that, if so, it would have been better for him to have left them unspoken.

"Why should I be dismissed from your room without a reason?" said Mrs Proudie. "Cannot Dr Tempest understand that a wife may share her husband's counsels—as she must share his troubles? If he cannot, I pity him very much as to his own household."

"Dr Tempest," said the bishop, "Mrs Proudie takes the greatest possible interest in everything concerning the diocese."

"I am sure, my lord," said the doctor, "that you will see how unseemly it would be that I should interfere in any way between you and Mrs Proudie. I certainly will not do so. I can only say again that if you will communicate to me your wishes in writing, I will attend to them—if it be possible."

"You mean to be stubborn," said Mrs Proudie, whose prudence was beginning to give way under the great provocation to which her temper was being subjected.

"Yes, madam; if it is to be called stubbornness, I must be stubborn. My lord, Mrs Proudie spoke to me on this subject in the breakfast-room after you had left it, and I then ventured to explain to her that in accordance with such light as I have on the matter, I could not discuss it in her presence. I greatly grieve that I failed to make myself understood by her—as, otherwise, this unpleasantness might have been spared."

"I understood you very well, Dr Tempest, and I think you to be a most unreasonable man. Indeed, I might use a much harsher word."

"You may use any word you please, Mrs Proudie," said the doctor.

"My dear, I really think you had better leave us for a few minutes," said the bishop.

"No, my lord—no," said Mrs Proudie, turning round upon her husband. "Not so. It would be most unbecoming that I should be turned out of a room in this palace by an uncourteous word from a parish clergyman. It would be unseemly. If Dr Tempest forgets his duty, I will not forget mine. There are other clergymen in the diocese besides Dr Tempest who can undertake the very easy task of this commission. As for his having been appointed rural dean I don't know how many years ago, it is a matter of no consequence whatever. In such a preliminary inquiry any three clergymen will suffice. It need not be done by the rural dean at all."

"My dear!"

"I will not be turned out of this room by Dr Tempest—and that is enough."

"My lord," said the doctor, "you had better write to me as I proposed to you just now."

"His lordship will not write. His lordship will do nothing of the kind," said Mrs Proudie.

"My dear!" said the bishop, driven in his perplexity beyond all carefulness of reticence. "My dear, I do wish you wouldn't—I do indeed. If you would only go away!"

"I will not go away, my lord," said Mrs Proudie.

"But I will," said Dr Tempest, feeling true compassion for the unfortunate man whom he saw writhing in agony before him. "It will manifestly be for the best that I should retire. My lord, I wish you good morning. Mrs Proudie, good morning." And so he left the room.

"A most stubborn and a most ungentlemanlike man," said Mrs Proudie, as soon as the door was closed behind the retreating rural dean. "I do not think that in the whole course of my life I ever met with anyone so insubordinate and so ill-mannered. He is worse than the archdeacon." As she uttered these words she paced about the room. The bishop said nothing; and when she herself had been silent for a few minutes she turned upon him. "Bishop," she said, "I hope that you agree with me. I expect that you will agree with me in a matter that is of so much moment to my comfort, and I may say to my position generally in the diocese. Bishop, why do you not speak?"

"You have behaved in such a way that I do not know that I shall ever speak again," said the bishop.

"What is this that you say?"

"I say that I do not know how I shall ever speak again. You have disgraced me."

"Disgraced you! I disgrace you! It is you that disgrace yourself by saying such words."

"Very well. Let it be so. Perhaps you will go away now and leave me to myself. I have got a bad headache, and I can't talk any more. Oh dear, oh dear, what will he think of it!"

"And you mean to tell me that I have been wrong!"

"Yes, you have been wrong—very wrong. Why didn't you go away when I asked you? You are always being wrong. I wish I had never come to Barchester. In any other position I should not have felt it so much. As it is I do not know how I can ever show my face again."

"Not have felt what so much, Mr Proudie?" said the wife, going back in the excitement of her anger to the nomenclature of old days. "And this is to be my return for all my care in your behalf! Allow me to tell you, sir, that in any position in which you may be placed I know what is due to you, and that your dignity will never lose anything in my hands. I wish that you were as well able to take care of it yourself." Then she stalked out of the room, and left the poor man alone.

Bishop Proudie sat alone in his study throughout the whole day. Once or twice in the course of the morning his chaplain came to him on some matter of business, and was answered with a smile—the peculiar softness of which the chaplain did not fail to attribute to the right cause. For it was soon known throughout the household there had been a quarrel. Could he quite have made up his mind to do so—could he have resolved that it would be altogether better to quarrel with his wife—the bishop would have appealed to the chaplain, and have asked at any rate for sympathy. But even yet he could not bring himself to confess his misery, and to own himself to another to be the wretch that he was. Then during the long hours of the day he sat thinking of it all. How happy could he be if it were only possible for him to go away, and become even a curate in a parish, without his wife! Would there ever come to him a time of freedom? Would she ever die? He was older than she, and of course he would die first. Would it not be a fine thing if he could die at once, and thus escape from his misery?

What could he do, even supposing himself strong enough to fight the battle? He could not lock her up. He could not even very well lock her out of his room. She was his wife, and must have the run of his house. He could not altogether debar her from the society of the diocesan clergymen. He had, on this very morning, taken strong measures with her. More than once or twice he had desired her to leave the room. What was there to be done with a woman who would not obey her husband—who would not even leave him to the performance of his own work? What a blessed thing it would be if a bishop could go away from his home to his work every day like a clerk in a public office—as a stone-mason does! But there was no such escape for him. He could not go away. And how was he to meet her again on this very day?

And then for hours he thought of Dr Tempest and Mr Crawley, considering what he had better do to repair the shipwreck of the morning. At last he resolved that he would write to the doctor; and before he had again seen his wife, he did write his letter, and he sent it off. In this letter he made no direct allusion to the occurrence of the morning, but wrote as though there had not been any fixed intention of a personal discussion between them. "I think it will be better that there should be a commission," he said, "and I would suggest that you should have four other clergymen with you. Perhaps you will select two yourself out of your rural deanery; and, if you do not object, I will name as the other two Mr Thumble and Mr Quiverful, who are both resident in the city." As he wrote these two names he felt ashamed of himself, knowing that he had chosen the two men as being special friends of his wife, and feeling that he should have been brave enough to throw aside all considerations of his wife's favour—especially at this moment, in which he was putting on his armour to do battle against her. "It is not probable", he continued to say in his letter, "that you will be able to make your report until after the trial of this unfortunate gentleman shall have taken place, and a verdict shall have been given. Should he be acquitted, that, I imagine, should end the matter. There can be no reason why we should attempt to go beyond the verdict of a jury. But should he be found guilty, I think we ought to be ready with such steps as it will be becoming for us to take at the expiration of any sentence which may be pronounced. It will be, at any rate, expedient that in such case the matter should be brought before an ecclesiastical court." He knew well as he wrote this, that he was proposing something much milder than the course intended by his wife when she had instigated him to take proceedings in the matter; but he did not much regard that now. Though he had been weak enough to name certain clergy-men as assessors with the rural dean, because he thought that by doing so he would to a certain degree conciliate his wife—though he had been so far a coward, yet he was resolved that he would not sacrifice to her his own judgment and his own conscience in his manner of proceeding. He kept no copy of his letter, so that he might be unable to show her his very words when she should ask to see them. Of course he would tell her what he had done; but in telling her he would keep to himself what he had said as to the result of an acquittal in a civil court. She need not yet be told that he had promised to take such a verdict as sufficing also for an ecclesiastical acquittal. In this spirit his letter was written and sent off before he again saw his wife.

He did not meet her till they came together in the drawing-room before dinner. In explaining the whole truth as to circumstances as they existed at the palace at that moment, it must be acknowledged that Mrs Proudie herself, great as was her courage, and wide as were the resources which she possessed within herself, was somewhat appalled by the position of affairs. I fear that it may now be too late for me to excite much sympathy in the mind of any reader on behalf of Mrs Proudie. I shall never be able to make her virtues popular. But she had virtues, and their existence now made her unhappy. She did regard the dignity of her husband, and she felt at the present moment that she had almost compromised it. She did also regard the welfare of the clergymen around her, thinking of course in a general way that certain of them who agreed with her were the clergymen whose welfare should be studied, and that certain of them who disagreed with her were the clergymen whose welfare should be postponed. But now an idea made its way into her bosom that she was not perhaps doing the best for the welfare of the diocese generally. What if it should come to pass that all the clergymen of the diocese should refuse to open their mouths in her presence on ecclesiastical subjects, as Dr Tempest had done? This special day was not one on which she was well contented with herself, though by no means on that account was her anger mitigated against the offending rural dean.

During dinner she struggled to say a word or two to her husband, as though there had been no quarrel between them. With him the matter had gone so deep that he could not answer her in the same spirit. There were sundry members of the family present—daughters, and a son-in-law, and a daughter's friend who was staying with them; but even in the hope of appearing to be serene before them he could not struggle through his deep despondence. He was very silent, and to his wife's words he answered hardly anything. He was courteous and gentle with them all, but he spoke as little as was possible, and during the evening he sat alone, with his head leaning on his hand—not pretending even to read. He was aware that it was too late to make even an attempt to conceal his misery and his disgrace from his own family.

His wife came to him that night in his dressing-room in a spirit of feminine softness that was very unusual with her. "My dear," said she, "let us forget what occurred this morning. If there has been any anger we are bound as Christians to forget it." She stood over him as she spoke, and put her hand upon his shoulder almost caressingly.

"When a man's heart is broken, he cannot forget it," was his reply. She still stood by him, and still kept her hand upon him: but she could think of no other words of comfort to say. "I will go to bed," he said. "It is the best place for me." Then she left him, and he went to bed.

L. C.

ON MRS PROUDIE (I)
"That she-Beelzebub . . ."—*Archdeacon Grantly*

L. C.

ON MRS PROUDIE (II)
". . . that pestilent woman . . ."—*Rev. Josiah Crawley*

L. C.

Grace Crawley and the Archdeacon

———•———

"Grace, my dear," said Mrs Robarts, coming up into the nursery in which Miss Crawley was sitting with the children, "come out here a moment, will you?" Then Grace left the children and went out into the passage. "My dear, there is a gentleman in the drawing-room who asks to see you."

"A gentleman, Mrs Robarts! What gentleman?" But Grace, though she asked the question, conceived that the gentleman must be Henry Grantly. Her mind did not suggest to her the possibility of any other gentleman coming to see her.

"You must not be surprised, or allow yourself to be frightened."

"Oh, Mrs Robarts, who is it?"

"It is Major Grantly's father."

"The archdeacon?"

"Yes, dear; Archdeacon Grantly. He is in the drawing-room."

"Must I see him, Mrs Robarts?"

"Well, Grace—I think you must. I hardly know how you can refuse. He is an intimate friend of everybody here at Framley."

"What will he say to me?"

"Nay; that I cannot tell. I suppose you know ———"

"He has come, no doubt, to bid me have nothing to say to his son. He need not have troubled himself. But he may say what he likes. I am not a coward, and I will go to him."

"Stop a moment, Grace. Come into my room for an instant. The children have pulled your hair about." But Grace, though she followed Mrs Robarts into the bedroom, would have nothing done to her hair. She was too proud for that—and we may say, also, too little confident in any good which such resources might effect on her

245

behalf. "Never mind about that," she said. "What am I to say to him?" Mrs Robarts paused before she replied, feeling that the matter was one which required some deliberation. "Tell me what I must say to him?" said Grace, repeating her question.

"I hardly know what your own feelings are, my dear."

"Yes, you do. You do know. If I had all the world to give, I would give it all to Major Grantly."

"Tell him that, then."

"No, I will not tell him that. Never mind about my frock, Mrs Robarts. I do not care for that. I will tell him that I love his son and his granddaughter too well to injure them. I will tell him nothing else. I might as well go now." Mrs Robarts, as she looked at Grace, was astonished at the serenity of her face. And yet when her hand was on the drawing-room door Grace hesitated, looked back, and trembled. Mrs Robarts blew a kiss to her from the stairs; and then the door was opened, and the girl found herself in the presence of the archdeacon. He was standing on the rug, with his back to the fire, and his heavy ecclesiastical hat was placed on the middle of the round table. The hat caught Grace's eye at the moment of her entrance, and she felt that all the thunders of the Church were contained within it. And then the archdeacon himself was so big and so clerical, and so imposing! Her father's aspect was severe, but the severity of her father's face was essentially different from that expressed by the archdeacon. Whatever impression came from her father came from the man himself. There was no outward adornment there; there was, so to say, no wig about Mr Crawley. Now the archdeacon was not exactly adorned; but he was so thoroughly imbued with high clerical belongings and sacerdotal fitnesses as to appear as a walking, sitting, or standing impersonation of parsondom in its severest aspect.

"Miss Crawley, I believe?" said he.

"Yes, sir," said she, curtseying ever so slightly, as she stood before him at some considerable distance.

His first idea was that his son must be indeed a fool if he was going to give up Cosby Lodge and all Barsetshire, and retire to Pau, for so slight and unattractive a creature as he now saw before him. But this idea stayed with him only for a moment. As he continued to gaze at her during the interview he came to perceive that there was very much more than he had perceived at the first glance, and that his son, after all, had had eyes to see, though perhaps not a heart to understand.

"Will you not take a chair?" he said. Then Grace sat down, still at a distance from the archdeacon, and he kept his place upon the rug. He felt that there would be a difficulty in making her feel the full force of his eloquence all across the room; and yet he did not know how to bring himself nearer to her. She became suddenly very important in his eyes, and he was to some extent afraid of her. She was so slight, so meek, so young; and yet there was about her something so beautifully feminine—and, withal, so like a lady—that he felt instinctively that he could not attack her with harsh words. Had her lips been full, and her colour high, and had her eyes rolled, had she put forth against him any of that ordinary artillery with which youthful feminine batteries are charged, he would have been ready to rush to the combat. But this girl, about whom his son had gone mad, sat there as passively as though she were conscious of the possession of no artillery. There was not a single gun fired from beneath her eyelids. He knew not why, but he respected his son now more than he had respected him for the last two months—more, perhaps, than he had ever respected him before. He was as eager as ever against the marriage—but in thinking of his son in what he said and did after these few first moments of the interview, he ceased to think of him with contempt. The creature before him was a woman who grew in his opinion till he began to feel that she was in truth fit to be the wife of his son—if only she were not a pauper, and the daughter of a mad curate, and, alas! too probably, of a thief. Though his feeling towards the girl was changed, his duty to himself, his family, and his son, was the same as ever, and therefore he began his task.

"Perhaps you had not expected to see me?" he said.

"No, indeed, sir."

"Nor had I intended when I came over here to call on my old friend, Lady Lufton, to come up to this house. But as I knew that you were here, Miss Crawley, I thought that upon the whole it would be better that I should see you." Then he paused as though he expected that Grace would say something; but Grace had nothing to say. "Of course you must understand, Miss Crawley, that I should not venture to speak to you on this subject unless I myself were very closely interested in it." He had not yet said what was the subject, and it was not probable that Grace should give him any assistance by affecting to understand this without direct explanation from him. She sat quite motionless, and did not even aid him by showing by her altered colour that she understood his purpose. "My son has told me", said he, "that he has professed an attachment for you, Miss Crawley."

Then there was another pause, and Grace felt that she was compelled to say something. "Major Grantly has been very good to me," she said, and then she hated herself for having uttered words which were so tame and unwomanly in their spirit. Of course her lover's father would despise her for having so spoken. After all it did not much signify. If he would only despise her and go away, it would perhaps be for the best.

"I do not know about being good," said the archdeacon. "I think he is good. I think he means to be good."

"I am sure he is good," said Grace, warmly.

"You know he has a daughter, Miss Crawley?"

"Oh, yes; I know Edith well."

"Of course his first duty is to her. Is it not? And he owes much to his family. Do you not feel that?"

"Of course I feel it, sir." The poor girl had always heard Dr Grantly spoken of as the archdeacon, but she did not in the least know what she ought to call him.

"Now, Miss Crawley, pray listen to me; I will speak to you very openly. I must speak to you openly, because it is my duty on my son's behalf—but I will endeavour to speak to you kindly also. Of yourself I have heard nothing but what is favourable, and there is no reason as yet why I should not respect and esteem you." Grace told herself that she would do nothing which ought to forfeit his respect and esteem, but that she did not care two straws whether his respect and esteem were bestowed on her or not. She was striving after something very different from that. "If my son were to marry you, he would greatly injure himself, and would very greatly injure his child." Again he paused. He had told her to listen, and she was resolved that she would listen—unless he should say something which might make a word from her necessary at the moment. "I do not know whether there does at present exist any engagement between you?"

"There is no engagement, sir."

"I am glad of that—very glad of it. I do not know whether you are aware that my son is dependent upon me for the greater part of his income. It is so, and as I am so circumstanced with my son, of course I feel the closest possible concern in his future prospects." The archdeacon did not know how to explain clearly why the fact of his making a son an annual allowance should give him a warmer interest in his son's affairs than he might have had had the major been altogether independent of him; but he trusted that Grace would understand this by her own natural lights. "Now, Miss Crawley, of course I cannot wish to say a word that shall hurt your feelings. But there are reasons——"

"I know," said she, interrupting him. "Papa is accused of stealing money. He did not steal it, but people think he did. And then we are so very poor."

"You do understand me then—and I feel grateful, I do indeed."

"I don't think our being poor ought to signify a bit," said Grace. "Papa is a gentleman and a clergyman, and mamma is a lady."

"But, my dear——"

"I know I ought not to be your son's wife as long as people think that papa stole the money. If he had stolen it, I ought never to be Major Grantly's wife—or anybody's wife. I know that very well. And as for Edith—I would sooner die than do anything that would be bad to her."

The archdeacon had now left the rug, and advanced till he was almost close to the chair on which Grace was sitting. "My dear," he said, "what you say does you very much honour—very much honour indeed." Now that he was close to her, he could look into her eyes, and he could see the exact form of her features, and could under-stand—could not help understanding—the character of her coun-tenance. It was a noble face, having in it nothing that was poor, nothing that was mean, nothing that was shapeless. It was a face that promised infinite beauty, with a promise that was on the very verge of fulfilment. There was a play about her mouth as she spoke, and a curl in her nostril as the eager words came from her, which almost made the selfish father give way. Why had they not told him that she was such a one as this? Why had not Henry himself spoken of the speciality of her beauty? No man in England knew better than the archdeacon the difference between beauty of one kind and beauty of another kind in a woman's face—the one beauty, which comes from health and youth and animal spirits, and which belongs to the miller's daughter, and the other beauty, which shows itself in fine lines and a noble spirit—the beauty which comes from breeding. "What you say does you very much honour indeed," said the archdeacon.

"I should not mind at all about being poor," said Grace.

"No; no; no," said the archdeacon.

"Poor as we are—and no clergyman, I think, ever was so poor—I should have done as your son asked me at once, if it had been only that—because I love him."

"If you love him you will not wish to injure him."

"I will not injure him. Sir, there is my promise." And now as she spoke she rose from her chair, and standing close to the archdeacon, laid her hand very lightly on the sleeve of his coat. "There is my promise. As long as people say that papa stole the money, I will never marry your son. There."

The archdeacon was still looking down at her, and feeling the slight touch of her fingers, raised his arm a little as though to wel-come the pressure. He looked into her eyes, which were turned eagerly towards his, and when doing so was quite sure that the promise would be kept. It would have been sacrilege—he felt that it would have been sacrilege—to doubt such a promise. He almost relented. His soft heart, which was never very well under his own control, gave way so far that he was nearly moved to tell her that, on his son's behalf, he acquitted her of the promise. What could any man's son do better than have such a woman for his wife? It would have been of no avail had he made her such offer. The pledge she had given had not been wrung from her by his influence, nor could his influence have availed aught with her towards the alteration of her purpose. It was not the archdeacon who had taught her that it would not be her duty to take disgrace into the house of the man she loved. As he looked down upon her face two tears formed themselves in his eyes, and gradually trickled down his old nose. "My dear," he said, "if this cloud passes away from you, you shall come to us and be my daughter." And thus he also pledged himself. There was a dash of generosity about the man, in spite of his selfishness, which always made him desirous of giving largely to those who gave largely to him. He would fain that his gifts should be the bigger, if it were possible. He longed at this moment to tell her that the dirty cheque should go for nothing. He would have done it, I think, but that it was impossible for him so to speak in her presence of that which moved her so greatly.

He had contrived that her hand should fall from his arm into his grasp, and now for a moment he held it. "You are a good girl," he said—"a dear, dear, good girl. When this cloud has passed away, you shall come to us and be our daughter."

"But it will never pass away," said Grace.

"Let us hope that it may. Let us hope that it may." Then he stooped over her and kissed her, and leaving the room, got out into the hall and thence into the garden, and so away, without saying a word of adieu to Mrs Robarts.

As he walked across the court, whither he was obliged to go, because of his chaise, he was lost in surprise at what had occurred. He had gone to the parsonage, hating the girl, and despising his son. Now, as he retraced his steps, his feelings were altogether changed. He admired the girl—and as for his son, even his anger was for the moment altogether gone. He would write to his son at once and implore him to stop the sale. He would tell his son all that had occurred, or rather would make Mrs Grantly do so. In respect to his son he was quite safe. He thought at that moment that he was safe. There would be no use in hurling further threats at him. If Crawley were found guilty of stealing the money, there was the girl's promise. If he were acquitted, there was his own pledge. He remembered perfectly well that the girl had said more than this—that she had not confined her assurance to the verdict of a jury, that she had protested that she would not accept Major Grantly's hand as long as people thought that her father had stolen the cheque; but the archdeacon felt that it would be ignoble to hold her closely to her words. The event, according to his ideas of the compact, was to depend upon the verdict of the jury. If the jury should find Mr Crawley not guilty, all objection on his part to the marriage was to be withdrawn. And he would keep his word! In such case it should be withdrawn.

When he came to the rags of the auctioneer's bill, which he had before torn down with his umbrella, he stopped a moment to consider how he would act at once. In the first place he would tell his son that his threats were withdrawn, and would ask him to remain at Cosby Lodge. He would write the letter as he passed through Barchester, on his way home, so that his son might receive it on the following morning; and he would refer the major to his mother for a full explanation of the circumstances. Those odious bills must be removed from every barn-door and wall in the county. At the present moment his anger against his son was chiefly directed against his ill-judged haste in having put up those ill-omened posters. Then he paused to consider what must be his wish as to the verdict of the jury. He had pledged himself to abide by the verdict, and he could not but have a wish on the subject. Could he desire in his heart that Mr Crawley should be found guilty? He stood still for a moment thinking of this, and then he walked on, shaking his head. If it might be possible he would have no wish on the subject whatsoever.

"Well!" said Lady Lufton, stopping him in the passage—"have you seen her?"

"Yes; I have seen her."

"Well?"

"She is a good girl—a very good girl. I am in a great hurry, and hardly know how to tell you more now."

"You say that she is a good girl?"

"I say that she is a very good girl. An angel could not have behaved better. I will tell you all some day, Lady Lufton, but I can hardly tell you now."

When the archdeacon was gone old Lady Lufton confided to young Lady Lufton her very strong opinion that many months would not be gone by before Grace Crawley would be the mistress of Cosby Lodge. "It will be great promotion," said the old lady, with a little toss of her head.

When Grace was interrogated afterwards by Mrs Robarts as to what had passed between her and the archdeacon, she had very little to say as to the interview. "No, he did not scold me," she replied to an inquiry from her friend. "But he spoke about your engagement?" said Mrs Robarts. "There is no engagement," said Grace. "But I supposed you acknowledged, my dear, that a future engagement is quite possible?" "I told him, Mrs Robarts," Grace answered, after hesitating for a moment, "that I would never marry his son as long as papa was suspected by anyone in the world of being a thief. And I will keep my word." But she said nothing to Mrs Robarts of the pledge which the archdeacon had made to her.

L. C.

THE DANGEROUS AGE

... for real true love, love at first sight, love to devotion, love that robs a man of his sleep ... we believe the best age is from forty-five to seventy; up to that men are generally given to mere flirting.

B. T.

INSINCERITY

It is one thing for a young lady to make prudent, heart-breaking suggestions, but quite another to have them accepted.

D. T.

R.I.P.

Things were very gloomy at the palace. It has been already said that for many days after Dr Tempest's visit to Barchester, the intercourse between the bishop and Mrs Proudie had not been of a pleasant nature. He had become so silent, so sullen, and so solitary in his ways, that even her courage had been almost cowed, and for a while she had condescended to use gentler measures, with the hope that she might thus bring her lord round to his usual state of active submission; or perhaps, if we strive to do her full justice, we may say of her that her effort was made conscientiously, with the idea of inducing him to do his duty with proper activity. For she was a woman not without a conscience, and by no means indifferent to the real service which her husband, as bishop of the diocese, was bound to render to the affairs of the Church around her. Of her own struggles after personal dominion she was herself unconscious; and no doubt they gave her, when recognised and acknowledged by herself, many stabs to her inner self, of which no single being in the world knew anything. And now, as after a while she failed in producing any amelioration in the bishop's mood, her temper also gave way, and things were becoming very gloomy and very unpleasant.

The bishop and his wife were at present alone in the palace. Their married daughter and her husband had left them, and their unmarried daughter was also away. How far the bishop's mood may have produced this solitude in the vast house I will not say. Probably Mrs Proudie's state of mind may have prevented her from having other guests in the place of those who were gone. She felt herself to be almost disgraced in the eyes of all those around her by her husband's long absence from the common rooms of the house and by his dogged silence at meals. It was better, she thought, that they two should be alone in the palace.

Her own efforts to bring him back to something like life, to some activity of mind if not of body, were made constantly; and when she failed, as she did fail day after day, she would go slowly to her own room, and lock her door, and look back in her solitude at all the days of her life. She had agonies in these minutes of which no one near her knew anything. She would seize with her arm the part of the bed near which she would stand, and hold by it, grasping it, as though she were afraid to fall; and then, when it was at the worst with her, she would go to her closet—a closet that no eyes ever saw unlocked but her own—and fill for herself and swallow some draught; and then she would sit down with her Bible before her, and read it sedulously. She spent hours every day with her Bible before her, repeating to herself whole chapters, which she almost knew by heart.

It cannot be said that she was a bad woman, though she had in her time done an indescribable amount of evil. She had endeavoured to do good, failing partly by ignorance and partly from the effects of an unbridled, ambitious temper. And now, even amidst her keenest sufferings, her ambition was by no means dead. She still longed to rule the diocese by means of her husband—but was made to pause and hesitate by the unwonted mood that had fallen upon him. Before this, on more than one occasion, and on one very memorable occasion, he had endeavoured to combat her. He had fought with her, striving to put her down. He had failed, and given up the hope of any escape for himself in that direction. On those occasions her courage had never quailed for a moment. While he openly struggled to be master, she could openly struggle to be mistress—and could enjoy the struggle. But nothing like this moodiness had ever come upon him before.

She had yielded to it for many days, striving to coax him by little softnesses of which she herself had been ashamed as she practised them. They had served her nothing, and at last she determined that something else must be done. If only for his sake, to keep some life in him, something else must be done. Were he to continue as he was now, he must give up his diocese, or, at any rate, declare himself too ill to keep the working of it in his own hands. How she hated Mr Crawley for all the sorrow that he had brought upon her and her house!

And it was still the affair of Mr Crawley which urged her on to further action. When the bishop received Mr Crawley's letter he said nothing of it to her; but he handed it over to his chaplain. The chaplain, fearing to act upon it himself, handed it to Mr Thumble, whom he knew to be one of the bishop's commission, and Mr Thumble, equally fearing responsibility in the present state of affairs at the palace, found himself obliged to consult Mrs Proudie. Mrs Proudie had no doubt as to what should be done. The man had abdicated his living, and of course some provision must be made for the services. She would again make an attempt upon her husband, and therefore she went into his room holding Mr Crawley's letter in her hand.

"My dear," she said, "here is Mr Crawley's letter. I suppose you have read it?"

"Yes," said the bishop; "I have read it."

"And what will you do about it? Something must be done."

"I don't know," said he. He did not even look at her as he spoke. He had not turned his eyes upon her since she had entered the room.

"But, bishop, it is a letter that requires to be acted upon at once. We cannot doubt that the man is doing right at last. He is submitting himself where his submission is due; but his submission will be of no avail unless you take some action upon his letter. Do you not think that Mr Thumble had better go over?"

"No, I don't. I think Mr Thumble had better stay where he is," said the irritated bishop.

"What, then, would you wish to have done?"

"Never mind," said he.

"But, bishop, that is nonsense," said Mrs Proudie, adding something of severity to the tone of her voice.

"No, it isn't nonsense," said he. Still he did not look at her, nor had he done so for a moment since she had entered the room. Mrs Proudie could not bear this, and as her anger became strong within her breast, she told herself that she would be wrong to bear it. She had tried what gentleness would do, and she had failed. It was now imperatively necessary that she should resort to sterner measures. She must make him understand that he must give her authority to send Mr Thumble to Hogglestock.

"Why do you not turn round and speak to me properly?" she said.

"I do not want to speak to you at all," the bishop answered.

This was very bad—almost anything would be better than this. He was sitting now over the fire, with his elbows on his knees, and his face buried in his hands. She had gone round the room so as to face him, and was now standing almost over him, but still she could not see his countenance. "This will not do at all," she said. "My dear, do you know that you are forgetting yourself altogether?"

"I wish I could forget myself."

"That might be all very well if you were in a position in which you owed no service to anyone; or, rather, it would not be well then, but the evil would not be so manifest. You cannot do your duty in the diocese if you continue to sit there doing nothing, with your head upon your hands. Why do you not rally, and get to your work like a man?"

"I wish you would go away and leave me," he said.

"No, bishop, I will not go away and leave you. You have brought yourself to such a condition that it is my duty as your wife to stay by you; and if you neglect your duty, I will not neglect mine."

"It was you that brought me to it."

"No, sir, that is not true. I did not bring you to it."

"It is the truth." And now he got up and looked at her. For a moment he stood upon his legs, and then again he sat down with his face turned towards her. "It is the truth. You have brought on me such disgrace that I cannot hold up my head. You have ruined me. I wish I were dead; and it is all through you that I am driven to wish it."

Of all that she had suffered in her life this was the worst. She clasped both her hands to her side as she listened to him, and for a minute or two she made no reply. When he ceased from speaking he again put his elbows on his knees and again buried his face in his hands. What had she better do, or how was it expedient that she should treat him? At this crisis the whole thing was so important to her that she would have postponed her own ambition and would have curbed her temper had she thought that by doing so she might in any degree have benefited him. But it seemed to her that she could not rouse him by conciliation. Neither could she leave him as he was. Something must be done. "Bishop," she said, "the words that you speak are sinful, very sinful."

"You have made them sinful," he replied.

"I will not hear that from you. I will not indeed. I have endeavoured to do my duty by you, and I do not deserve it. I am endeavouring to do my duty now, and you must know that it would ill-become me to remain quiescent while you are in such a state. The world around you is observing you, and knows that you are not doing your work. All I want of you is that you should arouse yourself, and go to your work."

"I could do my work very well", he said, "if you were not here."

"I suppose, then, you wish that I were dead?" said Mrs Proudie. To this he made no reply, nor did he stir himself. How could flesh and blood bear this—female flesh and blood—Mrs Proudie's flesh and blood? Now, at last, her temper once more got the better of her judgment, probably much to her immediate satisfaction, and she spoke out. "I'll tell you what it is, my lord; if you are imbecile, I must be active. It is very sad that I should have to assume your authority ——"

"I will not allow you to assume my authority."

"I must do so, or must else obtain a medical certificate as to your incapacity, and beg that some neighbouring bishop may administer the diocese. Things shall not go on as they are now. I, at any rate, will do my duty. I shall tell Mr Thumble that he must go over to Hogglestock and arrange for the duties of the parish."

"I desire that you will do no such thing," said the bishop, now again looking up at her.

"You may be sure that I shall," said Mrs Proudie, and then she left the room.

He did not even yet suppose that she would go about this work at once. The condition of his mind was in truth bad, and was becoming worse, probably, from day to day; but still he did make his calculations about things, and now reflected that it would be sufficient if he spoke to his chaplain to-morrow about Mr Crawley's letter. Since the terrible scene that Dr Tempest had witnessed, he had never been able to make up his mind as to what great step he would take, but he had made up his mind that some great step was necessary. There were moments in which he thought that he would resign his bishopric. For such resignation, without acknowledged incompetence on the score of infirmity, the precedents were very few; but even if there were no precedents, it would be better to do that than to remain where he was. Of course there would be disgrace. But then it would be disgrace from which he could hide himself. Now there was equal disgrace; and he could not hide himself. And then such a measure as that would bring punishment where punishment was due. It would bring his wife to the ground—her who had brought him to the ground. The suffering should not be all his own. When she found that her income, and her palace, and her position were all gone, then perhaps she might repent the evil that she had done him. Now, when he was left alone, his mind went back to this, and he did not think of taking immediate measures—measures on that very day—to prevent the action of Mr Thumble.

But Mrs Proudie did take immediate steps. Mr Thumble was at this moment in the palace waiting for instructions. It was he who had brought Mr Crawley's letter to Mrs Proudie, and she now returned to him with that letter in her hand. The reader will know what was the result. Mr Thumble was sent off to Hogglestock at once on the bishop's old cob, and—as will be remembered—fell into trouble on the road. Later in the afternoon he entered the palace yard, having led the cob by the bridle the whole way home from Hogglestock.

Some hour or two before Mr Thumble's return Mrs Proudie returned to her husband, thinking it better to let him know what she had done. She resolved to be very firm with him, but at the same time she determined not to use harsh language, if it could be avoided. "My dear," she said, "I have arranged with Mr Thumble." She found him on this occasion sitting at his desk with papers before him, with a pen in his hand; and she could see at a glance that nothing had been written on the paper. What would she have thought had she known that when he placed the sheet before him he was proposing to consult the archbishop as to the propriety of his resignation! He had not, however, progressed so far as to write even the date of his letter.

"You have done what?" said he, throwing down the pen.

"I have arranged with Mr Thumble as to going out to Hogglestock," said she firmly. "Indeed he has gone already." Then the bishop jumped up from his seat, and rang the bell with violence. "What are you going to do?" said Mrs Proudie.

"I am going to depart from here," said he. "I will not stay here to be the mark of scorn for all men's fingers. I will resign the diocese."

"You cannot do that," said the wife.

"I can try, at any rate," said he. Then the servant entered. "John," said he, addressing the man, "let Mr Thumble know the moment he returns to the palace that I wish to see him here. Perhaps he may not come to the palace. In that case let word be sent to his house."

Mrs Proudie allowed the man to go before she addressed her husband again. "What do you mean to say to Mr Thumble when you see him?"

"That is nothing to you."

She came up to him and put her hand upon his shoulder, and spoke to him very gently. "Tom," she said, "is that the way in which you speak to your wife?"

"Yes, it is. You have driven me to it. Why have you taken upon yourself to send that man to Hogglestock?"

"Because it was right to do so. I came to you for instructions, and you would give none."

"I should have given what instructions I pleased in proper time. Thumble shall not go to Hogglestock next Sunday."

"Who shall go, then?"

"Never mind. Nobody. It does not matter to you. If you will leave me now I shall be obliged to you. There will be an end of all this very soon—very soon."

Mrs Proudie after this stood for a while thinking what she would
say; but she left the room without uttering another word. As she
looked at him a hundred different thoughts came into her mind.
She had loved him dearly, and she loved him still; but she knew
now—at this moment felt absolutely sure—that by him she was
hated! In spite of all her roughness and temper, Mrs Proudie was in
this like other women—that she would fain have been loved had it
been possible. She had always meant to serve him. She was conscious
of that! conscious also in a way that, although she had been industri-
ous, although she had been faithful, although she was clever, yet she
had failed. At the bottom of her heart she knew that she had been a
bad wife. And yet she had meant to be a pattern wife! She had meant
to be a good Christian; but she had so exercised her Christianity
that not a soul in the world loved her, or would endure her presence
if it could be avoided! She had sufficient insight to the minds and
feelings of those around her to be aware of this. And now her
husband had told her that her tyranny to him was so overbearing
that he must throw up his great position, and retire to an obscurity
that would be exceptionally disgraceful to them both, because he
could no longer endure the public disgrace which her conduct

brought upon him in his high place before the world! Her heart was too full for speech; and she left him, very quietly closing the door behind her.

She was preparing to go up to her chamber, with her hand on the bannisters and with her foot on the stairs, when she saw the servant who had answered the bishop's bell. "John," she said, "when Mr Thumble comes to the palace, let me see him before he goes to my lord."

"Yes, ma'am," said John, who well understood the nature of these quarrels between his master and his mistress. But the commands of the mistress were still paramount among the servants, and John proceeded on his mission with the view of accomplishing Mrs Proudie's behests. Then Mrs Proudie went upstairs to her chamber, and locked her door.

Mr Thumble returned to Barchester that day, leading the broken-down cob; and a dreadful walk he had. He was not good at walking,

and before he came near Barchester had come to entertain a violent hatred for the beast he was leading. The leading of a horse that is tired, or in pain, or lame, or even stiff in his limbs, is not pleasant work. The brute will not accommodate his paces to the man, and will contrive to make his head very heavy on the bridle. And he will not walk on the part of the road which the man intends for him, but will lean against the man, and will make himself altogether very disagreeable. It may be understood, therefore, that Mr Thumble was not in a good humour when he entered the palace yard. Nor was he altogether quiet in his mind as to the injury which he had done to the animal. "It was the brute's fault," said Mr Thumble. "It comes generally of not knowing how to ride 'em," said the groom. For Mr Thumble, though he often had a horse out of the episcopal stables, was not ready with his shillings to the man who waited upon him with the steed.

He had not, however, come to any satisfactory understanding respecting the broken knees when the footman from the palace told him he was wanted. It was in vain that Mr Thumble pleaded that he was nearly dead with fatigue, that he had walked all the way from Hogglestock and must go home to change his clothes. John was peremptory with him, insisting that he must wait first upon Mrs Proudie and then upon the bishop. Mr Thumble might perhaps have turned a deaf ear to the latter command, but the former was one which he felt himself bound to obey. So he entered the palace, rather cross, very much soiled as to his outer man; and in this condition went up a certain small staircase which was familiar to him, to a small parlour which adjoined Mrs Proudie's room, and there awaited the arrival of the lady. That he should be required to wait some quarter of an hour was not surprising to him; but when half an hour was gone, and he remembered himself of his own wife at home, and of the dinner which he had not yet eaten, he ventured to ring the bell. Mrs Proudie's own maid, Mrs Draper by name, came to him and said that she had knocked twice at Mrs Proudie's door, and would knock again. Two minutes after that she returned, running into the room with her arms extended, and exclaiming, "Oh, heavens, sir; mistress is dead!" Mr Thumble, hardly knowing what he was about, followed the woman into the bedroom, and there he found himself standing awestruck before the corpse of her who had so lately been the presiding spirit of the palace.

R.I.P.

The body was still resting on its legs, leaning against the end of the side of the bed, while one of the arms was close clasped round the bed-post. The mouth was rigidly closed, but the eyes were open as though staring at him. Nevertheless there could be no doubt from the first glance that the woman was dead. He went close up to it, but did not dare to touch it. There was no one as yet there but he and Mrs Draper—no one else knew what had happened.

"It's her heart," said Mrs Draper.

"Did she suffer from heart complaint?" he asked.

"We suspected it, sir, though nobody knew it. She was very shy of talking about herself."

"We must send for the doctor at once," said Mr Thumble. "We had better touch nothing till he is here." Then they retreated and the door was locked.

In ten minutes everybody in the house knew it except the bishop; and in twenty minutes the nearest apothecary with his assistant were in the room, and the body had been properly laid upon the bed. Even then the husband had not been told—did not know either his relief or his loss. It was now past seven, which was the usual hour for dinner at the palace, and it was probable that he would come out of his room among the servants, if he were not summoned. When it was proposed to Mr Thumble that he should go in to him and tell him, he positively declined, saying that the sight which he had just seen and the exertions of the day together, had so unnerved him, that he had not the physical strength for the task. The apothecary, who had been summoned in a hurry, had escaped, probably being equally unwilling to be the bearer of such a communication. The duty there-fore fell to Mrs Draper, and under the pressing instance of the other servants she descended to her master's room. Had it not been that the hour of dinner had come, so that the bishop could not have been left much longer to himself, the evil time would have been still postponed.

She went very slowly along the passage, and was just going to pause ere she reached the room, when the door was opened and the bishop stood close before her. It was easy to be seen that he was cross. His hands and face were unwashed and his face was haggard. In these days he would not even go through the ceremony of dressing himself before dinner. "Mrs Draper," he said, "why don't they tell me that dinner is ready? Are they going to give me any dinner?" She stood a moment without answering him, while the tears streamed down her face. "What is the matter?" said he. "Has your mistress sent you here?"

"Oh, laws!" said Mrs Draper—and she put out her hands to support him if such support should be necessary.

"What is the matter?" he demanded angrily.

"Oh, my lord—bear it like a Christian. Mistress isn't no more." He leaned back against the door-post, and she took hold of him by the arm. "It was the heart, my lord. Dr Fillgrave hisself has not been yet; but that's what it was." The bishop did not say a word, but walked back to his chair before the fire.

L. C.

HUMBUG

"The proverb of De mortuis is founded on humbug."—*Archdeacon Grantly*

L. C.

Map Making
in
Barsetshire

Map Making in Barsetshire

"I almost fear that it will become necessary, before this history be completed, to provide a map of Barsetshire."

L. C.

". . . the new shire which I had added to the English counties. . . . . This [Framley Parsonage] *was the fourth novel of which I had placed the scene in Barsetshire, and as I wrote it I made a map of the dear county."*

Autobiography.

The starting point of the cartography of Barsetshire is Anthony Trollope's own sketch map. Its authority is binding and not to be disputed. That is obvious. At the same time it must be said that this precious document is not entirely satisfactory to the would-be rambler along Barset lanes. It is only a very rough sketch and a hasty improvisation with little attempt at scale. Details are tantalisingly scanty.[1]

The next step is the evidence to be found in the six Barsetshire novels. This is sometimes direct, sometimes indirect and, sometimes, but not often, contradictory. The whole builds up to a very complete picture.

Trollope's sketch sets out the broad outlines of the county. Barchester, of course, is the focal point. To the east lies Puddingdale, Boxall Hill and Greshamsbury. Plumstead Episcopi is to the south.

---

[1] Thanks to the efforts of that great biographer and bibliographer of Anthony Trollope, Mr Michael Sadleir, this map was recovered for posterity. It is reproduced *facsimile* in the 1927 editions of Mr Sadleir's "Trollope: A Commentary". The editor's own sketchmap is printed on the end-papers of this volume.

Framley is to the north, with Hogglestock still further away. Silverbridge is in the same quarter, but more westerly; it is, in fact, in the western division of Barset. The main line railway runs eastwards from Silverbridge towards London, and is joined by the branch from Barchester running north-east from that city. Chaldicotes, Uffley and Courcy lie to the west of Barchester.

All this is vital, but the sketch tells little about the distances from one place to another or of the location of the lanes and roads. The "old coach road" is indicated, running from Courcy east to Barchester and thence through Puddingdale towards London, but that is all.

At the top of the map Trollope has written: "Silverbridge 20 to Barchester," and "Hogglestock 15 to Barchester".

That is the most vital of Trollope's cartography. The rest must be deduced from the evidence in the novels.

Hogglestock to Barchester

As a starting point it is convenient to take the road from Hogglestock to Barchester. The distance according to Trollope's map is fifteen miles, and this is supported by further evidence. *The Last Chronicle* stresses the fact—indeed, it might be said that much of its drama depends upon it. It was this road along which Josiah Crawley trudged to Barchester palace where, with the famous words, "Peace, woman," he humbled Mrs Proudie to the dust. True, Crawley did not walk all the way. He was cajoled into accepting a lift in Farmer Mangle's cart as far as Framley Mill. At that point he was half-way to Barchester; but he footed it all the way back, proudly forbearing to turn off the road to the mill, where the faithful Mangle waited vainly until six o'clock.

"Now Hogglestock was fifteen miles from Barchester" (so says *The Last Chronicle*, ch. 17). Yet evidence in *Framley Parsonage* is in apparent contradiction. When Mrs Crawley was stricken with typhus Mark Robarts at once set forth to help his sorely pressed brother cleric. Whilst on the road he met Dean Arabin on a like errand. Arabin had, in his concern for his old friend, "undertaken a journey of nearly forty miles" (ch. 36). Half forty is twenty, and the facile deduction is that Barchester is twenty miles from Hogglestock.

What, then, of the evidence elsewhere? Fortunately the seeming discrepancy is easily explained. The fact is the conclusion is wrong because the premise is wrong. It is assumed that Arabin had ridden over from his Barchester deanery. Trollope does not say this, and it is surely not unreasonable to assume that he was, at that time, staying with his brother-in-law, Archdeacon Grantly, at Plumstead Episcopi. This place, as will be shown later, is five miles from Barchester. Five and fifteen is twenty, and it may be recalled that Major Grantly, V.C., was in later years to undertake a journey of similar length from Plumstead when he hurried to Hogglestock with the news that all was well in the matter of the cheque. As *The Last Chronicle* (ch. 73) puts it, "The distance was very nearly twenty miles . . ."

The Framley Puzzle

The location of Framley at first gives difficulty. Silverbridge, as has been seen, is twenty miles from Barchester and lies in the western division. Hogglestock is to the east, in the northern extremity of the eastern division of Barset. There is the authority of Trollope's own map. Now Framley "lies slightly off the road from Hogglestock to Barchester—so much so as to add perhaps a mile to the journey if the traveller goes by the parsonage gate"—thus *The Last Chronicle*, ch. 74.

Since the route from Barchester to Hogglestock has been established as fifteen miles, then the journey *via* Framley must be sixteen miles in length. Turning now to *Framley Parsonage* (ch. 14) it can be read that "Hogglestock . . . adjoins Framley, though the churches are as much as seven miles apart". If Framley is seven miles from Hogglestock, as is seen, then obviously Framley is sixteen less seven, that is nine, miles from Barchester.

All this is of the utmost value. Framley is seven miles from Hogglestock and nine from Barchester. How far from Silverbridge? Turn again to *Framley Parsonage* (ch. 10) and it has it that "Framley is only four miles from Silverbridge, and . . . Silverbridge . . . was on the direct road to the west". Here is a third fix, and it would seem that Framley has been located as accurately as could be desired.

But there is a snag. What is the best way from Barchester to Silverbridge? Why not go, first, to Framley (nine miles) and then on to Silverbridge (reputedly four miles), making thirteen miles in all? But Barchester to Silverbridge is twenty miles. There is the undeniable evidence of Trollope's map, and *The Last Chronicle* (ch. 11) says "Barchester is twenty miles from Silverbridge by road, and more than forty by railway". It can scarcely be pleaded, with hope of conviction, that the longer route was invariably preferred. Even if the roads to Framley were "deep" (as Trollope puts it) they are hardly likely to have been so bad that wayfarers consistently went seven miles out of their way to avoid them.

A more critical examination of the evidence does away with the need for such an explanation. A host of cartographical difficulties are swept aside if a simple and not improbable clerical error is assumed. If it has remained uncorrected for so long it is because Trollope, as is well known, took little notice of his work after publication. It may be remembered also that *Framley Parsonage* was written with *Castle Richmond* still on the stocks, when doubtless Trollope was pressed more than usual.

He wrote of Mark Robarts dashing off to Exeter on the news of the death of his father. It was, Trollope hastily wrote, four miles to Silverbridge, and there Robarts was on the direct road to the west. But almost certainly what Trollope really meant to say was that it was four miles to the Silverbridge *Road*, and there Robarts was on the direct route to the west. A trifling error in itself—just a little hasty writing and imperfect revision—but it might have been highly misleading.

Framley is no mere pin point on the map. *Framley Parsonage*, ch. 2, says "The high road went winding . . . for a mile and a half, not two hundred yards of which ran in a straight line; and there was a cross-road which passed down through the domain, whereby there came to be a locality called Framley Cross. Here stood the 'Lufton Arms' . . ." And *The Last Chronicle* (ch. 17) has "Now Framley Mill was only half a mile off the direct road to Barchester, and was almost half-way from Hogglestock parsonage to the city". Clearly, since Farmer Mangle dropped Crawley at the mill and not on the main highway, he must have turned off the road some distance before. Indeed, when Crawley was returning from Barchester "He passed the turning going down to Framley with courage, but when he came to the further turning, by which the cart would return from Framley to the Hogglestock road . . ." (*The Last Chronicle*, ch. 18). From Framley Cross "Framley church was distant . . . just a quarter of a mile, and stood immediately opposite to the chief entrance to Framley Court" (*Framley Parsonage*, ch. 2).

From all this it can be seen that the roads form a rough triangle based on the Barchester-Hogglestock highway (with the two sides together one mile longer than the base) and that the apex is formed by Framley Cross. Framley Mill is half a mile from the main road, and undoubtedly most houses of the scattered village lie between the Cross and the Mill.

Framley, as has been seen, is four miles from the Silverbridge Road. It will later transpire, as the map takes shape, that it is a further eight miles into Silverbridge itself. Framley is in reality twelve miles from that town.

Hogglestock

The cure of Jos. Crawley is not the most inviting corner of Barsetshire, but nevertheless the location of Hogglestock is of cartographical importance. It is already established as fifteen miles from Barchester and seven miles from Framley. How far from Silverbridge?

This brings another difficulty, to explain which it is first necessary to look at the hamlet of Hoggle End. *The Last Chronicle*, ch. 12, has it that "Mr Crawley went forth and made his way with rapid steps to a portion of his parish nearly two miles distant from his house, through which was carried a canal, affording water communication . . . to both London and Bristol". That is clear enough, and the same reference gives—" 'How did you get back from Silverbridge yesterday, Dan?' 'Footed it,—all the blessed way.' 'It's only eight miles.' "

Hoggle End, then, is two miles from Hogglestock and eight miles from Silverbridge. It looks as if Silverbridge is six miles from Hogglestock. Yet turn now to *The Last Chronicle*, ch. 61, and Dr Tempest may be found saying to Crawley " 'You have walked eight miles. . . .' " Geometrically, of course, there is nothing against both Hogglestock and Hoggle End being eight miles from Silverbridge and two from each other. Geographically there is everything against it, because it is quite impossible for Silverbridge to be twenty miles from Barchester, Hogglestock fifteen miles from Barchester, and Silverbridge eight miles from Hogglestock—impossible because the Barchester–Silverbridge road will later be found to pass close by Hogglestock.

What then? The first assumption—namely, six miles—fits in with the rest of the data. Dr Tempest's figure does not. Possibly Dr Tempest was speaking loosely. He may have lived some way out of Silverbridge. A host of possibilities come to mind, but six miles is the utmost distance that can be allowed from Silverbridge to Hogglestock.

Silverbridge

The Silverbridge–Barchester road is known to be twenty miles. The problem is now to determine its precise location. The outline of the map that can so far be constructed, as well as Trollope's sketch, shows a direct bee-line to be out of the question—and a circuitous route offers many alternatives.

Fortunately there is indirect evidence to settle the matter. When the clerical commission, convened by Dr Tempest to look into the Crawley affair, broke up after its first and only meeting, it may be recalled that Thumble and Quiverful departed at once for Barchester. "Mark Robarts and Caleb Oriel left Silverbridge in another gig by the same road, and soon passed their brethren" (*The Last Chronicle*, ch. 54). Robarts and Oriel were on their way to Framley, so the Silverbridge–Barchester road must coincide, for at least part of the way, with the Silverbridge–Framley route.

Now this latter road passes fairly close to Hogglestock, for it can be read (*The Last Chronicle*, ch. 20) that "Mr Robarts . . . drove himself into Silverbridge, passing very close to Mr Crawley's house on his road". Obviously, then, Thumble and Quiverful, trailing behind their speedier brethren, must have subsequently joined the Hogglestock–Barchester highway in order to reach the cathedral city. The requirements of the already established distances enable the road to be drawn with accuracy.

It now transpires that the Silverbridge Road runs east from Silverbridge; after something over five miles there is a turning north for Hogglestock, nearly a mile further on; a mile and a half further it runs into the Hogglestock–Barchester road; then, four miles short of Framley, it branches east again, where it goes on to Greshamsbury and eventually joins the old coach road from Barchester to London.

Greshamsbury

This pleasant Barset village is, at first, located with the utmost simplicity. *Doctor Thorne*, ch. 3, says "Greshamsbury was only fifteen miles from Barchester . . . but eight from Silverbridge". What could be clearer? But, if only eight miles from Silverbridge why do the Greshamburians, without exception, use the railway station at Barchester? The station at Silverbridge is not only seven miles nearer but, since it is on the main line, presumably better served with trains than Barchester on the branch.

Trollope's own map indicates the figure of eight miles to be wrong. Greshamsbury lies to the south of the branch line well to the east of Barchester. Even making every possible allowance for lack of scale, no amount of ingenuity will make it fit. That being so, what is the true figure? Here the methods of so-called Higher Criticism prove their value. Examination of the circumstances under which *Doctor Thorne* was written makes it apparent that an odd slip of the pen is not to be wondered at. Turning to the *Autobiography*, ch. 7, it can be read, "As I journeyed across France to Marseilles, and made thence a terribly rough voyage to Alexandria, I wrote my allotted number of pages every day. On this occasion more than once I left my papers on the cabin table, rushing away to be sick in the privacy of my state room." This stupendous piece of authorship refers to *Doctor Thorne*.

What, then, is more probable that a sudden spell of nausea caused "eight" to be written, when what Trollope really intended to convey was "eighteen"? It can, in fact, be safely assumed that this was the case. All map-making anomalies vanish if the distance of eighteen miles between Silverbridge and Greshamsbury is taken as a fact. Neatly and snugly the village appears to the south of the Barchester branch line in accordance with the requirements of Trollope's own sketch.

So much for internal resources. Reference to outside sources brings about a striking confirmation of the deduction. *The Prime Minister* is not, of course, within the Barset saga, but chapter 34 has "Greshamsbury, the seat of Francis Gresham Esq., who was a great man in these parts, was about twenty miles from Silverbridge . . ."

It seems that most cultural ties of Greshamsbury are with Barchester, but commercially the village is more closely connected with Silverbridge. The postal centre is the latter town, as is shown when Mary Thorne, quite ignorant of the procedure, imagines that her letter to Frank Gresham will be sent by the post-mistress straight up to the Hall. Instead it had to be sent all the way into Silverbridge and back again, by which time her beloved had departed for London.

The Courcy District

The location of Courcy, to the west of Barchester on the old coach road, is simple. There is the authority of so accurate a witness as Planty Pal, who obviously rarely made errors on matters of fact. *The Small House* has it, in ch. 23, that "Plantagenet Palliser . . . remarked . . . that he believed it was only twelve miles to Silverbridge". It was his slight banter on the subject with Lady Dumbello that gave rise to the grave *scandale* which led to the old Duke threatening to cut off his nephew with a beggarly few thousands a year.

There is a railway station. *Doctor Thorne* (ch. 15) has it that "there was a railway station a mile and a half distant . . ." It was a station evidently little used, and the mails certainly avoided it, for it is recorded in *The Last Chronicle* (ch. 5) ". . . that letter to Framley . . . went into Barchester by the Courcy night mail-cart, which, on its road, passes through the villages of Uffley and Chaldicotes . . ."

Chaldicotes was the home of the unfortunate and rascally Nat

Sowerby, and where Mark Robarts got himself into such a pickle by endorsing one of Sowerby's little bits of "paper". There is some measure of conflicting testimony about its distance from Barchester. *Framley Parsonage* (ch. 3) has Sowerby whispering to Robarts, " 'Fancy having to drive ten miles after dusk, and ten miles back, to hear Harold Smith talk for two hours about Borneo!' " Yet four chapters later one reads of Robarts' anxiety lest he should be late with the sermon which he is to give in Chaldicotes Church and of his asking himself "whether it was good that he should be waiting there, in painful anxiety, to gallop over a dozen miles in order . . ." etc.

The evidence in neither case is of a precise order. Sowerby was obviously speaking loosely, and he was not the most accurate of men when it was a matter of figures. And of course the distance from Sowerby's home to Barchester might well differ appreciably from the distance between the "Dragon of Wantly" and Chaldicotes Church. In actual fact a figure of ten miles between the village of Chaldicotes and Barchester fits in well with Trollope's sketch and the outline of the map drawn thus far. It can be taken, then, that this is the correct distance. Having located Chaldicotes, and then fixed Courcy in its proper relation both to that place and to Silverbridge—here Trollope's map is of great assistance—it is found that the distance from Courcy to Barchester is about twelve miles.

The journeys of Mark Robarts about Barsetshire have afforded such insight into the geography of the county that it is a matter of regret to record that one of his trips gives another indication of hasty and unrevised writing by Trollope. In *Framley Parsonage* (ch. 2) when Robarts was preparing for his disastrous visit to Chaldicotes it has it that "He was to start after lunch on that day, driving himself in his own gig, so as to reach Chaldicotes, some twenty-four miles distant, before dinner". And in the following chapter " 'Is that Mr Robarts?' said Mrs Harold Smith, getting up to greet him, and screening her pretended ignorance under the veil of the darkness. 'And have you really driven over four-and-twenty miles of Barsetshire roads on such a day as this . . .' "

This is evidence clearer than some, but, unfortunately, it will not do! Even if Robarts had to travel all the way round by Barchester the distance is less than that—nine miles from Framley into Barchester, and ten miles out from the cathedral city to Chaldicotes, is only nineteen miles at the most. It is here that the map itself solves a ticklish problem. Measurement with the dividers discloses the fact that a fairly straight road between Framley and Chaldicotes is twelve miles. Twelve miles! Just half the distance! The explanation is obvious. What Trollope had in mind was the return journey, and in his haste—remember that he was writing *Castle Richmond* at that time as well—omitted to make this clear.

Plumstead Episcopi and others

So far little has been said of Plumstead Episcopi, a place of no little importance in Barsetshire. The great Archdeacon Grantly exercised his mighty influence from that solid, comfortable rectory, an influence in Barset affairs extending over all things social, ecclesiastical and, doubtless, political. Alas! it is over Plumstead Episcopi that Trollope slips in a manner that can only be explained as a downright error, without benefit of seasickness, miscalculation or confusion of nomenclature.

Barchester Towers (ch. 25) has it that "Plumstead is nine miles from Barchester, and Puddingdale but four". There is never reason to doubt the figure for Puddingdale, where acquaintance is first made with the Reverend Mr Quiverful and his brood, but that for Plumstead is nowhere in accord with the rest of the evidence. When at Plumstead Dr Fillgrave is reckoned as ". . . some five or six miles out of town, at Plumstead" (*Doctor Thorne*, ch. 12). Since the worthy doctor's precise abode in Barchester is not known this may be taken as in accord with *The Last Chronicle* (ch. 73) which has it that "a run into Barchester and back . . . was under ten miles".

It can only be assumed that the later evidence is correct, and that Plumstead Episcopi is five miles to the south of Barchester. It must not be forgotten, of course, that Trollope, in chronicling *Barchester Towers* was less familiar with the county than he afterwards became.

No further problems present themselves. Boxall Hill, which passed from the ownership of the Greshams to the Scatcherds and back again, "lay half-way between Greshamsbury and Barchester . . ." (so it has in *Doctor Thorne*, ch. 3). Crabtree Parva, the living of which was held by Septimus Harding—it is queer that his activities as a pluralist never seemed to trouble his conscience—is on the old coach road to the west, according to Trollope's map; and ". . . . Crabtree Church was not quite a mile and a half from the cathedral . . ." (*The Warden*, ch. 16). Again Trollope's sketch gives authority for Stogpingum, Eiderdown and Crabtree Canonicorum—the latter on no account to be confused with Crabtree Parva; the rich glebe lands of Crabtree Canonicorum were enjoyed by the extravagant Stanhopes in distant Italy. Then, turning to the north of Barset, there is Spigglewick Hill. Here Mr Thumble's borrowed cob broke its knees and it clearly lies a little to the south of Hogglestock on the main road from Barchester. The location of Hoggle End, two miles to the north of Hogglestock, has already been established.

The site of Gatherum Castle, the most splendid, staggering edifice in the whole of the county, is marked on Trollope's map, and internal evidence makes it plain that this lavish pile is more than six miles from Courcy. Frank Gresham, offended by the manifest imperfections of the Duke as a host, had walked that distance before he was overtaken by the Honourable George, hiccuping his appreciation of the Gatherum cellars.

The master's own sketch is again resorted to for the location of Scarington (not, by the way, Scannington, as some cartographers have written). For other places mentioned in *Doctor Thorne*—Annesgrove, Hesterwell Park, Mill Hill and The Grange—mathematical precision is not possible; but they are obviously in the Greshamsbury area. So with Cosby Lodge, Major Henry Grantly's home in *The Last Chronicle* which nearly came beneath the auctioneer's hammer. It is obviously not far from Silverbridge. Similarly *Barchester Towers* has evidence to indicate Knowle Park, The Elms and Rosebank as being in the neighbourhood of Ullathorne: Ullathorne is within the parish of St Ewold's and, according to *Barchester Towers*, ch. 14, "St Ewold is a parish lying just without the city of Barchester . . . not much above a mile distant from the city gate."

The Railways

Barset railways present no problems of note. Silverbridge is on the main line—obviously the Great Western and one can hardly imagine it being any other—and Barchester on the branch. To the west of Silverbridge is Burleybridge station. Beyond the railway goes into the next county, where Guestwick serves as the station for Allington. For all this there is the confirmation of Trollope's map.

An additional detail is Courcy station, already shown to be a mile and a half from the village. It is obviously on an extension of the Barchester branch line. Then there is another station within reach of both Framley and Hogglestock. *Framley Parsonage* (ch. 14) has it that "Framley is . . . just to the south of the grand trunk line of railway from which the branch to Barchester strikes off at a point some thirty miles nearer to London. The station for Framley Court is Silverbridge . . . Hogglestock is to the north of the railway, the line of which, however, runs through a portion of the parish . . ." Yet it may be recalled that when Crawley went to London to lay his cause *in forma pauperis* before Mr Toogood he found it unnecessary to go all the way into Silverbridge. Instead he avoided the night mail (which stopped only at Silverbridge) and was able to get a third class return ticket at single fare and was able to "get in and out of the train at a station considerably nearer to him than Silverbridge". Thus *The Last Chronicle* (ch. 32).

Mark Robarts obviously used the same station when "he had gone to Silverbridge by railway . . ." (*The Last Chronicle*, ch. 68). He probably travelled first class. It makes it clear, then, that a station exists between Hogglestock and Framley. This station, obviously no more than a halt, can only lie at the intersection of the railway and the Hogglestock–Barchester road.

The rail journey from Silverbridge to Barchester has already been shown to be over forty miles. It is, in fact, much more than that. The route is via the junction, where Doctor Thorne took such a poor opinion of the tea.

It has been wondered why Adolphus Crosbie elected to go to Courcy all the way round by Barchester, instead of alighting at Silverbridge, the same distance away. Crosbie, however, had left Allington unnecessarily early and, even in Barchester, had time to kill. It is probable, too, that Crosbie felt it was "not done" to arrive at Courcy Castle from so plebian a spot as Silverbridge. As for Courcy station, that was obviously impossible. There is no record of anyone using the railway there. The service must have been hopeless. There are places like that to-day.

Woods and Rivers

Barset roads are not good. Trollope invariably wrote of their being "deep" and "muddy". The Countess de Courcy was loud in her complaints when she arrived so indecently late for the Ullathorne sports. Not that her remarks are to be trusted, but the roads can hardly have been very good, or else she would have fabricated some other excuse.

The largest stretch of woodland is the Chase of Chaldicotes. It was once crown property, but it was bought by the Thornes—the Thornes of Chaldicotes, not of Ullathorne—despite the desire of the Duke of Omnium to add it to his already vast estates. It is on record that it once extended all the way to Silverbridge.

Probably a surviving part of this once extensive woodland—the distance from Chaldicotes to Silverbridge is about ten miles—is Cobbold's Ashes, where the hunting prowess of Mark Robarts brought disapproval from old Lady Lufton. As can be seen from *Framley Parsonage* (ch. 14), Cobbold's Ashes ". . . was not in Framley parish, nor in the next parish to it. It was half-way across to Chaldicotes—in the western division . . ."

Plumstead Coppices mark the boundary between the lands of Archdeacon Grantly and the estate of Thorne of Ullathorne. It was here that a fox was once trapped, probably by the man at Darvell's Farm which, of course, is in the neighbourhood. This was about the most shocking crime Trollope ever had to write about. In this area, too, is St Ewold's Down and also Goshall Spring. Hoggle Bushes, about the foxes in which Major Grantly seemed to know a good deal, is one of the few pleasant spots in the Hogglestock corner of the county.

Barset is no angler's paradise—Lord Lufton found it necessary to go all the way to Norway for salmon fishing—and the only river mentioned by Trollope is the one skirting Hiram's Hospital in Barchester. The nomenclature of Silverbridge clearly indicates a river there, and it is not unreasonable to assume it to be the same. Part of its course between the two places obviously forms the boundary between the eastern and western divisions of Barset.

The canal at Hoggle End—where Crawley received the immortal advice, "It's dogged as does it!"—has been shown to lead in one direction to Bristol and London. In the other it can only lead to the river at Silverbridge.

A glance over the completed map of Barsetshire recalls the differing character of one region and another. Around Hogglestock, stretching perhaps as far south as the Silverbridge Road, it is barren, inhospitable and depressing. As Trollope has recorded, it really should be in another county. It taints even the town of Silverbridge, a place of business with few attractions for the tourist.

Nor does Courcy, twelve miles to the south, share the full richness of Barsetshire. It has the air of slight decay, of shabby tinsel, from which even the wealth of Gatherum Castle does not entirely free itself. There are some broken fences in West Barset, and tenant farmers hard pressed to pay their rent.

Not so in the other division. The fat glebe lands of Plumstead Episcopi, the old oaks of Ullathorne, the rich pastures of Greshamsbury, the fertile corn lands of Framley—all these indicate prosperity rooted deep in good English earth. And in Barchester City the shady nooks, the quiet corners, the hallowed cloisters and the sacred, time-weathered stones of the cathedral express to God the mute gratitude of those worthy folk who live and work and play and die in the dearest of English counties. Long may it and they endure!

A
Handy Guide to
Barsetshire

ALLINGTON

This pleasant village is not in Barsetshire, but in its western neighbour. Principal residences: The Great House; also The Small House. Church. Inn: The Red Lion (one bedroom only). P.O. Railway station: Guestwick, about four miles.

ANNESGROVE

A gentleman's estate in the neighbourhood of Greshamsbury.

BARCHESTER

The capital of Barsetshire is a quiet town famed for the beauty of its cathedral and the antiquity of its monuments. It is an assize town and amongst the most ancient cities in the country. Its name is believed to have been derived from "Baronum Castrum", the title of the old Roman settlement on the site. (In this connection it is not without interest to note that Bishops of Barchester sign "Barnum", a derivation from the Roman foundation of the city.) The principal points of interest for the visitor are the cathedral, the bishop's palace and the old foundation of Hiram's Hospital. This charitable institution was founded by John Hiram in 1434, and the lands he made over for this purpose, namely, Hiram's Butts and Hiram's Patches, still contribute to its income. The hospital adjoins the river and is perhaps the most charming spot in the city. The gateway is particularly fine. The Church of St Cuthbert's is one of the smallest parish churches extant. It is a Gothic building built over the gateway to the

Cathedral Close and is only about 27 feet by 18 feet. The wood carving of the interior oak beams is unique.

The Bishopric of Barchester is worth £5,000 per annum, having formerly been £9,000. The wardenship of Hiram's Hospital is in the Bishop's gift. Its value is £450, having once been £800. The former custom of combining the precentorship of the cathedral (of which the stipend is £70) is now discontinued. The Dean of Barchester has £1,200 per annum, and the prebendary stalls are worth £600, having been reduced from £900. The rector of St Cuthbert's gets £75 a year.

Inns: The Dragon of Wantly, The Brown Bear, The White Horse, and The Compasses. Railway station: on the Barchester Branch Line. (There are about three trains per day each way, and an omnibus runs to the station from the centre of the city.)

Barchester is represented by member of parliament.

BARSETSHIRE

This, the most typical of English counties, is mainly agricultural in its pursuits. For administrative purposes the old shire was divided into two sections, East Barset and West Barset, each returning a member of parliament, at the time of the Reform Bill in the 1830's.

BOXALL HILL

An extensive estate situated half-way between Barchester and Greshamsbury. By Barset standards the estate is a new one, the residence having been built in the middle of the nineteenth century. BOXALL GORSE is held in high esteem by sportsmen. Its partridges are famous, and it is noted in fox hunting circles as being almost certain to "draw".

BURLEYBRIDGE

A station on the main railway line to the west of Silverbridge.

CHALDICOTES

Another Barset spot famous for its shooting. The village of Chaldicotes lies ten miles to the west of Barchester, a little to the north of the Old Coach Road and not far from Courcy. Principal residence: Chaldicotes House. Church.

The CHASE OF CHALDICOTES is the most famous of Barset woodlands and lies mainly in the parishes of Chaldicotes and Uffley. In historic times it reached all the way to Silverbridge. It was formerly crown property.

COBBOLD'S ASHES

This stretch of woodland lies about half-way between Chaldicotes and Framley, two parishes distant from the latter village, and in the western division of Barset.

COSBY LODGE

A gentleman's estate, with good sporting facilities, not far from Silverbridge on the road to Chaldicotes.

COURCY

A sleepy village about a dozen miles to the west of Barchester on the Old Coach Road. Principal residence: Courcy Castle. Inn: The Red Lion. Railway station: a mile and a half distant. (The service is poor; post horses may be obtained in Barchester, which offers better facilities for Courcy than does Silverbridge.)

CRABTREE CANONICORUM

A small village to the south-east of Barchester. The population is only 200. Church. The living is in the gift of the dean and chapter of Barchester; there are four hundred acres of glebe land, together with the great and small tithes, all of which accrue to the rector. The tithes alone are worth £400 per annum.

CRABTREE PARVA

A charming village a mile and a half to the west of Barchester. Church. The vicarage is famed for its garden. The living is valued at £80.

DARVELL'S FARM

This is part of the Ullathorne estate not far from Plumstead Coppices. Its bad reputation is due to a crime committed in the last century. The then tenant deliberately trapped a fox.

EIDERDOWN

A parish to the east of Plumstead. Much of it is part of the famous Grantly estates. The living is united with that of the neighbouring parish of Stogpingum (more properly Stoke Pinquium or Stoke Pinguium).

THE ELMS

A residence in the Ullathorne district.

FRAMLEY

A straggling village extending along a mile and a half of winding lanes between Hogglestock and Barchester, but lying a little off the main road. Principal residence: Framley Court, sometimes known as Framley Hall. (The house is unpretentious, but the gardens superb.) Church. Inn: The Lufton Arms. P.O. Railway station: none, though some trains stop at The Halt, situated at the intersection of the Hogglestock road and the railway. Framley Mill is one of the few mills in Barset, not a great corn growing county.

The living of Framley is a valuable one. It is worth £900 per annum. The Lufton family hold the advowson.

GATHERUM CASTLE

A noble pile standing on an eminence deep in West Barset. It is built of white stone and was erected at enormous expense in the 1840's. GATHERUM WOODS are fairly extensive.

GOSHALL SPRINGS

These are on the Ullathorne estate, not far from the Plumstead boundary.

THE GRANGE

A gentleman's residence near Greshamsbury.

GRESHAMSBURY

Situated in the heart of East Barset this village claims to be amongst the most charming spots in the county. It is about fifteen miles from Barchester and consists of a straggling street a mile long and turning at right angles in the centre. Principal residence: Greshamsbury House, one of the finest examples of Tudor architecture in the country; its gardens are also famous; Greshamsbury Park lies distinct from the house. Church. P.O. (mail being forwarded via Silverbridge.) Railway station: none, Barchester being the most convenient centre.

The living (annual value unknown) belongs to the Gresham family.

GUESTWICK

Not in Barsetshire, this quiet market town lies in its western neighbour. Inn: The Magpie. Railway station: on the main line from Paddington. GUESTWICK MANOR, a few miles away, is the principal residence of the locality.

HAMERSHAM

This is not in Barsetshire, but the county town of its western neighbour. The assize goes here.

HARTLEBURY

This is in Shropshire and the home of the Hartletops.

HESTERWELL PARK

An estate in East Barset in the neighbourhood of Greshamsbury.

HOGGLESTOCK

A village situated in the north of East Barset, seven miles from Framley and the other side of the main line railway. It lies in the poorest part of the shire. Principal residences: none. Church. P.O.: four miles distant. Railway station: none. (Silverbridge is normally used, though, when available, the Halt, which also serves Framley, offers nearer facilities.)

The living is a perpetual curacy and is in the gift of the Dean of Barchester. Its value is only £130 per annum.

Sporting facilities are few, but some sportsmen reckon that Hoggle Bushes will yield a brush as often as not.

HOGGLE END

An unsightly village situated on the banks of a canal and lying in the extreme north of the county, two miles beyond Hogglestock. It consists almost exclusively of workmen's dwellings, brickmaking being a flourishing industry in these parts. It lies within the parish of Hogglestock.

THE HORNS

A compact estate in Surrey belonging to the Omnium family.

THE JUNCTION

The railway centre for the county. Here the Barchester Branch Line joins the main line. There is a refreshment room.

KNOWLE PARK

An estate in the Ullathorne district.

LUFTON

A village in Oxfordshire. Lufton Park is in derelict condition and the family reside at Framley in Barsetshire.

MATCHING PRIORY

Another estate belonging to the Omnium family, but not in Barset.

MILL HILL

A hamlet near Greshamsbury.

A Handy Guide to Barsetshire

PLUMSTEAD EPISCOPI

This village lies a few miles south of Barchester in the midst of a prosperous neighbourhood. Principal residence: The Rectory, a large house with lodge gates. Church: a fine building, badly proportioned, but rich in good stone work matured to a yellow grey colour. P.O. Railway station: none.

Good sporting facilities are to be had in the neighbourhood. PLUMSTEAD COPPICES mark the boundary between Plumstead and the more northerly estate of Ullathorne.

The living is a valuable one and by custom given to the Archdeacon of Barchester. Together the annual value amounts to nearly £3,000 per annum.

PUDDINGDALE

A featureless village on the London road, about four miles east of Barchester. The living gives £400 per annum.

ROSEBANK

A small residence in the Ullathorne district.

ST EWOLD'S

A pleasing village, with a population of 1,200, lying between one and two miles from Barchester, slightly off the Plumstead road. The river flows here on its way to Barchester, where it skirts Hiram's Hospital. The view from the village across the well-wooded countryside towards the cathedral is especially pretty. Principal residence: Ullathorne Court. This extensive and ancient estate lies within the parish of St Ewold's, and more generally gives its name to the place as ULLATHORNE. It is an old building, on three stories and with a well matured exterior. Church. Railway station: Barchester is commonly used.

The living at St Ewold's is not a rich one, being valued at between three and four hundred pounds per annum. The old custom of associating the living with one of the offices in the cathedral choir fell into disuse in the middle of the last century, and the living is now attached to the rectory of Plumstead Episcopi.

SCARINGTON

A tiny village situated to the north of Greshamsbury. Owing to a misreading of the earliest known map of Barsetshire some commentators have named the village Scannington, but this is erroneous and conflicts with the historian, Trollope.

SILVERBRIDGE

A thriving market town situated towards the north of West Barset, to which it serves as capital. The distance from Barchester is twenty miles. Church. Inns: The George and Vulture, The Palliser Arms. P.O. Railway station: on the main Great Western Line from London.

SPIGGLEWICK HILL

A formidable obstacle on the road between Barchester and Hogglestock, lying a little to the south of Hogglestock. The road is very poor here.

STOGPINGUM

A small village south-east of Barchester. The living is united to that of Eiderdown nearby.

UFFLEY

A village between Chaldicotes and Courcy.

ULLATHORNE

See St Ewold's.

Who's Who in Barsetshire

Anne—Under-chambermaid at "The Dragon of Wantly". (LC)

Anticant, Dr Pessimist—A Scottish essayist and publicist. (W)

Apjohn, Mr—A Barchester attorney. (DT)

Applejohn, Mr—Butler at Framley Court. (FP)

Arabin, Mrs Eleanor—(*See* Miss Eleanor Harding.)

Arabin, Very Rev. Dr Francis—One time Fellow of Lazarus College, Oxford; instituted Vicar of St Ewold's; subsequently Dean of Barchester. (BT, FP, LC)

Arabin, Susan (Posy)—A young daughter of Dr and Mrs Arabin. (LC)

Arabin, Elly—A young daughter of Dr and Mrs Arabin. (LC)

Armstrong—First mortgage holder of the Greshamsbury estates. (DT)

Athelings, the Misses—Daughters of a clergyman in the Greshamsbury neighbourhood. (DT)

Athill, Rev. Mr—One time holder of a living near Greshamsbury; vicar of Eiderdown. (DT)

Athill, Mrs—Wife of the above. (FP)

Auldreekie, Marquis of—Scottish nobleman, heir to the title Lord of the Isles. (SHA)

Austen, John—The elder of the brothers "Tozer" (q.v.). (FP)

Bagley, Mr—A Barchester chorister. (DT)

Baker, Mr—Resident at "Mill Hill". (DT)

Baker, Henry (Harry)—Son of the above and friend of Frank Gresham. (DT)

Bangles, Mr Peter—Of Burton & Bangles, Wine Merchants, of Hook Court. (LC)

Barlow, Mrs—Guest at Courcy Castle. (DT)

Barrell, Master—A coachman. (BT)

Bateson, Mr—Of "Annesgrove". (DT)

Bateson, Mrs—Wife of the above. (DT)

Bateson, Miss—Daughter of Mr Bateson. A spinster of 50. (DT)

Bates, John—Butler at the Great House, Allington. (LC)

Baxter, Mrs—The Arabins' housekeeper at Barchester deanery. (LC)

Bell, Johnny—Inmate of Hiram's Hospital. (W)

Bideawhile, Mr—A London lawyer, member of the firm of Slow & Bideawhile. (DT)

Biddle—Late president of the Goose and Glee Club, Barchester. (LC)

Blackie's—A shop in Regent Street. (LC)

Boanerges, Lord—Guest at Gatherum Castle. (FP)

Bob—Sowerby's groom at Chaldicotes. (FP)

Boggs—Messenger in the General Committee Office. (SHA)

Bold, Mrs Eleanor—(*See* Miss Eleanor Harding.)

Bold, John—A young surgeon of Barchester; first husband of Miss Eleanor Harding. (W)

Bold, Johnny—Posthumous son of John and Mrs Bold. (BT)

Bold, Mary—Elder sister of John Bold. (W, BT, FP)

Bolus—One time apothecary at Scarington. (DT)

Borleys & Bonstock—Solicitors of Barchester. (LC)

Boulger—A friend of John Eames. (LC)

Bounce, Bounce and Bounce—West End bankers. (LC)

Boyce, Rev. Mr—Vicar of Allington. (SHA, LC)

Boyce, Mrs—Wife of the above. (SHA, LC)

Boyce, Bessy—Daughter of Rev. Mr Boyce. (SHA, LC)

Boyce, Charles—Son of Rev. Mr Boyce. (SHA)

Boyce, Dick—Son of Rev. Mr Boyce. (SHA)

Boyce, Florence—Daughter of Rev. Mr Boyce. (SHA)

Boyce, Jane—Daughter of Rev. Mr Boyce. (SHA, LC)

Boyce, Susan—Daughter of Rev. Mr Boyce. (SHA)

Bradley's—Corn chandlers in Barchester High Street. (BT)

Brawl, Baron—Guest at Gatherum Castle. A puisne judge. (FP)

Bridget—Servant of Dr Thorne. (DT)

Brittleback, Lord—A politician. (FP)

Brock, Lord—Prime Minister. (FP, SHA)

Broughton, Dobbs—A city man. Also known at Market Harboro'. (LC)

Broughton, Mrs Maria—née Maria Clutterbuck; wife of the above. (LC)

Brown, Rev. Mr—A member of the Proudie faction. (BT)

Buckish, Lord—A nephew of Lady Arabella Gresham. (DT)

Buffle, Sir Raffle—A civil servant. Chief Commissioner of the Income Tax Office. (SHA, LC)

Buffle, Lady—Wife of the above. (SHA)

Buggins—Messenger in the Petty Bag Office. (FP)

Bumpter—Resident in Barchester High Street; the last member of the Goose and Glee Club. (LC)

Bumpwell, Dr—A former Barchester doctor. (BT)

Bunce, John—Senior almsman at Hiram's Hospital. (W, LC)

Burslem, Dr—A former Barchester prebendary. (FP)

Burton & Bangles—Wine merchants of Hook Court. (LC)

Bushers, PC—Policeman at Paddington. (SHA)

Butterwell, Mr—Secretary of the General Committee Office. (SHA, LC)

Butterwell, Mrs—Wife of the above. (SHA, LC)

Cantabili, Signor—Barchester music master patronised by the Greshams. (DT)

Carson—A servant of the Robarts. (FP)

Carter—A city man. (LC)

Carter, Ricketts and Carter—A city firm. (LC)

Cecile—A maid of Griselda, Marchioness of Hartletop. (LC)

Century, Dr—A Barsetshire doctor. (DT)

Chadwick, Mr—Steward to the Bishop of Barchester. (W, BT, FP, LC)

Chadwick, Mrs—Wife of the above. (BT)

Chadwick, Augustus—Son of Mr Chadwick. (BT)

Chadwick, Frederick—Son of Mr Chadwick. (BT)

Chadwick, Mr John—A Barchester lawyer, nephew of Mr Chadwick (LC)

Champion, Rev. Mr—A Barchester prebendary; a friend of Dowager Lady Lufton. (LC)

Chumpend—A London butcher. (SHA)

Clandidlem, Lady—A guest at Courcy Castle. (SHA)

Clantantrum, Mrs—A Barchester resident. (BT)

Clantelbrocks, Lady—A London hostess. (FP)

Clarke, Rev. Mr—The parson who visited the dying Sir Roger Scatcherd. (DT)

Clodheve, Sexton—Sexton of St Ewold's. (BT)

Clontarf—A friend of Lord Lufton. (FP)

Closerstil (or Closerstill)—An election agent. (DT, FP)

Clutterbuck, Maria—Maiden name of Mrs Dobbs Broughton. (LC)

Colepepper—A friend of Lord Porlock. (SHA)

Connor, Mrs—A servant at Guestwick Manor. (SHA)

Corner, Lord Tattenham—An acquaintance of Archdeacon Grantly. (BT)

de Courcy, Earl—Of Courcy Castle; a member of Her Majesty's Household. (DT, SHA)

de Courcy, Countess—Wife of the above. (BT, DT, SHA, LC)

de Courcy, Hon. George—Their second son. (BT, DT, FP, SHA, LC)

de Courcy, Hon. John—Their third son. (BT, DT, SHA, LC)

de Courcy, Lady Amelia—Daughter of the Earl and Countess de Courcy; married Mortimer Gazebee. (DT, SHA, LC)

de Courcy, Lady Alexandrina—Eldest daughter of the de Courcys; married Adolphus Crosbie. (DT, SHA, LC)

de Courcy, Lady Arabella—(See Lady Arabella Gresham.)

de Courcy, Lady Margaretta—Daughter of the de Courcys. (BT, DT, SHA)

de Courcy, Lady Rosina—Daughter of the de Courcys. (DT, SHA) de Courcy, Lady Selina—Daughter of the de Courcys. (DT)

de Courcy, Mrs George—Wife of Hon. George de Courcy. (SHA)

Cox, Mrs—Parishioner of Hogglestock. (LC)

Cox and Cumming—Attorneys of Lincoln's Inn. (W)

Cradell, Joseph—Clerk in the Income Tax Office. (SHA, LC)

Cradell, Mrs Amelia—(*See* Miss Amelia Roper.)

Cradell, Mrs—A barrister's widow; mother of Joseph. (SHA)

Crawley, Rev. Josiah—Sometime perpetual curate of Hogglestock; vicar of St Ewold's. (FP, LC)

Crawley, Mrs Mary—Wife of the above. (FP, LC)

Crawley, Grace—Daughter of Rev. Jos. Crawley; married Major Henry Grantly, V.C. (FP, LC)

Crawley, Jane—Sister of Grace. (LC)

Crawley, Bob—Son of Rev. Jos. Crawley; student at Marlborough College. (FP, LC)

Crawley, Frank—Son of Rev. Jos. Crawley. (FP)

Crawley, Harry—Son of Rev. Jos. Crawley. (FP)

Crawley, Kate—Daughter of Rev. Jos. Crawley. (FP)

Crimpton, Miss—A pupil at Miss Prettyman's School, Silverbridge. (LC)

Crofts, Dr James—A Guestwick doctor; married Isabella Dale. (SHA, LC)

Crofts, Mrs—(*See* Isabella Dale.)

Crosbie, Adolphus—A civil servant in the General Committee Office; one time fiancé of Lily Dale; married Lady Alexandrina de Courcy. (SHA, LC)

Crosbie, Mrs—(*See* Lady Alexandrina de Courcy)

Crowdy, Squire—Of Creamclotted Hall, Devon; married Blanche Robarts. (FP)

Crump, Mr—Attorney; partner of Mr Toogood. (LC)

Crump, Mrs—Postmistress at Allington. (SHA)

Crumple, Jonathan—Inmate of Hiram's Hospital. (W)

Culpepper, Captain—A friend of Lord Lufton. (FP)

Cumming—(*See* Cox & Cumming.)

Curling—A Barchester attorney. (FP)

Dale, Captain Bernard—Son of Colonel Orlando and Lady Fanny Dale; nephew of Squire Dale of Allington; R.E.; married Emily Dunstable. (SHA, LC)

Dale, Christopher—Squire of Allington. (SHA, LC)

Dale, Lady Fanny—A sister of Earl de Guest; married to Col Orlando Dale; resident in Torquay. (SHA)

Dale, Isabella—Elder sister of Lilian Dale; married Dr James Crofts of Guestwick. (SHA, LC)

Dale, Kit—The father of Christopher Dale. (SHA)

Dale, Lilian—Niece of Squire Dale; once engaged to Adolphus Crosbie; a spinster. (SHA, LC)

Dale, Mrs—Mother of Lilian and Isabella Dale; resident in the Small House at Allington; widow of Philip Dale, a land surveyor. (SHA, LC)

Dale, Old Mrs—The mother of Squire Dale and one time resident in the Small House at Allington. (SHA)

Dale, Colonel Orlando—Formerly of the 19th Dragoons; second brother of Squire Dale; father of Bernard. (SHA)

Dale, Philip—Third brother of Squire Dale; father of Isabella and Lilian Dale. (SHA)

Dalrymple, Conway—A fashionable artist and intimate of John Eames. (LC)

Darvel—An employee of Earl de Guest. (SHA)

Darvels—Lodger with Dan Morris in Hoggle End. (LC)

Davis—A man who owed money to Mark Robarts. (FP)

Deeds, Mr Vellum—A Barchester attorney. (BT)

Demolines, Sir Confucius—One time a physician of Paris. (LC)

Demolines, Lady—Widow of the above; resident in Bayswater. (LC)

Demolines, Madalina—Daughter of Sir Confucius Demolines. (LC)

Dick—A servant of Dean Arabin. (LC)

Dickson, "Young"—A Barchester bank clerk. (W)

Die, Neversaye—A London counsel. (DT)

Dingles—Gamekeeper at Allington. (SHA)

Dobbs, Montgomerie—A friend of Adolphus Crosbie. (SHA)

Dolland's—Spectacle makers, of London. (LC)

Draper, Mrs—Mrs Proudie's maid. (LC)

Dumbello, Lord—Viscount; eldest son of the Marquis and Marchioness of Hartletop; married Griselda Grantly. (FP, LC)

Dumbello, Lady—(*See* Griselda Grantly.)

Dumbello, Lord (2)—Son of Lord and Lady Dumbello after their succession to Marquisate of Hartletop. (LC)

Dunn, Onesiphorous—An Irish friend of Mrs Thorne. (LC)

Dunstable, Emily—Niece of Martha Dunstable; engaged to Captain Bernard Dale. (LC)

Dunstable, Miss Martha—A wealthy heiress; married Dr Thomas Thorne, of Greshamsbury; of Chaldicotes, West Barset, and Berkeley Square, London. (DT, FP, LC)

Dunstable, Old Dr—One time uncle of Martha Dunstable who made a fortune out of "Ointment of Lebanon". (LC)

Eames, John—From Guestwick; civil servant employed in the Income Tax Office. (SHA, LC)

Eames, Mary—Sister of John Eames; sometimes called "Molly" by her brother. (SHA, LC)

Eames, Mrs—Of Guestwick; mother of the above; a sister of Mrs Mary Crawley. (SHA, LC)

Easyman, Dr—Physician of Miss Martha Dunstable. (DT)

Everbeery, Mr—He lived near Taunton and married his cook. (DT)

Fanfaron, Mr—A lawyer at Hamersham assizes. (SHA)

Fiasco, Major—Member of the board of the General Committee Office. (SHA)

Fillgrave, Dr—The most fashionable Barchester physician. (BT, DT, LC)

Finnie (or Finney)—An attorney of Barchester. (W, BT, DT)

Finnie, Mrs—Wife of the above. (BT)

Fisher—A clerk in the Income Tax Office. (LC)

Fitzgerald, Burgo—A friend of Lady Glencora MacCluskie. (SHA)

Fitzhoward—One time secretary to Sir Raffle Buffle. (SHA, LC)

Fitzplush, James—Footman of the Proudies. (BT)

Fitzwhiggin, Sir Nicholas—A Government "big wig". (BT)

Fletcher, Mr—A butcher of Silverbridge. (LC)

Flurry—Gamekeeper to Archdeacon Grantly. (LC)

Flurry, Martha—Wife of the above. (LC)

Forrard, Mrs—Landlady of the "Red Lion", Allington. (LC)

Forrest, Mr—Barchester bank manager. (FP)

Foster, Frank—Of "The Elms"; a guest at Ullathorne. (BT)

Fothergill—Agent of the Duke of Omnium. (DT, FP, SHA, LC)

Frummage, Mrs—Shopkeeper in Allington. (SHA)

Gagebee, "Young"—(*See* Mortimer Gazebee)

Gazebee, Lady Amelia—(*See* Lady Amelia de Courcy.)

Gazebee, Mortimer—A London lawyer, of Gumption, Gazebee and Gazebee; MP for Barchester; married Lady Amelia de Courcy (DT, FP, SHA, LC)

Gazebee, de Courcy—Eldest child of the above. (SHA)

Gazy, William—Inmate of Hiram's Hospital. (W)

Giggs, Sir Rickety—A counsel. (DT)

Giles, Mrs—Cleaner of Allington church. (LC)

Goodenough, Rev. Mr—One time vicar of St Ewold's. (BT)

Goodenough, Mrs—Wife of the above. (BT)

Goodygaffer, Dowager Lady—A friend of Lady Lufton. (FP)

Gorse, Sir Harkaway—A guest at Ullathorne. (BT)

Granger, Mrs—Wife of a Framley farmer. (FP)

Grantly, Rt Rev. Dr—Bishop of Barchester; father of Archdeacon Grantly. (W, BT, LC)

Grantly, Ven. Dr Theophilus—Son of the Rt Rev. Dr Grantly; archdeacon of Barchester; rector of Plumstead Episcopi; married Miss Susan Harding. (W, BT, DT, FP, SHA, LC)

Grantly, Mrs Susan—Formerly Susan Harding, daughter of Rev. Septimus Harding; wife of Archdeacon Grantly. (W, BT, DT, LC)

Grantly, Rev. Charles James—Son of Archdeacon Grantly. (W, LC)

Grantly, Major Henry, V.C.—Son of Archdeacon Grantly; widower with one daughter, Edith; married Grace Crawley. (W, LC)

Grantly, Samuel—Son of Archdeacon Grantly. (W)

Grantly, Edith—Daughter of Major Henry Grantly by his first wife. (LC)

Grantly, Florinda—Daughter of Archdeacon Grantly. (W, BT, FP)

Grantly, Griselda (Grizzel)—Daughter of Archdeacon Grantly; married Lord Dumbello; later Marchioness of Hartletop. (W, BT, FP, SHA, LC)

Grantly, Lady Anne—Wife of Rev. Charles Grantly. (LC)

Green—A Silverbridge tradesman. (LC)

Green, Rev. Augustus—A curate. (BT)

Green, Mr—A friend of Captain Bernard Dale and visitor to Allington. (LC)

Green, Mrs Opie—A widow who lived a mile from Greshamsbury. (DT)

Greenacre, Farmer—A churchwarden of St Ewold's. (BT)

Greenacre, Mrs—Wife of the above. (BT)

Greenacre, Harry—Son of Farmer Greenacre. (BT)

Gregory—Groom at Framley Court. (FP)

Gregory (2)—Under-gardener at Allington. (LC)

Gresham, John Newbold—Of Greshamsbury; first commoner in Barsetshire; MP for, first, Barset, then (after the Reform Bill) East Barset; grandfather of Frank Gresham. (DT)

Gresham, Francis Newbold—Father of Frank Gresham; married Lady Arabella de Courcy. (DT, SHA)

Gresham, Francis Newbold (Frank)—Son of the above; graduate of Cambridge; married Mary Thorne. (DT, FP, SHA, LC)

Gresham, Lady Arabella—Sister of Earl de Courcy; married Francis Newbold Gresham; mother of Frank Gresham. (DT, FP)

Gresham, Mrs Frank—(*See* Mary Thorne.)

Gresham, Augusta—Daughter of Francis Newbold Gresham. (DT)

Gresham, Beatrice—Daughter of Francis Newbold Gresham. (DT)

Gresham, Helina—Daughter of Francis Newbold Gresham. (DT)

Gresham, Matilda—Daughter of Francis Newbold Gresham. (DT)

Gresham, Nina—Daughter of Francis Newbold Gresham. (DT)

Gresham, "Pussy"—Daughter of Francis Newbold Gresham. (DT)

Gresham, Selina—Daughter of Francis Newbold Gresham. (DT)

Gresham, Sophy—Daughter of Francis Newbold Gresham. (DT)

Grey, Rev. Optimus—A curate of the Proudies. (BT, FP)

Greyson—A London apothecary attendant on Sir Louis Scatcherd. (DT)

Grobury—A Silverbridge baker. (LC)

Gruffen, Dr—A doctor of Guestwick. (SHA)

Gruffen, the Misses—Residents in Guestwick. (SHA)

de Guest, Earl—Of Guestwick Manor; a distinguished farmer. (SHA, LC)

de Guest, Lady Julia—Sister of the above. (SHA, LC)

de Guest, Lady Jemima—One time aunt of Earl de Guest. (SHA)

Guffern, Mrs—A farmer's wife; guest at Ullathorne. (BT)

Guffern, John—Son of the above. (BT)

Gumption, Mr—Solicitor of Nathaniel Sowerby. (DT, FP)

Gumption, Gazebee and Gazebee—London solicitors. (DT)

Gumption and Gagebee—London solicitors. (FP). (*See* above.)

Gushing, Miss—A Greshamsbury resident; later Mrs Rantaway. (DT)

Gwynne, Dr—Master of Lazarus College, Oxford. (BT)

Hall—A Silverbridge tradesman. (LC)

Handy, Abel—Inmate of Hiram's Hospital. (W)

Hannah—Servant of Lady Scatcherd. (DT, FP)

Haphazard, Sir Abraham—Attorney-general; most distinguished Q.C. (W, DT)

Harding, Rev. Septimus—One time warden of Hiram's Hospital; precentor Barchester Cathedral; rector Crabtree Parva; rector St Cuthbert's of Barchester; refused Deanery of Barchester; later vicar of St Ewold's; author "Harding's Church Music". (W, BT, FP, SHA, LC)

Harding, Eleanor—Daughter of the above; married (1) by whom issue posthumously, John Bold, (2) Very Rev. Dr Francis Arabin. (W, BT, DT, FP, SHA, LC)

Harding, Susan—(*See* Mrs Susan Grantly.)

Hartletop, Marchioness of—Friend of the Duke of Omnium; mother of Lord Dumbello. (FP, SHA)

Hartletop, Marchioness of (2)—(*See* Griselda Grantly.)

Hartletop, Marquis of—Of Hartlebury, Shropshire. (FP, SHA)

Hartletop, Marquis of (2)—One time Viscount Dumbello (LC)

Hatherly, Sir Frederick—Of Hatherly Court, Glos. (DT)

Hearne (Hearn, Heard), Mrs—Widow of a former vicar of Allington; friend of Lilian Dale. (SHA, LC)

Hesterwell, the Misses—Of Hesterwell Park. (DT)

Hoggett, Giles—A labourer of Hoggle End. (LC)

Holt, Mrs—A shopkeeper of Silverbridge. (LC)

Hopkins—Head gardener at the Great House at Allington. (LC)

Hyandry, Dr—A Church dignitary. (W)

Jackson—Of "The Grange". (DT)

Jackson, Mrs—Wife of the above. (DT)

Jackson (2)—Partner of Sir Roger Scatcherd in the "York and Yeovil Grand Central". (DT)

Jane—Personal maid of Griselda Grantly. (FP)

Jane (2)—Servant of Miss Martha Dunstable. (FP)

Jane (3)—Parlour maid in the Small House at Allington. (SHA, LC)

Jane (4)—Maid of the Walkers in Silverbridge. (LC)

Janet—A maid of Dr Thomas Thorne. (DT)

Jemima—A servant of Lady Scatcherd. (FP)

Jemima (2)—Cook at Framley Parsonage. (FP)

Jemima (3)—Parlour maid of Mrs Roper. (SHA)

Jemima (4)—Maid of Lady Julia de Guest. (LC)

Jenkins—Friend of Sir Louis Scatcherd. (DT)

John—Servant of Rev. Mark Robarts. (FP)

John (2)—Servant at Guestwick Manor. (SHA)

John (3)—Postman at Allington. (SHA)

John (4)—Footman at Barchester Palace. (LC)

John (5)—Old waiter at the "Dragon of Wantly". (LC)

"John, Old Sir"—MP for East Barset. (FP)

Johnson, Matilda—A resident of Barchester. (W)

Jolliffe—Bailiff of Allington. (SHA)

Jonah—Valet of Sir Louis Scatcherd. (DT)

Jones, Rev. John Joseph—M.A.; curate St Peter's, Northgate, Guestwick. (SHA)

Jones, Miss—Governess to children of Dr Arabin. (LC)

Jones, Miss (2)—Daughter of the Framley curate. (FP)

Jones, Mrs—A correspondent of Mrs Dale. (LC)

Jones, Rev. Evan—Curate of Mark Robarts at Framley. (FP)

Jones'—A London chemist. (LC)

Juniper, Mr—A friend of Amelia Roper. (SHA)

Kensington Gore, Marquis of—Lord High Steward of the Pantry Board. (BT)

Kerrigy, Miss—A friend of Miss Martha Dunstable. (FP)

Kissing, Mr—Clerk in the Income Tax Office; secretary to the board. (SHA, LC)

Knowle, Miss—A guest at Ullathorne. (BT)

Knowle, "Old Lady"—A guest at Ullathorne. (BT)

Knowle, "Young"—A guest at Ullathorne; of Knowle Park. (BT)

Larron, Mlle—French governess at Greshamsbury Park. (DT)

Lookaloft, Augustus—A guest at Ullathorne. (BT)

Lookaloft, Mrs—A guest at Ullathorne. (BT)

Lookaloft, Miss—A guest at Ullathorne. (BT)

Lookaloft, "Bab"—A guest at Ullathorne. (BT)

Love, Mr—Clerk in the Income Tax Office. (SHA)

Lufton, Lord Ludovic—Of Lufton, Oxfordshire, and Framley, East Barset. (FP, LC)

Lufton, Lady—(*See* Lucy Robarts.)

Lufton, Dowager Lady—Mother of Lord Lufton. (FP, LC)

Lupex, Mr—A lodger at Mrs Roper's boarding house. (SHA)

Lupex, Mrs—Wife of the above. (SHA)

MacCluskie, Lady Glencora—Only child of the Lord of the Isles; a wealthy heiress; married Plantagenet Palliser. (SHA, LC)

MacMull, Lady Julia—A lady jilted by Lord Dumbello. (FP)

Mangle, Mr—A farmer of Hogglestock. (LC)

Martin, Jack—A witness to the codicil of Sir Roger Scatcherd's will. (DT)

Mason—An attorney of Silverbridge. (LC)

Maynew, Sir Lamda—A famous London doctor. (BT)

Medlicote, Judge—A judge of the high court. (LC)

Meredith, Sir George—Son-in-law of Dowager Lady Lufton. (FP)

Meredith, Lady Justinia—Daughter of Dowager Lady Lufton; married to Sir George Meredith. (FP)

Moffat, Gustavus—One time suitor of Augusta Gresham. (DT, SHA)

Moffat, Miss—Sister of the above. (DT)

Monsell, Miss Fanny—(*See* Mrs Fanny Robarts.)

Moody, Greg—Inmate of Hiram's Hospital. (W)

Morell, Mrs—A London dressmaker. (LC)

Morris, Dan—A brick-maker of Hoggle End. (LC)

Morris, Mrs—Wife of the above. (LC)

Muggeridge—A clerk in the Income Tax Office. (SHA)

Musselboro, Augustus— A city man, partner to Dobbs Broughton. (LC)

Mutters, Joe—An old clerk of Archdeacon Grantly. (W)

Nearthewind—An election agent. (DT)

Neroni, Signora Madeline—Daughter of Hon. and Rev. Dr Vesey Stanhope; married Paulo Neroni in Italy; a cripple. (BT)

Neroni, Paulo—A captain in the Pope's guard; husband of the above. (BT)

Neroni, Julia—Baby daughter of Paulo and Madeline Neroni. (BT)

Oaklerath, Farmer—A tenant of the Greshams. (DT)

Oaklerath, Mrs—Wife of the above. (DT)

O'Flaherty, Hon. Miss—A bridesmaid at the wedding of Adolphus Crosbie and Lady Alexandrina de Courcy. (SHA)

Omnium, Duke of—The first resident of Barsetshire; of Gatherum Castle, West Barset, and elsewhere. (DT, FP)

Optimist, Mr—Chairman of the board of the General Committee Office. (SHA, LC)

Oriel, Rev. Caleb—Rector of Greshamsbury; married Beatrice Gresham. (DT, FP, LC)

Oriel, Patience—Sister of the above. (DT)

Outonites—A clerk in the civil service. (SHA)

Outonites, Sir Constant—A cousin of the above. (SHA)

Palliser, Lady Glencora—(*See* Lady Glencora MacCluskie.)

Palliser, Plantagenet—Nephew of the Duke of Omnium; MP for Silverbridge; married Lady Glencora MacCluskie. (SHA)

Partridge, Miss—A lady Bernard Dale used "to talk about". (LC)

Peebles, Haddington—A friend of Lord Lufton. (FP)

Peter—The stud groom at Greshamsbury. (DT)

Phillips, Mrs—The nurse at the death of Bishop Grantly. (BT)

Pie, Sir Omicron—A famous London consultant. (BT, DT, FP, SHA)

Plomacy, Mr—Steward of Ullathorne. (BT)

Podgens, Mr—Grocer, clerk and sexton; of Framley. (FP)

Podgens, Mrs—Wife of the above; pew opener of Framley church. (FP)

Podgens, Baby—A child of the above. (FP)

Pole, Mrs—A resident in Exeter. (FP)

Ponsonby—A barrister; guest at dinner party of Dobbs Broughton. (LC)

Ponsonby, Mrs—Wife of the above. (LC)

Porlock, Lord—Eldest son and heir of the Earl de Courcy. (DT, SHA)

Pot Sneuf, Baron—A celebrated German diplomat. (SHA)

Potter—An accountant. (FP)

Potts—A livery stableman of London. (LC)

Pounce—Head groom of Lord Lufton. (FP)

Pratt, Fowler—A friend of Adolphus Crosbie. (SHA, LC)

Prettyman, Miss Annabella—Proprietress of a school for young ladies in Silverbridge. (LC)

Prettyman, Miss Anne—Younger sister of the above. (LC)

Pritchard—A maid of Lady Julia de Guest. (LC)

Proudie, Rt Rev. Dr Thomas—Bishop of Barchester; nephew of an Irish baron on his mother's side; husband of Mrs Proudie. (BT, DT, FP, LC)

Proudie, Mrs—Niece of a Scotch earl; a great antagonist of low church sympathies; her husband, Thomas, was Bishop of Barchester. (BT, DT, FP, LC)

Proudie, Netta—Daughter of the above. (BT, FP)

Proudie, Augusta—Daughter of Rt Rev. Dr Thomas Proudie. (BT, FP)

Proudie, Olivia—Daughter of Rt Rev. Dr Thomas Proudie; married Rev. Tobias Tickler, a widower with three children and incumbent of the Trinity district church in Bethnal Green. (BT, FP)

Quiverful, Rev. Mr—One time vicar of Puddingdale; subsequently Warden of Hiram's Hospital. (W, BT, LC)

Quiverful, Mrs Letitia—Wife of the above; mother of fourteen children; matron of Hiram's Hospital. (W, BT, LC)

Quiverful, George—Son of Rev. Mr Quiverful. (BT)

Quiverful, Sam—Son of Rev. Mr Quiverful. (BT)

Quiverful, Tom—Son of Rev. Mr Quiverful. (BT)

Quiverful, Bessy—Daughter of Rev. Mr Quiverful. (BT)

Quiverful, Jane—Daughter of Rev. Mr Quiverful. (BT)

Quiverful, Jemima—Daughter of Rev. Mr Quiverful. (BT)

Rafferty—A messenger in the Income Tax Office. (SHA, LC)

Ramsby—A London wine merchant. (LC)

Rantaway, Mrs—(*See* Miss Gushing.)

Reddypalm—A Barchester publican; licensee of "The Brown Bear". (DT)

Rerechild, Mr—A Barchester surgeon. (BT, DT, LC)

Richard—A footman at Guestwick Manor. (SHA)

Richard (2)—A servant of Mortimer and Lady Amelia Gazebee. (SHA)

Richards—A maid of Lady Lufton. (FP)

Richards, Mrs—A maid of the Misses Proudie. (BT)

Richards, Mrs (2)—Housekeeper of the Greshams. (DT)

Robarts, Dr—A physician of Exeter; father of Rev. Mark Robarts. (FP)

Robarts, Rev. Mark—Vicar of Framley; educated Harrow and Oxford; married Miss Fanny Monsell. (FP, LC)

Robarts, Mrs Fanny—Wife of the above; an intimate of Dowager Lady Lufton. (FP, LC)

Robarts, Baby—A son of the above. (FP)

Robarts, Blanche—A sister of Rev. Mark Robarts; married Squire Crowdy (q.v.). (FP)

Robarts, Frank—The eldest son of Rev. Mark Robarts. (FP)

Robarts, Gerald—Younger brother of Rev. Mark Robarts; an Army officer. (FP)

Robarts, Jane—Sister of Rev. Mark Robarts. (FP)

Robarts, John—Youngest brother of Rev. Mark Robarts; a clerk at the Petty Bag Office. (FP)

Robarts, Lucy—Sister of Rev. Mark Robarts; married Lord Lufton. (FP, LC)

Robarts, Mary—Sister of Rev. Mark Robarts. (FP)

Robin—The postman at Framley. (FP)

Romer, Mr—A young barrister. (DT)

Roper, Amelia—Daughter of Mrs Roper, a widow who kept a boarding house in Burton Crescent, London; married Joseph Cradell. (SHA, LC)

Roper, James—Brother of the above. (SHA)

Roper, Mrs—Mother of the above. (SHA, LC)

Runter, Serjeant—A distant relative of Sir Confucius Demolines (LC)

Rusk, Betsey—A maid of Miss Monica Thorne. (BT)

"Sacerdos"—The pen name under which Archdeacon Grantly put forward his view on the Earl of Guilford and St Cross dispute. (W)

St Bungay, Duchess of—A famous hostess. (SHA)

Sark, Earl of—A politician. (SHA)

Scalpen—A retired apothecary. (BT)

Scatcherd, Sir Roger—One time stone mason of Barchester; a famous and wealthy railway magnate. (DT)

Scatcherd, Lady—Wife of Sir Roger; foster mother of Frank Gresham. (DT, FP)

Scatcherd, Sir Louis Phillipe—Son of Sir Roger; a dipsomaniac. (DT)

Scatcherd, Mary—Sister of Sir Roger Scatcherd; mother of Mary Thorne by Henry Thorne. (DT)

Scott, Sabrina—A friend of Lady Glencora MacCluskie. (SHA)

Scuttle, Jem—An ostler at the "Dragon of Wantly"; emigrated to New Zealand. (LC)

Sentiment, Mr Popular—A novelist. (W)

Shorter—A man who fled to Canada to avoid Madalina Demolines. (LC)

Sidonia—A politician. (FP)

Sims, Rev. Mr—A curate of Archdeacon Grantly. (LC)

Skulpit, Job—Inmate of Hiram's Hospital. (W, LC)

Slope, Rev. Obidiah—M.A.; chaplain to Bishop Proudie. (BT, FP)

Slow and Bideawhile—London lawyers. (DT, FP)

Smillie, Rev. Mr—A parson of Silverbridge. (LC)

Smith, Rev. Mr—Curate of Rev. Septimus Harding at Crabtree Parva. (W)

Smith, Harold—A member of Parliament. (FP, LC)

Smith, Mrs Harriet—A sister of Nathaniel Sowerby; wife of the above. (FP, LC)

Smithe, Mr—A friend of Miss Anne Prettyman. (LC)

Smithers & Smith—Lady Julia de Guest's solicitors; of 57 Lincoln's Inn Fields. (LC)

Snapper, Rev. Mr—Chaplain to the Bishop of Barchester. (LC)

Snapper, Mrs—Wife of the above. (LC)

Snilam, Mr—A counsel. (DT)

Soames, Mr—The agent of Lord Lufton. (LC)

Sowerby, Nathaniel—One time owner of Chaldicotes; MP for West Barset in the Omnium interest. (FP, LC)

Spermoil—A celebrity; guest at Miss Martha Dunstable's "At Home". (FP)

Spooner, Rev. Mr—A minor canon of Barchester Cathedral. (LC)

Spriggs, Mathew—Inmate of Hiram's Hospital. (W)

Spriggs, Mr—A churchwarden at St Ewold's. (BT)

Spruce, Miss Sally—A maiden lady; cousin of Mrs Roper. (SHA)

Stanhope, Hon. and Rev. Dr Vesey—A prebendary (Goosegorge Stall) of Barchester Cathedral; rector of Crabtree Canonicorum; rector of Stoke Pinquium; resident near Lake Como, Italy. (W, BT, FP)

Stanhope, Mrs—Wife of the above. (BT)

Stanhope, Charlotte—Eldest daughter of the above. (BT)

Stanhope, Ethelbert—Son of Hon. and Rev. Dr Vesey Stanhope; an artist; convert to Roman Catholicism; convert to Judaism. (BT, DT)

Stanhope, Madeline—(*See* Signora Madeline Neroni.)

Staples, Tom—Tutor of Lazarus College, Oxford. (BT)

Stiles, Mr—A churchwarden of St Ewold's. (BT)

Stock, Mr—A co-executor, with Dr Thorne, of Sir Roger Scatcherd's estate. (DT)

Stoddard—Grandmother of Dr James Crofts. (SHA)

Stopford, Rev. Dr—One time vicar of Framley. (FP)

Stringer, Dan—A relative of John Stringer. (LC)

Stringer, John—Landlord of "The Dragon of Wantly". (LC)

Stubbs—Employee of Rev. Mark Robarts; lived over the coach house at Framley Parsonage. (FP)

Stubbs, Mrs—Wife of the above. (FP)

Stubbs (2)—A policeman at Paddington station. (SHA)

Stubbs, Bob—A plasterer. (BT)

Stubbs, Mrs (2)—A parishioner of Rev. Jos. Crawley in Hogglestock. (FP)

Studge, Bobby—A pupil at Hogglestock Church School. (LC)

Subsoil, Farmer—A parishioner of Puddingdale. (BT)

Summerkin, William—A clerk in the Income Tax Office; engaged to Polly Toogood. (LC)

Supplehouse, Mr—A member of Parliament. (FP)

Swanton, Rev. Mr—Curate to Rev. Mr Boyce of Allington. (LC)

Tempest, Rev. Dr Mortimer—Rector of Silverbridge; rural dean of Barsetshire. (LC)

Tempest, Mrs—Wife of the above. (LC)

de Terrier, Lord—A politician. (FP)

Thomas—A groom of Dr Thorne. (DT)

Thomas (2)—A servant of the Proudies. (FP)

Thompson—A clerk in the General Committee Office. (LC)

Thompson (2)—Superintendent of the Silverbridge police. (LC)

Thompson, Sarah—A protegée of Dowager Lady Lufton. (FP)

Thorne, "Old" Dr—One time clerical dignitary of Barchester; father of Dr Thomas Thorne. (DT)

Thorne, Henry—The brother of Dr Thomas Thorne; natural father of Mary Thorne by Mary Scatcherd. (DT)

Thorne, Mary—Natural daughter of Henry Thorne; niece of Dr Thomas Thorne; married Frank Gresham. (DT, FP, LC)

Thorne, Miss Monica—Sister of Wilfred Thorne of Ullathorne; unmarried. (BT, DT, LC)

Thorne, Mrs Martha—(*See* Miss Martha Dunstable.)

Thorne, Dr Thomas—A doctor of Greshamsbury; a second cousin to Wilfred Thorne; married Miss Martha Dunstable. (DT, FP, LC)

Thorne, Wilfred—Squire of Ullathorne; unmarried. (BT, DT, FP, LC)

Thumble, Rev. Caleb—A clergyman attached to the Proudies. (LC)

Thumble, Mary Anne—Wife of the above. (LC)

Tickler, Rev. Tobias—Incumbent of the Trinity district church, Bethnal Green; widower, three children; married Miss Olivia Proudie. (FP, LC)

Tomlinson—A Barchester tradesman; married Mary Scatcherd; emigrated to Canada. (DT)

Toogood, Mr—Father of John Toogood; grandfather of John Eames. (LC)

Toogood, Mr John—A London solicitor; a cousin of Mrs Josiah Crawley; uncle of John Eames; partner of Toogood & Crump. (LC)

Toogood, Mrs Maria—Wife of the above. (LC)

Toogood, Miss Lucy—Daughter of Mr John Toogood. (LC)

Toogood, Miss Polly—Daughter of Mr John Toogood; engaged to William Summerkin. (LC)

Toogood & Crump—Solicitors; of Raymond's Buildings, Gray's Inn. (LC)

Towers, Tom—A journalist; of *The Jupiter*. (W, FP)

Tozer—A dealer in money bills. (FP)

Tozer, Tom—A dealer in money bills; brother of the above; also known as "John Austen". (FP)

Tozer, Rev. Mr—A chaplain of the Proudies. (LC)

Trefoil, Very Rev. Dr—One time Dean of Barchester. (BT)

Trefoil, Miss—Daughter of the above. (BT)

Turner, Dr—A physician; attended Rev. Josiah Crawley. (LC)

Tupper—A messenger in the Income Tax Office. (SHA)

Twistleton, Harriett—An acquaintance of Hon. John de Courcy. (SHA)

Twitch—A maid of Countess de Courcy. (SHA)

Umbleby, Mr Yates—Attorney and agent at Greshamsbury. (DT)

Umbleby, Mrs—Wife of the above. (DT)

Van Siever, Clara—Daughter of Mrs Van Siever. (LC)

Van Siever, Mrs—A rich widow of a Dutch merchant. (LC)

Vickers—Butler of Earl de Guest. (SHA)

Walker, Mr Green—MP for Crewe Junction; nephew of the Marchioness of Hartletop. (FP)

Walker, George—A solicitor of Silverbridge. (LC)

Walker, Mrs—Wife of the above. (LC)

Walker, John—Son of the above. (LC)

Walker, Mary—Daughter of the above. (LC)

Walker & Winthrop—Silverbridge solicitors. (LC)

White, Rev. Mr—A curate attached to the Proudies. (BT, FP)

Wiggins, Mrs—Widow of a tallow chandler; one time resident of Barchester close in the house of Hon. and Rev. Dr Vesey Stanhope. (FP)

Wilkins—A policeman of Silverbridge. (LC)

Winterbones, Mr—Confidential clerk to Sir Roger Scatcherd. (DT)

Winthrop, Mr Zachary—A solicitor of Silverbridge; partner of George Walker; clerk to the Silverbridge magistrates. (LC)

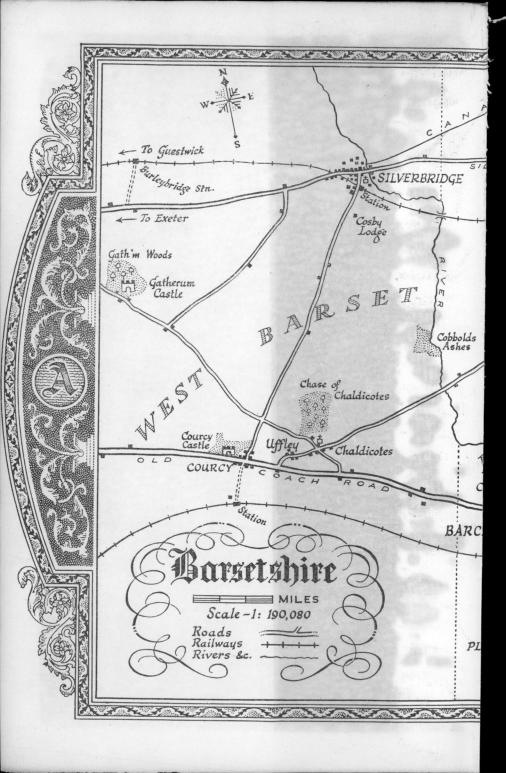